AS/A2
Revise
PE
for Edexcel
third edition

by

Dennis Roscoe
Jan Roscoe

CREDITS

AS/A1 Revise PE for Edexcel third edition

by
Dennis Roscoe
Jan Roscoe

Jan Roscoe Publications Ltd
An imprint of Heath Books Ltd

First edition published in 2009 by Jan Roscoe Publications.
Second edition May 2014.
Third edition August 2016.

Heath Books Ltd
Willow House, Willow Walk
Sutton
Surrey
SM3 9QQ
United Kingdom

tel: 020 8644 7788
fax: 020 8641 3377
email: sales@jroscoe.co.uk

A Catalogue record for this book is available from the British Library.

ISBN   978-1-901424-88-1.

Cover designs by Helen Roscoe-Rutter and David Roscoe-Rutter.

Published via Adobe InDesign, CorelDraw 10.410, Adobe Illustrator 9.0, Smartdraw 6.0, laid out and typeset by Dennis Roscoe

Printed and bound by

Hobbs the Printers Limited
Brunel Road
Totton
Hampshire
SO40 3WX
United Kingdom

tel: 023 8066 4800
fax: 023 8066 4801

email: estimating@hobbs.uk.com

INTRODUCTION

This Edexcel endorsed A level PE book has been written to address the changes in content and style of the Pearson Edexcel Level 3 Advanced Subsidiary GCE Level Physical Education (8PE0) and Pearson Edexcel Level 3 Advanced Year 1 GCE Level Physical Education (9PE0) syllabuses which commence in September 2016. The 2016 AS syllabus will be first examined in June 2017, and has been designed to be able to be co-taught with the first year of the A Level course to be first examined in June 2018. This means that students taking the AS Level in June 2017 can be taught in the same group as the first year of the two year A Level course to be examined in 2018.

These Physical Education syllabuses are multi-disciplinary in nature, covering applied anatomy and exercise physiology, skill acquisition and sports psychology, and historical and contemporary studies. These subject areas have generated a substantial quantity of specialist literature each with its own specific language. At times you may be overwhelmed by the amount of material covered, however this book addresses the problem of dealing with copious notes by summarising the content of the subject matter and attempting to explain in simple language what are sometimes complicated concepts or issues.

Questions are provided throughout the text and exam style questions are provided at the end of each chapter. Answers can be downloaded by going to the following link: http://www.jroscoe.co.uk/downloads/as_a1_revise_pe_edexcel/ on the JRP website. The answers will amplify the subject matter and provide clues as to how the exam itself should be approached. A new feature this time is the requirement that the final exam questions on each section of the syllabus shall include an essay type answer. This allows students to express their ability and knowledge in the context of properly written language (prose) with attention to grammar and punctuation. Question assessment guidelines and use of terminology are included immediately before the index section in this book.

Materials are presented in a concise and visual approach for effective and efficient revision. Modern terminology, nomenclature and units have been used wherever possible. At the end of the book there is a comprehensive index for easy reference.

HOW TO USE THIS REVISION GUIDE

The ideal use of this Revision Guide would be to purchase it at the start of the course and relate each of the summary pages to the specific areas of the syllabus as an aide memoire. The inclusion of specific questions and full answers (to be found on the following link: http://www.jroscoe.co.uk/downloads/as_a1_revise_pe_edexcel/ provide a means of self-testing. Each chapter has its own link specified on the questions pages. Don't be tempted to find out the answers before attempting a question.

In reality, whole examination questions contain a much broader content than those given in this guide. Examiners will attempt to examine more than one small area of the syllabus within the context of one full question and therefore it is important that you revise all aspects of your syllabus.

The main use of the Revision Guide should be during the final revision period leading up to your examinations, as it should help you to understand and apply concepts i.e. link summary content with examination question.

The aim of this Student Guide is to provide an aid that enhances syllabus analysis, and to raise your level of success in examinations.

THE QUALITY OF AUTHORS

The authors are experts in the physical education field and have considerable experience in teaching 'A' Level Physical Education. They have written examination syllabuses, and have set and marked examination questions within this subject area and taught at revision workshops throughout the UK. Much of the material within this book has been thoroughly student tested.

The authors hope that this Revision Guide will prove useful to staff and students. Jan Roscoe Publications will welcome any comments you would wish to make about the book's utility or layout. Thank you for using this work.

Dennis Roscoe
Jan Roscoe

ACKNOWLEDGMENTS

The authors wish to thank Bob Davis for his contribution in the Historical and Contemporary Issues elements of this book. Thanks are also due to Helen Roscoe-Rutter and David Roscoe-Rutter for their contributions as cover designers and photographers and Lois Cresswell, Jenny Pacey, Helen Roscoe-Rutter and Osian Jones for their patience as photographic models. The authors wish to thank members of the Belgian Olympic Athletics Squad for permission to use their images. **Dennis Roscoe -** *Editor*

ACKNOWLEDGMENTS FOR GRAPHICS

Figure

Figure	Source
1.17	Actionplus
4.19	istockphoto Ed Hidden
4.20	istockphoto Simone van den Berg
4.21	istockphoto Ron Summers
5.7	Physical Education and the Study of Sport 5e 9780723433750
5.8	Physical Education and the Study of Sport 5e 9780723433750
5.11	istockphoto Damir Spanic
5.12	istockphoto nikada
7.5	istockphoto.com/Toby Cramer
8.3	istockphoto Birgitte Magnus
8.22	The Stretching Institute
12.2	istockphoto Rich Legg
12.3	istockphoto bradleym
13.2	Wikimedia Creative commons/John the scone
13.12	GNU free documentation/Richard Giles
13.15	Sport Development Centre, Loughborough University
14.11	shutterstock/Albo
14.12	LTA Wimbledon
15.1	getty images/AFP/stringer
15.3	shutterstock Vladmir Wrangel
18.5	Wikimedia Creative Commons/Kelseye
19.7	courtesy of Anwar El Bizanti
19.10	GNU free documentation/Rocky Briggs/CC-BY-SA-3.0
20.2	istockphoto Michael Krinke

All other photographs or graphics are by Helen Roscoe-Rutter, Jan Roscoe, Dennis Roscoe, Bob Davis or other free sources.

PEARSON ENDORSEMENT STATEMENT

A Level year 2 Revise PE for Edexcel

HIGH QUALITY PHOTOS

QUALITY GRAPHS

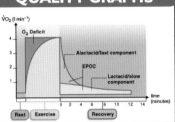

ROSCOE et al
A2 Revise PE for Edexcel
ISBN 978-1-911-24103-4

A2
Revise
PE
for
Edexcel
third edition

Dennis Roscoe
Bob Davis
Jan Roscoe

Jan Roscoe Publications Ltd

2016 Specification

REVISION SUMMARY NOTES

Factors affecting leader effectiveness

The following **leadership qualities** will determine a leader's effectiveness:
- Ability to communicate.
- Respect for group members.
- Enthusiasm.
- High ability.
- Deep knowledge of the sport and techniques or tactics.
- Charisma.

REVISION SUMMARY CHARTS

ANSWERS TO QUESTIONS are found on the JRP Website

3)   b) Why is blood doping an illegal ergogenic aid?
    3 marks
Answer
- WADA bans any means of artificially *enhancing performance* such as $\dot{V}O_{2max}$.
- Using chemicals or blood substitutes, and also blood doping can be *detrimental* to the athlete's health.
- Such as risk of infection from the reinfusion process.
- And high blood pressure.
- Because of a higher concentration of red blood cells, a much greater chance of thrombosis or blood clotting (possibly causing stroke or heart attack).
- Blood doping is in conflict with the general *spirit of sport*.

This new Revise Series covers all aspects of the examinable A Level year 2 Edexcel syllabus commencing September 2017. The book consists of student notes, full colour illustrations, photographs, exam questions and full answers. Key concepts are clearly defined with examples that can be used in answers to exam questions, enabling the student to self-test. This student revision guide supports a comprehensive revision plan and will enhance student grades.

CONTENTS

AS/A1 Revise PE for Edexcel

Topic 1

Applied anatomy and physiology

CONTENTS

APPLIED ANATOMY AND PHYSIOLOGY

CHAPTER I - 1.1 Muscular skeletal system

1.1.1 Names of muscles and bones

The skeletal system

- **The appendicular skeletal system** (figure 1.1) consists of the shoulder girdle, skull, hip girdle, leg and arm bones.
- **The axial skeleton** consists of the skull, vertebral column, ribs and sternum.

The functions of the skeletal system are to act as a lever system, as surface area for attachment of muscle, tendons and ligaments, and to give shape and support to the body. Also, red and white blood cells are manufactured within bone marrow, and bones store fats and minerals.

Types of bones and principal functions

- **Long bones**, for example, the femur (which acts as a lever).
- **Short bones**, for example, carpals (which have strength and lightness).
- **Flat bones**, for example, the pelvis (which has a large surface area for muscle & tendon attachments), the cranium (has the function of brain protection).
- **Irregular bones**, for example, the vertebrae (which protect the spinal cord), the patella (a sesamoid bone) which increases the mechanical advantage of the quadriceps tendon.

STUDENT NOTE

You need to familiarise yourself with the names of bones in figure 1.2 in relation to joints when you answer movement analysis questions.

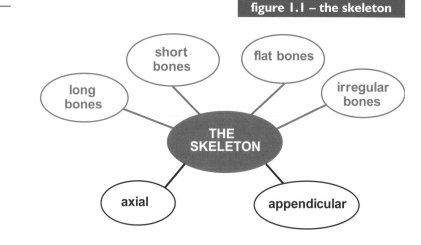

figure 1.1 – the skeleton

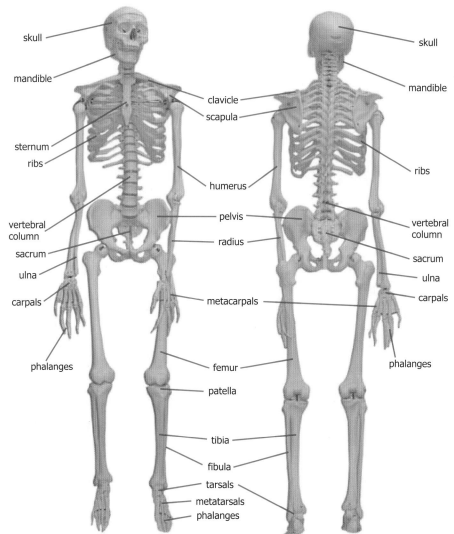

figure 1.2 – the human skeleton

Bony features

Protrusions and **depressions** act as the places on bones at which ligaments and muscle tendons attach (their shape increases the surface area on the bone available for attachment).

Cartilage

- **Hyaline (articular) cartilage** has a smooth, solid matrix which sits on the ends of bones, and forms the exact surfaces which are in contact and move across one another when a joint is used.
- **White fibro-cartilage** is tough and slightly flexible and exists between vertebrae.
- **Yellow elastic cartilage** is soft and elastic and exists in the ear lobes.

The structure and function of bone tissue

- The **periosteum** is an outer protective covering of bone which provides attachment for muscle tendons and ligaments. The deeper layers of the periosteum are responsible for growth in bone width.
- The **epiphyseal disc** or growth plate is the segment of a bone in which an increase in bone length takes place.
- **Compact bone** consists of solid bone tissue, located down the shaft of a long bone and the outer layers of short, flat and irregular bones. Its dense structure gives strength and support.
- **Cancellous bone** has a lattice-like or spongy appearance. It is light-weight and is located at the ends of a long bone, in addition to providing the internal bone tissue in short, flat and irregular bones.

Joints, movements and muscles

The articular system

Joints

Articulation is defined **'as a place where two or more bones meet to form a joint'**.

Joint types (figure 1.3) are:
- **Fibrous or immovable** – for example, between bones of the cranium.
- **Cartilaginous or slightly moveable** – for example, vertebral discs.
- **Synovial or freely moveable** (classified in table 1.1, page 15).

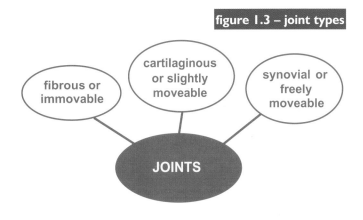

figure 1.3 – joint types

Synovial joint (figure 1.4)

- The **synovial fluid** reduces joint friction by lubrication, and maintains joint stability.
- The **synovial membrane** encloses fluid and secretes fluid.
- The **joint capsule** is a sleeve of tough, fibrous tissue surrounding the joint.
- A **ligament** is an extension of the joint capsule consisting of strong, fibrous connective tissue that provides stability by joining bone to bone.
- **Articular cartilage** prevents friction between bones, and cushions the ends of bones.
- **Bursae** prevent friction and wear.
- **Pads of fat** cushion the joint.
- **Menisci** help bones fit together and improve stabilisation of the joint.

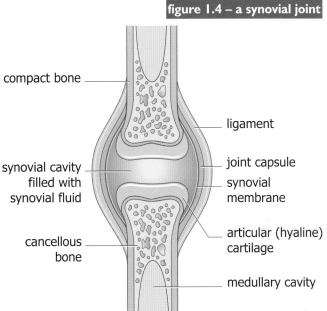

figure 1.4 – a synovial joint

Movement at joints – terminology

The possible ranges of movements within a synovial joint (see figures 1.5 and 1.6) vary according to the shape of the articular surfaces and therefore according to the joint type.

Abduction means to take away and so is characterised by movement away from the midline – for example, a cartwheel in gymnastics.

Adduction means to bring together and so is characterised by movement towards the midline – for example, bringing the lower legs back together from the inverted cartwheel.

Flexion means to bend, resulting in a decreased angle around the joint – for example, bending of the knee.

Extension means to straighten, resulting in an increased angle around the joint – for example, straightening of the knee from a bent-legged to straight-legged position.

Circumduction is a combination of flexion, extension, abduction and adduction – for example, when the upper arm moves (arm circling) so that it describes a cone with the shoulder joint at the apex.

Horizontal flexion (also known as horizontal adduction) occurs when the shoulder starts in a flexed position with the arm(s) parallel to the ground, followed by the shoulder joint moving towards the midline of the body – for example, during the press-out phase of a bench press, and the arm swing into the release phase of a discus throw.

Horizontal extension (also known as horizontal abduction) occurs when the shoulder joint, with the arm(s) parallel to the ground, move away from the midline of the body – for example, a seated row as the elbows are pulled back as far as possible, and the preparatory swing of a discus throw.

Depression describes movement of the shoulders downwards – for example, the preparation for a dead lift, gripping the bar.

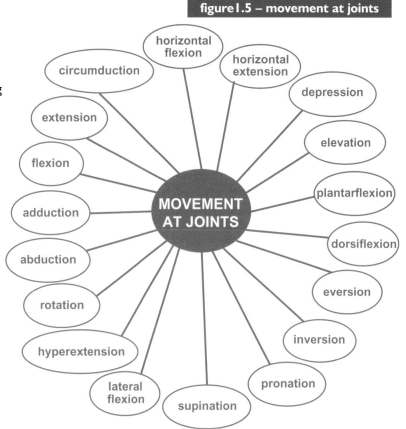

figure1.5 – movement at joints

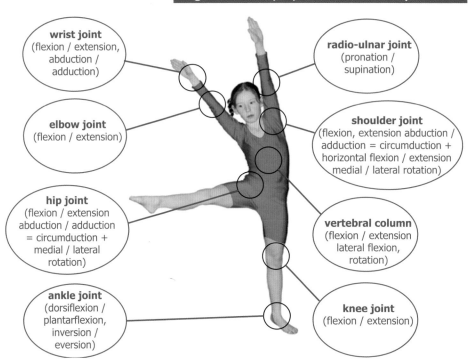

figure 1.6 – major joints – movement patterns

Elevation describes movement of the shoulders upwards – for example, a shoulder shrug.

Plantarflexion involves extending the toes thereby increasing the angle at the ankle – for example, standing on tip-toes.

Dorsiflexion describes movement of the foot towards the shin – for example, walking on one's heels.

Eversion is the joint action at the ankle characterised by the turning of the sole of the foot laterally outwards – for example, the kick action in breaststroke.

Inversion is the joint action at the ankle characterised by the turning of the sole of the foot medially inwards – for example, a football player inverts the foot to pass the ball with the outside of his or her boot.

Pronation is characterised by the rotation of the forearm medially so that the hand faces downwards – for example, a top-spin forehand in tennis.

Supination is characterised by the rotation of the forearm laterally so that the hand faces upwards – for example, the right hand action in a hockey flick.

Lateral flexion is sideways bending.

Hyperextension is the forced extension of a joint beyond its normal range of motion – for example, the arched spine that is created in the flight phase of the Fosbury Flop high jump technique.

Rotation is the turning of a structure around its long axis.
Rotation can be inwards, hence **medial rotation** of the humerus with the forearm flexed brings the hand towards the body – for example, in the breaststroke the humerus rotates medially as the hands enter the water.
Rotation can be outwards, hence **lateral rotation** of the humerus describes a movement whereby the hand moves away from the body – for example, the humerus rotates laterally in preparation for the forehand stroke in tennis.

Most movements that occur in physical activities are combinations of movements explained above.

Table 1.1 – **summary of synovial joint types and movement ranges**

synovial joint types	movement range	example body place: articulating bones
ball & socket	3 axes, flexion / extension, abduction / adduction, rotation, circumduction	**hip:** femur, acetabulum of pelvis **shoulder:** scapula, humerus
hinge	1 axis, flexion / extension	**knee:** femur, tibia **elbow:** humerus, radius, ulna
pivot	1 axis, rotation	**spine: atlas:** odontoid process of axis (turns head side to side) **elbow:** proximal ends of radius and ulna
condyloid (modified ball & socket)	2 axes, flexion / extension, abduction / adduction = circumduction	**knuckles:** joint of fingers: metacarpals, phalanges **wrist – radio-ulnar joint:** radius, carpals
saddle	2 axes, flexion / extension, abduction / adduction = circumduction	**joint at base of thumb:** carpal, metacarpal
gliding	a little movement in all directions	**centre of chest:** clavicle, sternum **spine:** articulating surfaces **wrist:** carpals **ankle:** tarsals

figure 1.7 – superficial anterior muscles

figure 1.8 – superficial posterior muscles

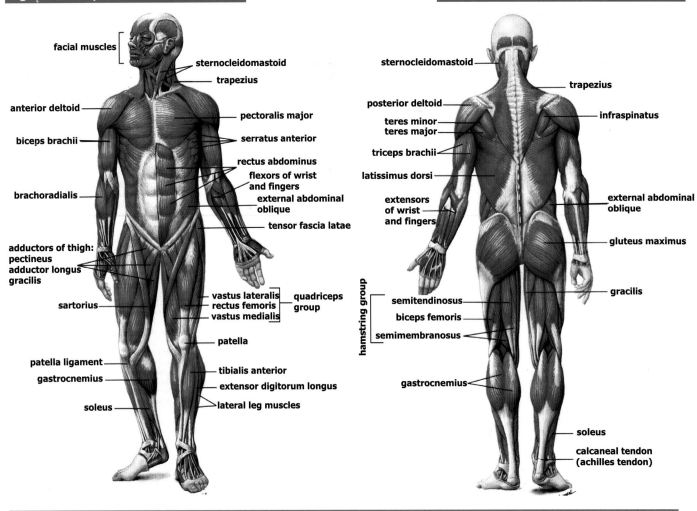

STUDENT NOTE

In your movement analysis you will need to identify major skeletal muscles of the human body (figures 1.7 and 1.8 above) in relation to joint activity and muscle analysis in tables 1.2 (page 17), 1.3 and 1.4 (page 18). The muscles identified in these tables give you plenty of choice to select from. However if you refer to your exam syllabus you may wish to focus on the muscles that your exam board has specified.

Question

Using the information on pages 12 to 14 above, complete the table below.

joint	joint type	articulating bones	associated movement patterns
shoulder			
elbow			
hip			
knee			
trunk			

Table 1.2 – **joints, movements and muscles in the wrists and arms**

body part / joint	movement pattern	active (agonist) muscles	movement examples
wrist	extension	**extensor carpi ulnaris**, extensor digitorum	follow through in an over-arm throw
	flexion	**flexor carpi radialis**, flexi carpi ulnaris	dumbbell wrist curls
arm / elbow	flexion	**biceps brachii**, brachialis	bicep curls
	extension	**triceps brachii**, anconeus (forearm)	follow through over-arm throw, bench press, triceps dips
forearm / radio-ulnar (pivot)	supination	**supinator**, biceps brachii	catching the bar during a clean
	pronation	**pronator teres**, pronator quadratus	putting top spin on a tennis ball
shoulder joint	adduction	**latissimus dorsi**, anterior deltoid, teres major / minor	recovery phase in overarm throw, triceps dips
	abduction	**medial deltoid**, supraspinatus	preparation phase shoulder pass
	flexion	**pectoralis major**, anterior deltoid, coracobrachialis	release phase in overarm throw, triceps dips
	extension	**posterior deltoid**, latissimus dorsi, teres major	shoulder position during javelin approach run
	medial rotation	**latissimus dorsi**, posterior deltoid, pectoralis major, teres major, subscapularis	forehand stroke / follow through at table tennis
	horizontal flexion	**pectoralis major**, anterior deltoid	arm swing into the release phase of a discus throw
	horizontal extension	**trapezius**, posterior deltoid, latissimus dorsi	preparatory swing (backward) of the arm in the discus
	lateral rotation	**infraspinatus**, teres minor	backhand stroke / follow through at table tennis
shoulder or pectoral girdle (scapula + clavicle)	elevation	**upper fibres of trapezius**, levator scapulae, rhomboids	a dumbbell shoulder shrug
	depression	**lower fibres of trapezius**, latissimus dorsi, pectoralis minor, serratus-anterior (lower fibres)	preparation for dead lift when gripping the bar
	protraction	serratus anterior	recovery phase during breaststroke
	retraction	rhomboids, trapezuis	pull phase during breaststroke
	upward rotation	**upper fibres of trapezius**, serratus anterior	arm recovery phase during butterfly stroke
	downward rotation	**rhomboids**	arm pull phase during butterfly stroke

STUDENT NOTE

The main agonist muscle for each movement is in **red bold** font type in table 1.2.

Table 1.3 – **joints, movements and muscles in the trunk and spine**

body part / joint	movement pattern	active (agonist) muscles	movement examples
trunk / spine	flexion	**rectus abdominus**, internal / external obliques,	sit ups
core stability muscles	extension / hyperextension supports lower back	**erector spinae group** - sacrospinalis / multifidu (deep lumbar portion)	extension - trunk position during netball shot at goal, hyperextension - flight phase of the Fosbury Flop
abdominal wall	rotation	**external obliques**, rectus abdominus, erector spinae	hammer throw swings, barani in trampolining / gymnastics
	lateral flexion	**internal obliques**, rectus abdominus, erector spinae, quadratus lumborum, sacrospinalis	side bends, twisting trunk / abdominal curls

body part / joint	movement pattern	active (agonist) muscles	movement examples
hip	flexion	**iliopsoas**, rectus femoris, pectineus, sartorius, tensor fascia latae, adductor longus / brevis	squat start (low) position, high knee lift during sprinting, moving the knees up into a tuck position
	extension	**gluteus maximus**, hamstring group, adductor magnus	high jump take-off, rear leg drive during sprinting
	adduction	**adductor longus / magnus / brevis**, pectineus, gracilis	cross over phase during javelin run-up, side footing a football
	abduction	**gluteus medius / minimus**, sartorius, tensor fascia latae, piriformis	movement into the inverted phase of a cartwheel
	medial rotation	**gluteus medius / minimus**, tensor fascia latae, iliopsoas, gracilis	hip movement across circle during travel phase of a discus turn
	lateral rotation	**gluteus maximus**, psoas major, adductors, piriformis, sartorious	movement into a yoga stork position
knee	extension	**quadriceps femoris group** - rectus femoris / vastus medialis / vastus intermedius, vastus lateralis	high jump take-off, rear leg sprint phase
	flexion	**hamstring group** - biceps femoris / semimembranosus / semitendinosus, + sartorius, gracilis, gastrocnemius	squat start (low) position, high knee lift during sprinting, moving the knees up into a tuck position
ankle	plantarflexion	**gastrocnemius**, soleus, tibialis posterior, peroneus, flexor digitorum longus	take-off phase during jumping
	dorsiflexion	**tibialis anterior**, extensor digitorum longus	landing phase from jump

STUDENT NOTE

The main agonist muscle for each movement is in **red bold** font type in tables 1.3 and 1.4.

1.1.2 The role of muscular contraction
- the stretch shortening cycle

figure 1.9 – isometric holds

During muscular contraction, a muscle may shorten, lengthen or stay the same. When a muscle changes its length, the contraction is classified as **dynamic**. When the muscle remains the same length, a **static** contraction occurs.

Static contractions – isometric muscle contraction

In **isometric contractions** (figure 1.9) the length of the muscle does not change, but the amount of tension **increases** during the contraction process.

In a training situation isometric work is done by exerting the maximum possible force in a fixed position for sets of 10 seconds, with 60 seconds recovery.

Isometric contractions are responsible for the constant length of postural muscles in the body and hence stabilise the trunk in many dynamic activities such as in sprinting.

figure 1.10 – concentric contraction

concentric muscle contraction (quadriceps)

Dynamic Muscle Contraction – concentric and eccentric contraction

Concentric muscle contraction

This type of contraction (figure 1.10) involves a muscle shortening under tension and is a form of **isotonic muscle contraction.** For example, in the driving upwards phase in a jump or squat, the quadriceps muscle group performs a concentric contraction as it shortens to produce extension of the knee joint.

figure 1.11 – eccentric contraction

Eccentric muscle contraction

This type of contraction (figure 1.11) involves a muscle lengthening under tension and is a form of **isotonic** muscle contraction. When a muscle contracts eccentrically it is acting as a brake, thus controlling the movement. This is called the **stretch shortening cycle**. For example, during the downward moving part of a jump or squat, the quadriceps femoris muscle group is lengthening under tension and so the work is labelled **eccentric** or **negative**. **Eccentric** muscle contraction produces the biggest overload in a muscle, thereby enhancing its development as far as strength is concerned. The chief practical use of eccentric muscle contraction is in **plyometric** or **elastic or explosive** strength work.

eccentric muscle contraction (quadriceps)

For eccentric contractions, the **agonist** muscle is the active muscle which in this case is lengthening. In the case of the landing from a jump or controlled downward movement in a squat, the quadriceps femoris muscle group lengthens under tension, and is therefore the **agonist**. To be the **agonist** in this situation, a muscle **must** be under tension. The **antagonist muscle action** during the example of a downward squatting movement would be the hamstring muscle group, which gets shorter and which relaxes or acts as a fixator for the hip joints.

Many muscle contractions involve a combination of dynamic and static work in which the muscles shorten by some amount, and the degree of tension increases.

Movement analysis of physical activity

figure 1.12 – high jump take-off and flight

figure b

figure a

STUDENT NOTE

In the following movement analysis examples not all agonist muscles have been listed.
The main agonist muscle for each movement is in **red bold** font type in table 1.5.
Refer to page 25 for the antagonist muscle action.

Table 1.5 – **the high jump**

After a continually accelerated run-up with a long penultimate stride, the jumper has a very fast last take-off stride before arriving at the position in figure 1.12 a.

physical activity	joint used	articulating bones	movement produced	agonist muscles	type of muscular contraction (isotonic)
high jump at take-off figure 1.12 a	ankle - take-off leg	talus, tibia, fibula	plantarflexion	**gastrocnemius**, soleus, tibialis posterior, peroneus, flexor digitorum longus	concentric
	knee - take-off leg	tibia, femur	extension	**quadriceps femoris group:** rectus femoris / vastus medialis / vastus intermedius / vastus lateralis	concentric
	shoulder girdle	clavicle, scapula	elevation	**upper fibres of trapezius**, levator scapulae, rhomboids	concentric
high jump in flight figure 1.12 b	hips	femur, acetabulum of pelvis	extension	**gluteus maximus**, adductor magnus, assisted by: **hamstring group:** biceps femoris / semimembranosus / semitendinosus	concentric
	spine	vertebrae	extension / hyperextension	**erector spinae group**	concentric

Question

Explain the differences between the following terms:

a) Concentric and eccentric muscle contraction.
b) Isometric and isotonic muscle contraction.
c) Agonist and antagonist muscle action.
d) Fixator and synergist muscle.
e) Extension and hyperextension.
f) Lateral and medial rotation.

figure 1.13 – sprint – a full stride

figure a   figure b   figure c

Table 1.6 – **sprinting leg action**

physical activity	joint type	movement produced	agonist muscles	antagonist muscles	type of muscular contraction
leg action in sprinting – figure 1.13 a left leg	ankle / hinge	plantarflexion	**gastrocnemius,** flexor digitorum longus	**tibialis anterior,** extensor digitorum longus	concentric
	knee / hinge	extension	**quadriceps femoris group**	**hamstring group**	concentric
action of hip joint figure 1.13 b - left leg	hip / ball and socket	flexion	**iliopsoas,** rectus femoris, adductor longus / brevis	**gluteus maximus,** hamstring group, adductor magnus	concentric
action of the trunk - figure 1.13 c	spine / cartilaginous	extension	**erector spinae group**	**rectus abdominus**	isometric

Question

Using figure 1.13c above, at the completion of the full stride of the left foot plant, identify:

a) The bones that form the ankle joint.
b) The joint type for the ankle.
c) The movement pattern produced as the left foot makes ground contact.
d) The main agonist responsible for this movement pattern.
e) The antagonist responsible for this movement pattern.
f) The type of muscular contraction taking place.

figure 1.14 – over arm throw

figure a   figure b   figure c

STUDENT NOTE

The main agonist muscle for each movement is in **red bold** font type in tables 1.7 and 1.8.

Table 1.7 – **the arm action in an over arm throw**

physical activity	joint used	articulating bones	movement produced	agonist muscles	type of muscular contraction (isotonic)
arm action in over arm throw - figure 1.14	elbow	humerus, radius, ulna	elbow joint extends as movement progresses	**triceps brachii**, anconeus	concentric
	shoulder girdle	scapula, clavicle	elevation, upward rotation	**elevation: upper fibres of trapezius**, levator scapulae. **upward rotation: upper fibres of trapezius**, serratus anterior	concentric
	radio-ulnar (wrist)	carpals, radius, ulna	supination to pronation	**pronator teres**, pronator quadratus	concentric

figure 1.15 – squat – down then up

figure a   b   c   d   e

STUDENT NOTE

You **must** list all muscles in the quadriceps femoris and hamstring groups when you analyse the actions of the knee and hips during physical activity.

Table 1.8 – **the full action of the squat - down then up**

physical activity	joint used	articulating bones	movement produced	agonist muscles	fixator muscles	type of muscular contraction (isotonic)
leg action in squat - figure 1.15	knee – figures a to c	tibia, femur	extension to flexion	**quadriceps femoris group**	adductor magnus	eccentric
	hip – figures c to e	femur, acetabulum of pelvis	flexion to extension	**gluteus maximus**, hamstring group, adductor magnus	erector spinae, transversus abdominus, gracilis	concentric

figure 1.16 – push-up – down then up

figure a

b

c

d

e

Note that during a very controlled downward phase in figures 1.16 a-c the **agonist** muscle at the elbow joint is the **triceps brachii** muscle. This is because the triceps brachii muscle is under extreme tension as it lengthens and so acts as a brake to control the downward phase of the action. The same explanation applies to the pectoralis major and anterior deltoid muscles, which act as the agonists at the shoulder joint.

STUDENT NOTE

The main agonist muscle for each movement is in **red bold** font type. The main antagonist muscle for each movement is in **blue bold** font type in table 1.9.

Table 1.9 – **the full action of the push-up - down then up**

physical activity	joint type	movement produced	agonist muscles	antagonist muscles	type of muscular contraction (isotonic)
arm action in push-up – down movement figure 1.16 a to c	elbow / hinge	flexion	**triceps brachii**, anconeus	**biceps brachii, brachialis**	eccentric
– up movement figure 1.16 c to e	shoulder / ball and socket	horizontal flexion	**pectoralis major**, anterior deltoid	**trapezius**, posterior deltoid	concentric

Question

1) a)   Explain how the type of muscle contraction changes as a weightlifter moves from the squat position, to the standing position, and back to the squat position.

    b)   Identify the main agonist muscle groups responsible for these movement patterns.

    c)   Identify a fixator muscle that is acting as a stabiliser for the action of the prime mover or agonist muscle from the low position in the squat to the upright position.

figure 1.17 – a kick

STUDENT NOTE

The main agonist muscle for each movement is in **red bold** font type in table 1.10.

STUDENT NOTE

As the ankle plantarflexes, during the foot strike of the ball, the tibialis anterior lengthens and is under extreme tension. Then as the ball leaves the foot this muscle will shorten (contract) and the foot will dorsiflex.

Table 1.10 – **leg action in a kick**

This sequence covers the strike phase only for the kick.

physical activity	joint type	movement produced	agonist muscles	synergist muscles (many possible examples)	type of muscular contraction (isotonic)
leg action in kicking (right leg) – figure 1.17	ankle / hinge	plantarflexion	tibialis anterior	rectus abdominus	eccentric
	knee / hinge	extension	quadriceps femoris group	rectus abdominus	concentric
	hip / ball and socket	flexion	iliopsoas, rectus femoris, adductor longus / brevis	rectus abdominus	concentric

Questions

1) Hockey involves movement at many joints in the body. Identify which bones articulate at each of the following joints:

   a) Shoulder.
   b) Knee.
   c) Elbow.
   d) Hip.
   e) Ankle.

2) Complete gaps in the table below naming the main agonist and antagonist in the named activity:

action	main agonist	main antagonist
elevating the shoulder		
extending the elbow joint		
flexing the knee joint		
dorsiflexing the ankle joint		
flexing the trunk		

1.1.3 Antagonist muscle action

This term describes the fact that muscles work in pairs (see figure 1.18).

- The **agonist** is the active muscle, the muscle under tension or doing work and functioning as the **prime mover** of a joint during the desired movement.

- The **antagonist** relaxes to allow the agonist to work as movement occurs.

- For example, curling a bar, the agonist = **biceps brachii muscle**, and the antagonist = **triceps brachii muscle.**

- A **synergist muscle** holds the body in position so that an agonist muscle can operate, thus preventing any unwanted movements that might occur as the prime mover contracts. For example, the trapezius muscle holds the shoulder in place during the bar curling exercise in figure 1.19.

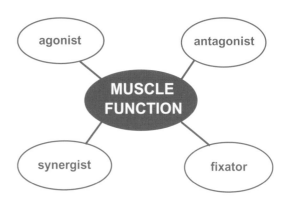

figure 1.18 – muscle function

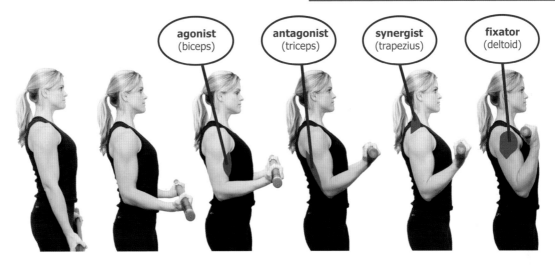

figure 1.19 – muscle function – curling a bar

- A **fixator** muscle by definition is a synergist muscle, but is more specifically referred to as a **fixator** or **stabiliser** when it immobilises the bone of the prime mover's origin, thus providing a stable base for the action of the prime mover. For example, the deltoid muscle stabilises the scapula during a bar curl.

Exam style questions

1) a) The diagram in figure 1.20 shows a shot putter during the delivery phase of the technique.
List the bones that articulate in the shoulder joint.   2 marks

   b) Briefly explain the movement sequence of the right arm during the delivery phase of the shot put.   3 marks

2) Describe the following movement terminology, and give a physical activity for each movement:
Abduction, circumduction, rotation and plantar flexion.
    8 marks

figure 1.20 – a shotputter

Exam style questions

figure 1.21 – long jump take-off and flight

figure c

figure b   a

3) Figure 1.21 a-c shows the final stride, take-off and flight phase of a long jump.

Use these three pictures to help you complete the following joint analysis.

a) Name the type of muscle contraction occurring in the left leg (foot in contact with the ground) in figure 1.21 a, name an agonist muscle responsible for this muscle contraction and explain why you have selected this muscle.   3 marks

b) Complete the following joint analysis below in table 1.11 for figure 1.21 b.   9 marks

Table 1.11 – **joint table**

joint	joint type	articulating bones	main agonist muscle
left ankle			
left knee			
left hip			

c) Describe the changes in movement patterns in the left ankle, knee, hip and trunk from figures 1.21 b to c. 4 marks

d) Suggest two factors which could affect the range of movement at the hip joint.   2 marks

e) Identify the predominant fibre type (refer to page 63) stressed during the take-off and give two reasons why this fibre type would be used. Identify the type of muscle contraction occurring during the take-off phase of the long jump.   4 marks

f) Why is it important to warm-up muscle tissue prior to long jumping?   2 marks

4) Figure 1.22 shows a tennis player completing a forehand drive. Use the figure to help you complete the following joint analysis.

figure 1.22 – tennis forehand

a) For the shoulder joint during horizontal flexion, identify the type of joint, the articulating bones, an agonist muscle, and the type of contraction for the agonist.   4 marks

b) Using the muscles that create flexion of the elbow during the forehand drive, explain what is meant by antagonistic muscle action.   4 marks

c) Identify the movement pattern produced and an agonist muscle responsible for the action on the right hand side of the trunk.   2 marks

d) For the right wrist, identify the articulating bones, a fixator or stabilising muscle, and the movement pattern at the completion of the forehand drive.   3 marks

5) Differentiate between concentric, eccentric and isometric muscle contraction, using practical examples to support your answer.   6 marks

Answers link: http://www.jroscoe.co.uk/downloads/as_a1_revise_pe_edexcel/EdexcelAS_A1_ch1_answers.pdf

CHAPTER 2 - *Muscular skeletal system - Biomechanics*

figure 2.1 – forces at origin and insertion

1.1.4 Components of a lever

The term **internal forces** describes the forces acting (figure 2.1) when a muscle pulls on its **origin O** and **insertion I**. The force on the origin (in red) is equal in size but opposite in direction to the force on the insertion (in black). This changes the **shape** of the person.

Levers

A lever is a **means of applying force at a distance** from the source of the force and has a **fulcrum (pivot)**, **effort** and **load**. In the human body, usually a **joint** and the **attached limbs** or bones act as a lever. **Force** is applied as **effort** by a **muscle** or group of muscles. The **load** is the **force applied** to the **surroundings** by the lever.

Classification of levers

figure 2.2 - elbow/triceps lever

a class 1 lever

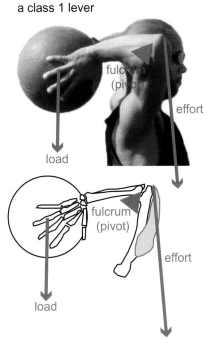

fulcrum (pivot)

effort

load

fulcrum (pivot)

effort

load

Class 1 lever

This is a see-saw lever with the fulcrum in between the effort and the load. It is found rarely in the body, for example the triceps/elbow/forearm lever (see figure 2.2), or the atlas/neck muscles used in the nodding movement.

Class 2 lever

This is a wheelbarrow lever where the load is bigger than the effort, and the fulcrum is at one end of the lever with the load in between the effort and the fulcrum. This is found rarely in the body, the main example being the Achilles tendon/calf muscles (gastrocnemius and soleus) and ankle joint lever (see figure 2.3). This is used in most running or walking movements with the fulcrum underneath the ball of the foot as it drives the body forward. This class of lever always has an advantage - the load is always bigger than the effort.

figure 2.3 - ankle/calf lever

a class 2 lever

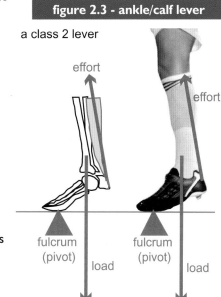

effort

effort

fulcrum (pivot)

fulcrum (pivot)

load

load

Class 3 lever

This class of lever again has the fulcrum at one end of the lever arm, with the effort in between the load and the fulcrum. It has a mechanical disadvantage, the effort is bigger than the load and is the most common system found in body. For example the elbow/biceps/forearm lever (see figure 2.4), or the knee/quadriceps/tibia/fibula systems (see figure 2.5 page 28).

figure 2.4 – the elbow and forearm lever

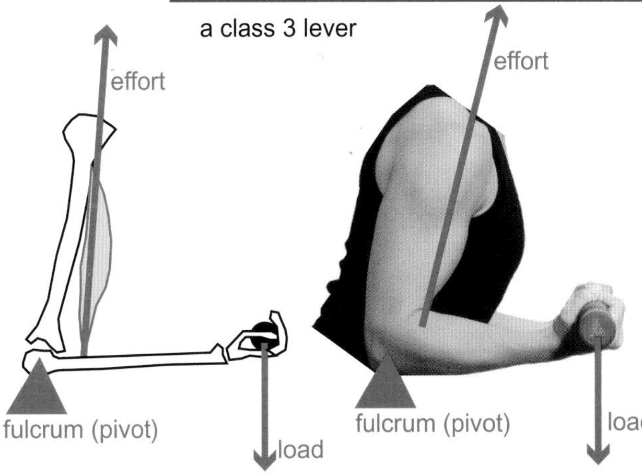

a class 3 lever

effort

effort

fulcrum (pivot)

load

fulcrum (pivot)

load

Effects of the length of lever

The **length of the lever** or **resistance arm** of the lever (**d** in figure 2.6) affects the **load** able to be exerted by the lever, and the **speed** at which the hand can move. The longer the lever **d**, the smaller the value of the load for a given biceps strength and value of the **effort arm** (distance between effort and pivot). The longer the lever arm **d**, the faster the load can be applied (as the limb moves through its range - a longer limb - the hand would move further in the same time).

This means that the hand of a thrower with long arms will be moving faster than the hand of a thrower with short arms if each is turning (rotating) at the same speed.

The **shorter** the **effort arm** the less load can be exerted. The shorter the load (resistance) arm of a person the bigger the load can be. This is why successful weightlifters tend to have short arms.

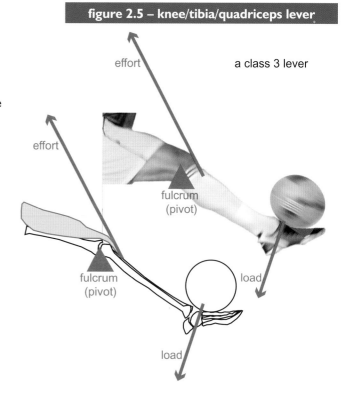

figure 2.5 – knee/tibia/quadriceps lever

a class 3 lever

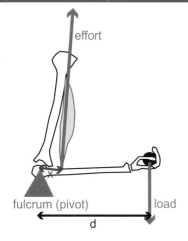

figure 2.6 – the length of a lever arm

1.1.5 Newton's laws of motion

Newton's first law

Newton's first law of motion describes what happens when **zero net force** acts, which means that all forces acting must cancel out. In figure 2.7 the forces (green arrows) **cancel out**. The vertical forces are the same size (arrows are the same length) but in opposite directions. The horizontal forces are also of the same size and in opposite directions, hence all forces cancel out.

When there is zero net force acting on an object:
*   The object is **stationary**.
*   **Or** the object moves at **constant velocity**.
Hence when any object moves at constant velocity, all forces must cancel out, the net force must be zero.

figure 2.7 – a sprinter at constant speed

Inertia

The first law is also known as the law of **inertia**. The concept of inertia is that a massive object will remain at rest and will require a force to shift it, and once moving, will require a force to change its motion (accelerate or decelerate it). Sometimes, the word **inertia** is used to represent the **mass** of a body or object.

Newton's second law

Newton's second law of motion describes what happens when a **net force acts** on a body. **A net force** produces **acceleration** or **deceleration** of the body or changes the direction of the body (swerving). In the motion of a sprinter the acceleration is produced by the net force applied, which must be forwards if the sprinter is accelerating forwards. When the sprinter **decelerates**, there is a net **force backwards**. In figure 2.8, the vertical arrows (representing vertical forces) are the same length but in opposite directions, and hence cancel out. The horizontal forces are both acting backwards, therefore there is a net force acting backwards on her. This means that she is **decelerating** (horizontally!).

figure 2.8– a sprinter decelerating

- Newton's second law also says that the bigger the **net** force, the greater the **acceleration** of the person.
- Hence a **stronger** sprinter should be able to **accelerate** out of the blocks quicker.
- However, the more mass an object has, the less the acceleration for a given force.
- Hence a heavier (more massive) sprinter will accelerate less than a lighter sprinter.

This is expressed mathematically as: **F = m x a**
(force = mass x acceleration)

As discussed above, slowing down (**deceleration**) is also caused by force. Hence a bike hitting a barrier encounters a large force, since a large deceleration slows the bike very quickly, possibly wrecking it and hurting the rider. However, if the cyclist had applied the brakes moderately, he or she would have encountered less deceleration, taking longer to stop, but would do so safely.

Newton's third law

Newton's third law of motion describes what happens when **two bodies** (or objects) exert forces on one another. Action and reaction are equal and opposite and always occur in pairs.

Action acts on one of the bodies, and the **reaction** to this action acts on the other body. At a sprint start, the athlete **pushes back** on the blocks as hard as possible (this is the **'action'** - see figure 2.9e), and the blocks **push forward** on the athlete (this push forward is the **'reaction force'**). The reaction provides forward acceleration on the athlete. In figure 2.9c , a swimmer pushes backwards on the water with hands and feet (this is the force in **black**, the **action**). At the same time, the water thrusts the swimmer forward (this is the force in red, the **reaction force**).

For **internal forces** within the body, for example in figure 2.1 on page 27, the origin (**O**) and insertion (**I**) of a muscle pull in opposite directions to change the shape of the body. In this example, the **action** is the pull of the muscle (red arrow) on the origin of the muscle, and the **reaction** is the pull of the muscle (**black arrow**) at its opposite end, on the insertion. The effect is to change the shape of the person, by pulling the origin towards the insertion, and bending the limb in question.

Reaction forces

Reaction forces are forces acting via Newton's third law as explained above. When one object pushes on another, the first object experiences a force equal but opposite in direction to the second (figure 2.9):

- a, the jumper pushes down on the ground (black arrow), the ground pushes up on the jumper (red arrow).

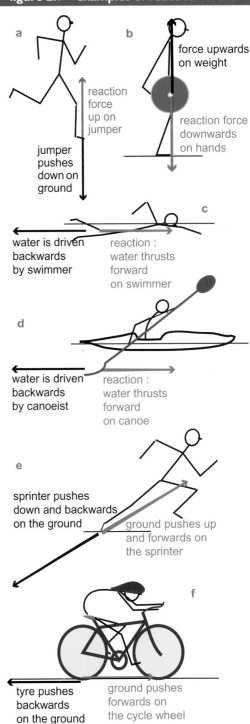

figure 2.9 – examples of reaction forces

a

b

force upwards on weight

reaction force up on jumper

reaction force downwards on hands

jumper pushes down on ground

c

water is driven backwards by swimmer

reaction : water thrusts forward on swimmer

d

water is driven backwards by canoeist

reaction : water thrusts forward on canoe

e

sprinter pushes down and backwards on the ground

ground pushes up and forwards on the sprinter

f

tyre pushes backwards on the ground

ground pushes forwards on the cycle wheel

Reaction forces (figure 2.9 on page 29)

- **b**, the weight lifter pulls up on the weight (black arrow), weight pulls down on lifter (red arrow).
- **c**, the swimmer pushes backwards on the water (black arrow), the water pushes forward on the swimmer (red arrow).
- **d**, canoeist pushes backwards on the water (black arrow), reaction force thrusts the canoe forward (red arrow).
- **e**, sprinter pushes back and down on the ground (black arrow), the ground pushes upwards and forwards on the sprinter (red arrow).
- **f**, in cycling, the tyre on the rear wheel pushes backward on the ground (black arrow), the ground pushes forward on the rear wheel (red arrow).

1.1.6 Stability and the Centre of Mass

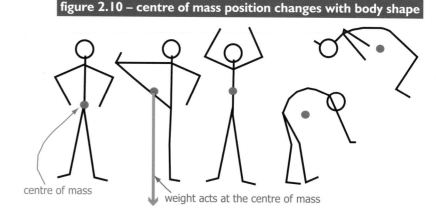

figure 2.10 – centre of mass position changes with body shape

centre of mass

weight acts at the centre of mass

Centre of mass

Centre of mass (CofM) is the single point (on a body) which represents **all the spread out mass** of the body. So, since gravity acts on mass to produce weight, the weight acts at the centre of mass of a body. In figure 2.10, the weight is marked as a green arrow, and it acts downward on the CofM. The CofM can be defined as **'the point of balance of the body'**. As limbs are moved, or the torso changes shape (as when bent over for example), so the position of the centre of mass of the body will move as in figure 2.10. Note that the CofM does not always lie within the body shape, when the torso is bent, it can lie well outside the body mass.

Note that the right hand image in figure 2.10 is that of the layout position for the Fosbury flop high jump technique. The CofM lies underneath the body, and can be below the bar even though the athlete clears the bar.

Balance

The CofM must be **over the base of support** if a person is to be balanced. In figure 2.11, with the leg stuck out sideways, the centre of mass moves to a position to the left of a vertical line through the foot. So, the weight (force) acts downwards through the centre of mass, and will topple the person to the left. Therefore to maintain balance, the person must lean to the right (as we look at her), and thereby bring the CofM back vertically over the supporting foot.

figure 2.11 – a gymnast topples to the left

weight causes toppling to the left

Toppling

Toppling is caused by the weight acting vertically at the CofM and therefore to **one side** of the near edge of the base of support. This fact can be used by divers or gymnasts to initiate a controlled spinning (twisting) fall. And hence lead into somersaults, cartwheels or twists.

figure 2.12 – unstable equilibrium

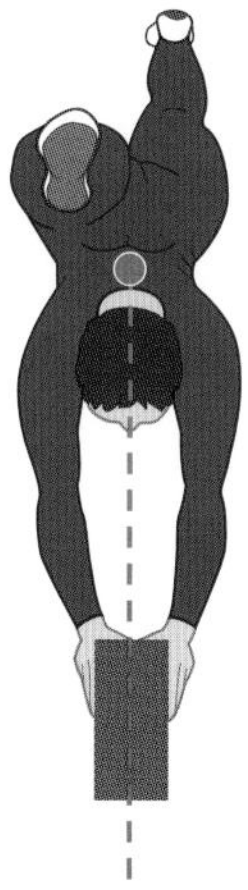

Stability

If an object has its CofM over the base of support, it is said to be in equilibrium. If a slight movement of the object will make it topple, then the object is said to be in unstable equilibrium. An example of this would be a beam gymnast who must carefully control the position of her CofM if she is to remain on the beam (figure 2.12).

The gymnast who lies on the floor would be said to be in neutral or stable equilibrium (figure 2.13). When pushed, he would remain in the same position (or nearly the same) without toppling or falling.

figure 2.13 – neutral or stable equilibrium

1.1.7 Calculation of force

figure 2.14 – direction of a vector

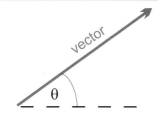

Force

Force is push or pull. The unit of force is the **newton** (10N is approximately the weight of 1 kg). Force changes the state of motion of an object, and causes acceleration or deceleration or change of direction.

One newton of force is the force required to produce an acceleration of 1 ms^{-2} in a mass of 1 kg. This is related to the inertial property of mass - the more force applied, the more acceleration produced (see Newton's second law, page 29).

Force has **direction** and size (**value**), and is therefore a vector. When describing a force it is important to explain where the force acts (the point of action), as well as the direction.

figure 2.15 – vectors cancel out

Vectors and scalars

The ideas behind **vectors** and **scalars** are used extensively in maths and physics. A **vector** is a quantity which has **size** (called magnitude) and **direction**. By quantity we mean something like weight, displacement, velocity, acceleration, force, and momentum, all of which are vectors, and therefore have to have a direction connected to them as well as value or size. For example, a force could be 100 newtons downward (the downward specifies the direction), an acceleration could be 10 metres per second squared forwards (the forwards specifies the direction).

Usually in maths, the direction is specified by the angle to the x-axis in a graph of an arrow drawn on the graph, with the size (magnitude) represented by the length of the arrow (figure 2.14).

A **scalar** is a quantity which has size or value only. Quantities like mass, speed, energy, power, and length have a value only. For example, a person could have a mass of 60 kg, or an amount of 1000 joules of energy are used up when performing an exercise. No directional angle is required when talking about these quantities.

figure 2.16 – forces cancel out

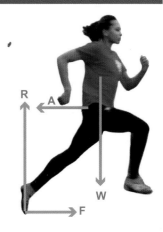

Net Force

The point of this is that when more than one vector has to be taken into account, then they must be added together taking note of the direction of each vector. In figure 2.15 for example, two forces of 500 newtons are acting, the green force acts upwards, and the red force acts downwards. Because they are acting in opposite directions, they add up to nil, in other words they exactly cancel out to give zero net force. Note that this gymnast is also in unstable equilibrium.

- In figure 2.16, the vertical forces acting on the sprinter are the weight (W = force due to gravity) acting downwards, and the ground reaction force (R) acting upwards. These two forces are identical in value but opposite in direction and therefore cancel out exactly to give zero net force vertically.
- The horizontal forces are the friction force (F) acting forwards, and the **air resistance** or drag (A) acting backwards. These two forces are equal in value but opposite in direction, and hence cancel out to give zero net force acting horizontally.
- Hence relatively large forces can act, but they can cancel out because of their direction. Note that zero net force does not mean that the sprinter is stationary, see Newton's first law of motion (page 28).
- Equally, when the forces are added up and there is an unbalanced **resultant** (the forces **do not cancel out**), then there is a **net force** acting. The body on which this force is acting will then accelerate in the **direction** of this net force as specified by Newton's second law (page 29).

Weight and mass

These two ideas are often confused. **Mass** is a scalar and represents the total quantity of matter in an object. **Weight** is the force due to gravity on a mass (with a direction towards the centre of the Earth) and can be calculated from the fact that the gravitational field strength at the Earth's surface is approximately 10 newtons for each kilogramme of mass. Hence if the mass of the sprinter in figure 2.16 is 50 kg, then her weight would be 50 x 10 = 500 newtons towards the centre of the Earth.

> **STUDENT NOTE**
>
> If this sprinter were to obtain astronaut status and visit the moon (where the gravitational field strength is 1.67 newtons per kilogramme), then her mass would still be 50 kg, but her weight would be 50 x 1.67 = 83.5 newtons towards the centre of the moon.

1.1.8 Response of muscular and skeletal systems to warm-up

Warm-up

Figure 2.17 provides an overview of the issues within an **active** warm-up. Warm-up usually consists of a series of low level aerobic exercises which can be sport specific or general in nature (jogging, SAQ, cycle ergometer, stretching). It includes a pulse-raiser, mobilising exercises for the joints, some stretching exercises for the muscles and a sport specific skill element.

The sport specific element usually includes exercises of increasing intensity up to the moment of game or competition beginning.

The aim of this element is to get the sportsperson into the rhythm and flow of their forthcoming activity, practise skills and movements expected later, and build confidence before the event starts.

figure 2.17 – warm-up overview

The benefits of warm-up on the muscular system

* Greater strength of contraction due to improved elasticity of muscle fibres.
* Faster speed of contraction due to an increased speed of nerve transmission to the muscle fibres.
* Faster speed of contraction and relaxation of the muscle fibres due to an increase in muscle temperature.
* Increased speed of strength of contraction due to an improvement in coordination between antagonistic pairs because of a reduction in muscle viscosity.
* Increased speed and strength of contraction due to an increase in enzyme activity in warmer muscle fibres.
* Reduced risk of injury despite an increase in speed of strength of contraction due to an increase in blood flow and oxygen to the muscle.
* Prepares tendons to improve the stability and contractile activity of skeletal muscles that are ready to react to increased activity.

Exam style question

1) A Level. Warm-up is considered to be an essential element of a training programme. Explain how the muscular and skeletal systems respond to a warm-up. Support your answer with details of intensity and duration of the warm-up for a sport of your own choice.
15 marks

The benefits of warm-up on the skeletal system

- Skeletal flexibility improves the range of motion possible around a specific joint or a series of articulations in preparation for the training session or competition.

- Warm-up increases the production of **synovial fluid** from the **articular cartilage** (McCutchen's weeping theory of lubrication).
- Synovial fluid is squeezed in and out of the articular cartilage at the points of contact, providing the articular surfaces with   nutrients and oxygen, and reduces friction between joints.

- The effect of warm-up on **bone density** is not known.

Intensity and duration

- The intensity and duration of warm-up depend on the demands of the sport, or the **demands** of the training session.

Warm-up can vary enormously in both factors, for example:
- An Olympic hurdler and sprinter taking 2 hours, for an event lasting less than 10 seconds, and incorporating multiple rhythmic and skill based movements specific to the event.
- The GB hockey team at the Olympics taking 1 hour, performing SAQ exercises, multiple passing and goal shooting plays, all with relatively low intensity.
- An Olympic weightlifter whose competitive effort involves a maximum of 6 efforts each lasting less than 2 seconds, including a systematic build-up for each of the two lifts, taking up to 2 hours and involving up to 90% of 1RM practice lifts.
- A rugby team taking 30 minutes with jogging, 80% sprinting and stretching, as well as some high intensity short duration exercises done to the accompaniment of verbal chanting to assist in the psychological preparation.

Exam style questions

2) a) Explain with diagrams what is meant by the centre of mass of a body.   2 marks

b) Explain with the aid of pin-man diagrams how the centre of mass of a long jumper changes from the take-off position to the flight phase shown in figure 2.18.
5 marks

figure 2.18 – a long jumper in flight

figure 2.19 – swimmer starting a race

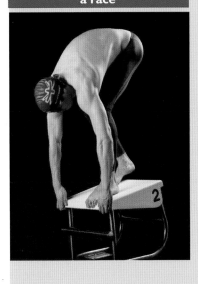

3) Figure 2.19 shows a swimmer holding a balance just before the start of a race. Explain how the position of the centre of mass can affect the swimmer's balance. Describe how the swimmer in figure 2.19 can use his knowledge of balance to achieve his most effective block start.
5 marks

figure 2.20 – long jumper taking off

4) Sketch the lever system which would represent the action of the biceps muscle in flexing the arm. Show on your diagram the resistance arm of the lever.   3 marks

5) In figure 2.20 of a jumper taking off, name, sketch and label the lever system operating at knee **B** during this action.   3 marks

Answers link: http://www.jroscoe.co.uk/downloads/as_a1_revise_pe_edexcel/EdexcelAS_A1_ch2_answers.pdf

6) In softball, what order (class) of lever is shown in the hitting action in figure 2.21? State **one** disadvantage and **one** advantage of reducing the bat length for a beginner.
3 marks

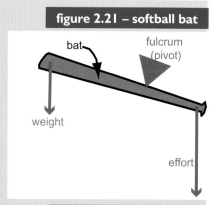

figure 2.21 – softball bat

7) Name, sketch and label the lever system which is operating at the ankle of leg **C** when doing the sprint set action illustrated in figure 2.22.
3 marks

figure 2.22 – ankle lever system

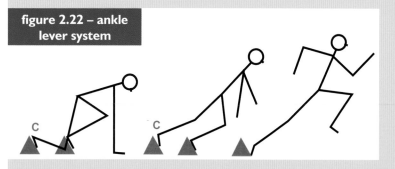

figure 2.23 – a press-up

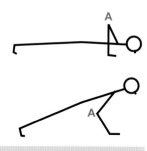

8) a) Figure 2.23 shows an elbow joint A of a person performing an exercise. Draw a simplified sketch to show the lever system, indicating the various forces operating.
4 marks

b) On your diagram draw and label the effort and resistance arm.
3 marks

c) Diagram 2.24 shows the elbow joint and the position of the triceps muscle in relation to it when supporting a load (a shot) behind the head. Draw a simplified sketch to show the lever system, indicating the various forces operating.
4 marks

figure 2.24 – elbow joint and triceps lever

d = 0.3m   x = 0.03m

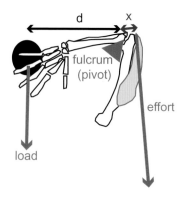

9) The table shows the speed of a 19 year-old male sprinter during a 200m race.

speed (ms⁻¹)	time (seconds)
0.0	0
6.0	1
7.5	2
8.2	3
8.4	4
8.5	5
8.5	7
8.4	8
8.3	10
8.2	13
8.1	18
8.0	22

a) Plot a graph of speed against time during this race. When does he reach maximum speed and what happens to his speed between 8 and 22 seconds?   7 marks

b) Acceleration is the change of speed per second. Use the graph to establish his speed at 0.5 seconds and 1.5 seconds and calculate the average acceleration between 0.5 and 1.5 seconds.
3 marks

c) Successful games players are often able to change their velocity rapidly in the game situation. Explain the biomechanics behind this ability using examples from a game of your choice.
6 marks

10) a) A sprinter uses her calf muscles to push on the blocks at the start of a run. Explain, using Newton's laws, how this enables her to accelerate forwards out of the blocks.
3 marks

b) If the resultant forward force was 300 newtons and the runner's mass was 60 kg, what would be her acceleration?
2 marks

c) What would be the speed of the runner after 1.5 seconds, assuming that the acceleration is the same over that period of time?
2 marks

d) A squash player drives forward into a forehand stroke. Show how Newton's third law of motion explains his ability to do this.
3 marks

e) Explain why the turn in the discus throw produces greater horizontal range than the standing throw.   3 marks

11) Figure 2.25 shows the distance/time graph for a 100m sprint.
  a) Describe the motion of the sprinter in sections A and B.
  2 marks
  b) Calculate the speed at points C and D and the average acceleration between the points.
  3 marks

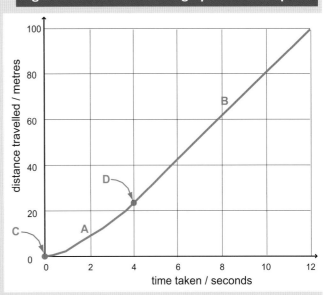

figure 2.25 – distance time graph for 100m sprint

12) a) Use the diagram in figure 2.26 of a basketballer just about to take off into a jump shot, and your knowledge of Newton's Laws of motion explain why the basketball jumper takes off.
  3 marks

  b) If the vertical upward ground reaction force on the jumper is 2000N, and the weight of the jumper is 800N, estimate the net upward force acting on him.
  1 mark

  c) The mass of the jumper is 80 kg, calculate his upward acceleration during this part of the jump.
  2 marks

13) a) The graph in figure 2.27 shows the start of a 100m sprint swim race. Using Newton's laws of motion, explain how the swimmer achieves the initial forward motion.
  3 marks

  b) Describe what has happened to the swimmer at point A and explain the motion that occurs.
  3 marks

figure 2.26 – basketballer about to take off

figure 2.27 – start of 100m swim race

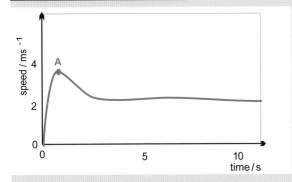

figure 2.28 – forces acting on a runner

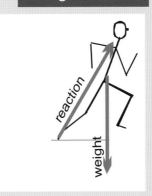

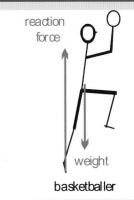

reaction force

weight

basketballer

14) a) What characterises a vector quantity?
  2 marks

  b) Figure 2.28 shows the forces acting on a runner at the start of a race. Use a vector diagram to show how you could work out the resultant force acting.
  3 marks

  c) Sketch a pin man drawing of a person standing still showing all the forces acting on him.
  2 marks

15) Tennis players have to change direction quickly during a match to recover to the centre of the court. Figure 2.29 shows a tennis player just after hitting a forehand and then starting to recover to the centre of the court in the direction shown.

  a) Draw a pin diagram of the tennis player as he pushes off the court surface to recover to the centre of the court, showing all forces acting on the tennis player at this point. All forces must be clearly identified.
  3 marks

  b) Explain the factors that affect the horizontal force at this point. Apply Newton's second law of motion to explain the effect of this force on the player.
  4 marks

figure 2.29 – a tennis player moves between strokes

moving

16) Explain the effects of warming up muscle tissue. Why is it more important to warm-up prior to an anaerobic training session as opposed to a 3 mile easy jog?
  6 marks

1.2.1 Anatomy and physiology of the cardiovascular, ciculatory and respiratory systems

This chapter deals with the respiratory system.

CHAPTER 3 - *The cardio-respiratory system*

1.2.2 The structure and function of the respiratory system

STUDENT NOTE	Prior knowledge of the structure and function of the respiratory system is assumed, but your syllabus requires understanding of the respiratory structures.

Respiratory structures

From figure 3.1 you will see that the **air pathway** as the air is breathed in follows the route:
nasal cavity to **pharynx** to **larynx** to **trachea** to **bronchi** to **bronchioles** to **respiratory bronchioles** (the smaller tubes which branch out from the bronchioles) to **alveolar ducts** (the tubes connecting the respiratory bronchioles to the alveoli) to **alveoli**.

The **trachea** consists of an incomplete ring of cartilage that keeps the airway open and allows swallowing. The nasal cavity, pharynx, larynx, trachea and bronchi have ciliated linings and **mucous glands** to provide a cleaning and filtering mechanism for incoming air.

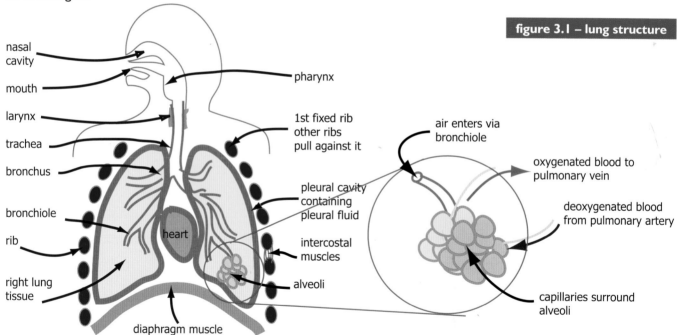

figure 3.1 – lung structure

Lung structure

The **pulmonary pleura** is a self-enclosed serous membrane covering the lungs. It lines the thoracic cavity, middle wall of the thorax and diaphragm. This membrane secretes pleural fluid into the pleural cavity thereby reducing friction between lung tissue and ribs, aiding inspiration as pleural pressure reduces, and expiration as pleural pressure increases.

Alveoli (see figure 3.1) are elastic, moist, and permeable (as single layered epithelium cells) and are surrounded by a network of capillaries. These are adapted for gaseous exchange, as oxygen travels through the capillary walls **from** the lung space **into** the blood within the capillaries, and carbon dioxide travels in the opposite direction through the capillary walls.

Pulmonary ventilation is '**the process by which we move air into and out of the lungs**'.

1.2.3 Mechanics of breathing and the physiology of the respiratory system

The actual mechanism of breathing is brought about by changes in air pressure (**intrapulmonary pressure**) in the lungs relative to atmospheric pressure, and as a result of the muscular actions of the 11 pairs of intercostal muscles and the diaphragm.

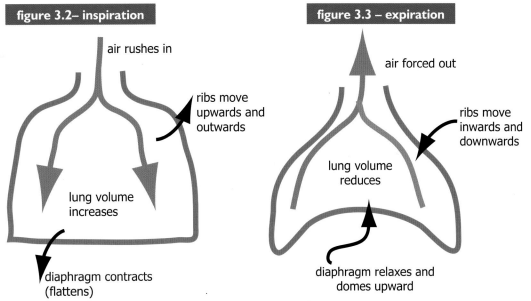

figure 3.2– inspiration

air rushes in

ribs move upwards and outwards

lung volume increases

diaphragm contracts (flattens)

figure 3.3 – expiration

air forced out

ribs move inwards and downwards

lung volume reduces

diaphragm relaxes and domes upward

STUDENT NOTE

For a summary view of the mechanics of breathing, see figure 3.2 for inspiration, 3.3 for expiration, and table 3.1.

Table 3.1 – **inspiration and expiration at rest and during exercise** (see figures 3.2 and 3.3)

inspiration	expiration
at rest	**at rest**
external intercostal muscles contract	external intercostal muscles relax - a passive process
diaphragm contracts – becomes flatter	diaphragm relaxes – domes upward into chest cavity – a passive process
internal intercostal muscles relax	
ribs and sternum move upwards and outwards	ribs and sternum move downwards and inwards
increase in chest cavity volume	decrease in chest cavity volume
pressure between pleural membranes is reduced	pressure between pleural membranes is increased
allows elastic pulmonary tissue to expand	compresses elastic pulmonary tissue
lung volume increases	lung volume decreases
pulmonary air pressure falls below atmospheric pressure (outside the body)	pulmonary air pressure is driven above atmospheric pressure (outside the body)
hence atmospheric air is forced into the lungs	hence atmospheric air is forced out of the lungs via the respiratory passages
until lung pressure equals the pressure outside again	until lung pressure equals the pressure outside again
during exercise	**during exercise**
additional muscles in the chest and torso contract (scalenes, sternocleidomastoid, pectoralis major / minor)	internal intercostal muscles and abdominal muscles contract powerfully, acting on ribs and body cavity
chest cavity volume further increased	chest cavity volume is further reduced
more air forced into the lungs	more pulmonary air is forced out of the lungs

The process of transport of respiratory gases

Several factors affect the rate at which the gases taking part in the respiration process are exchanged (figure 3.4).

Diffusion

The exchange of gases between lungs and blood and their movement at tissue level takes place passively by **diffusion.**

This is the movement of molecules through space by random collision with other molecules. This process would eventually result in random mixing of all the molecules present in a space. Molecules move using this process through gases and liquids, and can migrate through membranes (like tissue boundaries such as cell walls).

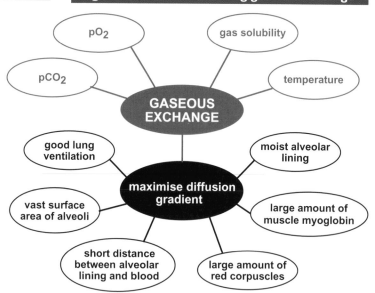

figure 3.4 – factors affecting gaseous exchange

A **diffusion gradient** is a situation where the concentration of molecules of a particular substance (say oxygen for example) is greater on one side of a space than on the other side of the same space. Hence a diffusion gradient will cause molecules to move across a space (or membrane) **by random** mixing or random molecular collision with membrane walls. Steep **diffusion gradients** are maintained by the factors shown in figure 3.4, and help move substances from higher concentrations to lower concentrations where they take part in the respiration process.

Gases diffuse from high to low pressure, and so the rate of exchange (either at lungs or tissue site) depends on the **partial pressure** of each gas (in blood or tissue site or alveolar air), **gas solubility** (in blood or tissue cell fluids), and **temperature.**

Partial pressure

Partial pressure (**p**) is defined as '**the pressure a gas exerts within a mixture of gases**', so pO_2 and pCO_2 are the partial pressures exerted by oxygen and carbon dioxide respectively within a mixture of these and other gases (for example nitrogen) present in the air or the tissues. The partial pressure of a gas is directly related to the concentration (number of molecules per cubic metre) of gas molecules in a space. At a given temperature, the bigger the **p**, the more molecules of gas are present.

Gaseous exchange

Gaseous exchange is the process whereby oxygen from the air **in the lungs** is transferred by diffusion to the blood flowing through the alveoli (see figure 3.5). At the same time, carbon dioxide is transferred from the blood arriving at the lungs, into the air in the lungs, which is subsequently breathed out. The gases travel **through** the capillary and alveolar walls, with oxygen diffusing into the blood, and carbon dioxide diffusing **out** of the blood.

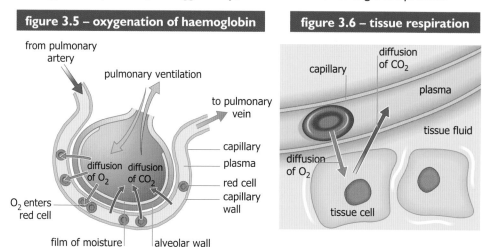

figure 3.5 – oxygenation of haemoglobin

figure 3.6 – tissue respiration

The reverse process happens at the **tissue site** (for example, active muscle tissue – see figure 3.6). Here, oxygen is carried by blood into the tissues and there it diffuses into tissue cells. At the same time, carbon dioxide diffuses **out of** tissue cells into the blood (which then flows back through the venous system and the heart and back to the lungs).

How gaseous exchange is achieved in the alveoli

The first step in oxygen transport involves the diffusion of oxygen **from** the **alveoli** into the blood.

In venous blood (arriving at the lungs from tissues) the partial pressure of oxygen (pO_2) = 5.3 kPa. The partial pressure of oxygen in alveolar air is 13.3 kPa, so the oxygen travels through the alveolar and capillary walls from the lung space **into** the blood where it combines with haemoglobin to form **oxyhaemoglobin** ($Hb(O_2)_4$) as follows:

$$Hb + 4O_2 \rightarrow Hb(O_2)_4$$

One of the **short-term effects** of physical activity is to cause a **small increase** in **pulmonary blood pressure**, which distorts red blood corpuscles within the alveolar capillary system, and this enables **10 times as much oxygen** to be picked up as at rest.

figure 3.7 – oxyhaemoglobin dissociation curve

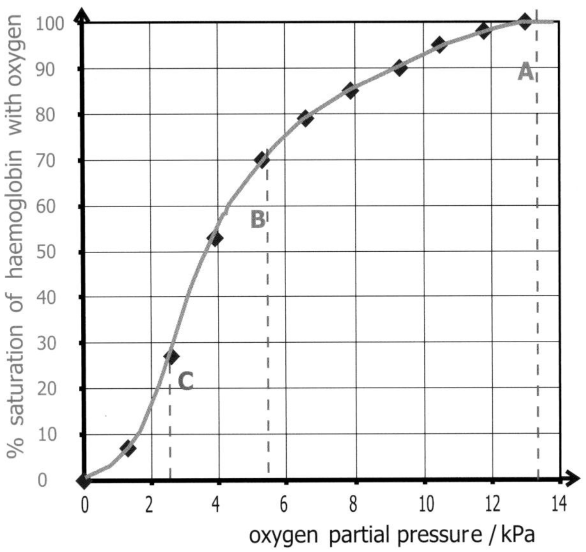

The **oxyhaemoglobin dissociation curve** (see figure 3.7) describes the percentage of haemoglobin saturated with oxygen at a given pO_2. At 13.3 kPa pressure, oxygen will combine with Hb at 98% of the **maximum possible** (see the red vertical line labelled **A** on figure 3.7, this is at 13.3kPa and intersects the graph line at almost 100%). This means that Hb leaving the lungs is almost completely saturated with O_2. (Note that 3% of oxygen dissolves in blood plasma).

Blood carrying this O_2 then travels out of the lungs to the heart via the pulmonary vein, then out to the body through the aorta and main arteries. At altitude, the pO_2 is less, which means that haemoglobin cannot carry as much oxygen as at sea level, therefore reducing the ability to perform physical work. This is called **hypoxia** (lowered pO_2).

At the same time, carbon dioxide is transferred in the opposite direction, from the blood into the alveolar air. The concentration of CO_2 in atmospheric air is about 0.049% (very small), and therefore pCO_2 in venous blood arriving (via the heart) from the body tissues is higher than in the alveoli air (breathed into the lungs). Therefore CO_2 diffuses through the alveolar membrane (from blood to air in lung) and is expired. Between 3% and 6% of air breathed out is CO_2 as shown in table 3.2.

Table 3.2 – **differences between inhaled and exhaled air**

	differences between inhaled and exhaled air		
	inhaled(%)	exhaled air at rest (%)	exhaled air during exercise (%)
O_2	21	17	15
CO_2	0.049	3	6

How gaseous exchange is achieved at the tissue cell site

The second step in oxygen transport involves the transfer of oxygen from the blood into tissue cells.

The role of myoglobin

Myoglobin is a substance somewhat similar to haemoglobin in that it attracts and binds to molecular oxygen. Myoglobin has a greater affinity for oxygen than haemoglobin and is located within cells, where its role is to enable oxygen to be carried across a cell to the **mitochondria** where the oxygen is consumed and energy transfer takes place (which, for example, enables muscle tissue to contract). Arriving (arterial) blood has an oxygen partial pressure (pO_2 = 13.3 kPa). This is greater than tissue pO_2 since the oxygen is being used up in the cells during the energy creating process. Because **myoglobin** in the tissue cells has a greater affinity for oxygen than does haemoglobin, oxygen diffuses **through** the capillary and cell walls **from** the blood **into** the tissue cells. Myoglobin then facilitates oxygen transfer to the mitochondria, notably at the start of exercise and during intense exercise when cellular pO_2 decreases considerably.

Oxygen transfer at rest

At a pO_2 of 5.5 kPa, which is the normal pO_2 in resting tissue capillaries, haemoglobin is about 70% saturated (this corresponds to red vertical line **B** in figure 3.7 on page 39). This means that approximately 30% of the oxygen bound to haemoglobin is released into the blood and can diffuse into the tissue spaces.

Oxygen transfer during vigorous exercise

During **vigorous exercise** the pO_2 in tissue spaces may decline to levels as low as 2.5 kPa. Therefore, looking at line **C** in figure 3.7, only about 25% of the haemoglobin remains saturated, and 75% of the oxygen bound to haemoglobin is released into the blood and can diffuse through the capillary walls into the active tissue spaces. The absorption and utilisation of oxygen from the blood leads to a difference in the oxygen content of arterial and venous blood. This difference is known as the **arterio-venous oxygen difference** or a-$\overline{v}O_{2diff}$.

The effect of pH, pCO_2 and temperature on oxygen release

Other factors influence the degree to which oxygen binds to haemoglobin. **During exercise**, tissue cell and blood temperature increases, pCO_2 increases due to the greater need for energy, and pH decreases due to the greater presence of H^+ ions from lactic acid or creation of H^+ from dissociating carbonic acid by the released CO_2. All these conditions cause reduction in the affinity of haemoglobin for oxygen. This means that more O_2 is released (than would be the case if no exercise were being taken), and hence more O_2 is then available to active tissue sites which are working harder. **So the harder the tissue is working, the more O_2 is released**.

The effect of increases in acidity, pCO_2 and temperature is to cause the oxyhaemoglobin dissociation curve to shift downward and to the right (enhanced unloading). This phenomenon is called the 'Böhr effect'.

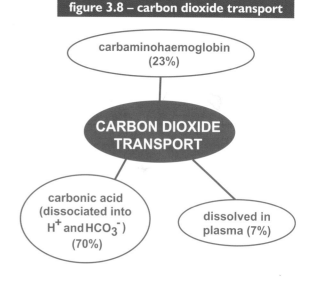

figure 3.8 – carbon dioxide transport

Carbon dioxide transport (figure 3.8)

CO_2 is produced in the cells as an end product of tissue cell respiration (production of energy from combination of fuel with oxygen). Hence, the fluid within muscle tissue cells has a higher pCO_2 than in the blood. Therefore CO_2 diffuses back through cell and capillary walls in the **opposite** direction (from tissue to departing blood).
CO_2 is transported in venous blood as:

- **Carbonic acid** mostly dissociated into H^+ and HCO_3^- (70%).
- **Carbaminohaemoglobin** (23%).
- **CO_2 dissolved in blood plasma** (7%).

In the lung capillaries carbon dioxide is released, then it diffuses from the blood into the alveoli and is expired out of the lungs.

1.2.4 Lung volumes and capacities

Interpretations from spirometer readings

A **spirometer** is a device that is used to measure pulmonary volumes. Figure 3.9 presents a typical lung volume trace resulting from a person breathing into a calibrated spirometer, at rest and during exercise. Note that during the exercise period tidal volume increases because of the encroachment on inspiratory reserve volume (IRV) and expiratory reserve volume (ERV), but more noticeably on the IRV.

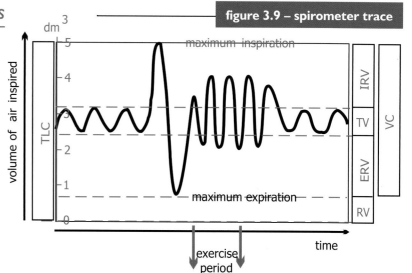

figure 3.9 – spirometer trace

Definitions for pulmonary volumes

Average values for male and females are shown in table 3.3 below.
Lung **volumes** vary with age, gender, body size and stature, and are defined and explained in table 3.3.

Table 3.3 – **lung volumes and definitions**

lung volumes		definitions	average values (ml)		change during exercise
			male	female	
TLC	total lung capacity	total volume of air in the lungs following maximum inspiration.	6000	4200	slight decrease
VC	vital capacity	maximum volume of air that can be forcibly expired following maximum inspiration.	4800	3200	slight decrease
TV	tidal volume	volume of air inspired **or** expired per breath.	600	500	increase
IRV	inspiratory reserve volume	volume of air that can be forcibly inspired above resting tidal volume.	3000	1900	decrease
ERV	expiratory reserve volume	volume of air that can be forcibly expired above resting tidal volume.	1200	800	decrease
RV	residual volume	volume of air remaining in the lungs after maximal expiration.	1200	1000	stays same
$\dot{V}E$=TV x f	minute ventilation	volume of air inspired **or** expired in one minute.	7200	6000	dramatic increase

Lung **capacities** are made up of combinations of lung volumes. The following list uses as examples the average **male** values from table 3.3 above.

Inspiratory capacity (IC)	= TV + IRV	(3600 ml)
Expiratory capacity (EC)	= TV + ERV	(1800 ml)
Vital capacity (VC)	= TV + IRV + ERV	(4800 ml)
Functional residual capacity (FRC)	= RV + ERV	(2400 ml)
Total lung capacity (TLC)	= VC + RV	(6000 ml)

Minute ventilation

Minute ventilation ($\dot{V}E$) is defined as '**the volume of air that is inspired or expired in one minute**'. Minute ventilation can be calculated by multiplying tidal volume (**TV**) by the number of breaths (**f**) taken in one minute (see the last row of table 3.3). Below are examples of minute ventilation values you would expect at rest and during differing intensities of exercise. A normal male resting breathing frequency is about 12 breaths per minute, and this is the value of **f** in the first row of the list below. This would increase to about 25 (breaths per minute) for submaximal exercise, and rapid breathing of about 55 breaths per minute during maximal exercise.

(dm³)	$\dot{V}E$	=	**TV**	x	**f**		
at rest	7.2	=	0.6	x	12	= 7.2	litres per minute or 7200 ml per minute – since 1 dm³ is 1 litre or 1000 ml.
sub-max	60	=	2.4	x	25	= 60	litres per minute or 60000 ml per minute.
max	121	=	2.2	x	55	= 121	litres per minute or 121000 ml per minute.

Hence from sub-maximal to maximal exercise breathing rate or respiratory frequency doubles. This dramatic increase often corresponds with the onset of anaerobic metabolism or the onset of blood lactate accumulation or **OBLA** at the expense of a decreasing tidal volume.

What is actually happening is a regulation of minute ventilation in response to **increased carbon dioxide** production and the need to get rid of carbon dioxide during expiration. The tidal volume decreases slightly because it is not physically possible to inspire the maximum possible volume of air during maximal exercise at a high breathing rate. This regulatory response is discussed further on page 43.

Ventilation – short-term response to exercise

STUDENT NOTE	You will be required to sketch and interpret these patterns in your exam.

Figure 3.10 compares the changes in minute ventilation with time during low intensity and high intensity exercise.

During the short period before exercise begins, during the exercise period, and during the recovery period immediately after exercise (see graph in figure 3.10) the following describes the reasons for the changes in rate of ventilation or minute ventilation.

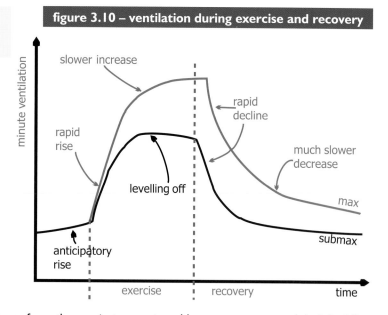

figure 3.10 – ventilation during exercise and recovery

- **Anticipatory rise** in $\dot{V}E$ is due to the hormonal action of **adrenaline** and **noradrenaline** on the respiratory centre in the brain. This rise is caused by the excitement in anticipation of exercise beginning.

- **Rapid rise** of $\dot{V}E$ on exercise beginning is due to **proprioceptor** sensory **stimulation**, and also due to continued release of hormones. During this period, exercise is anaerobic in nature and does not require oxygen from the respiratory system. However, an oxygen debt is building up, and this will need to be dealt with later.

- During **sub-maximal** exercise, a **levelling off** of $\dot{V}E$ occurs as a **steady state** is developed between oxygen required and provided by the respiratory system. Some recovery of O_2 debt (aerobic) occurs.

- During **maximal** workloads there is a continued **slower increase** in $\dot{V}E$ as anaerobic systems continue to be stressed. This produces lactic acid + CO_2 + K^+, which stimulate **chemoreceptors** at maximal level. The main stimulant for increased rates of ventilation is the presence of carbon dioxide in the blood flowing past chemoreceptors. See page 43 for details of the location and function of these receptors which stimulate the respiratory centre in the brain.

- As exercise ends, there is a **rapid decline** in $\dot{V}E$ due to cessation of proprioceptive stimuli and the withdrawal of hormones, then a levelling out to pre-exercise values.

- Later, after maximal work, there is a **much slower decrease** in $\dot{V}E$ due to the clearance of metabolites such as **lactic acid** and **carbon dioxide** as systems return to normal resting values.

Neural regulation of pulmonary ventilation

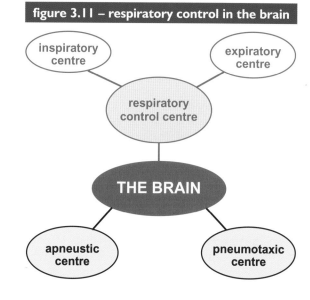

figure 3.11 – respiratory control in the brain

The **respiratory control centre** (**RCC**, see figure 3.11) is located within the medulla oblongata of the brain and regulates pulmonary ventilation. Rate of breathing (also called the **frequency** of breathing (**f**) and defined as **'the number of breaths taken in one minute'**) and **depth of breathing** (known as **tidal volume** (**TV**) and defined as **'the volume of air inspired or expired in one breath'**) are controlled by neurones within the medulla. Although the medullary neurones establish a basic rhythm of breathing, their activities can be influenced by input from other parts of the brain and by input from peripherally located receptors discussed in figure 3.12.

The RCC consists of two parts: the **inspiratory** and **expiratory** centres:

- The **inspiratory centre** is responsible for the basic rhythm of ventilation. At rest impulses are sent via the phrenic and intercostal nerves to the external intercostal muscles and diaphragm causing these muscles to contract to bring about inspiration. When stimulation ceases these muscles relax causing expiration.

- The **expiratory centre** is inactive during quiet breathing. However, during forceful breathing such as during exercise, the expiratory centre actively sends impulses to stimulate the muscles of expiration (sternocleidomastoid, scalenes, pectoralis major and minor) to increase the **rate of breathing** (refer to table 3.1 on page 37 to remind yourself of the mechanics of breathing).

Factors and neural control of breathing

Two additional **brain centres** aid the control of breathing:

- The **apneustic centre** controls the intensity of breathing. It does this by prolonging the firing of the inspiratory neurones, thereby increasing **TV**.

- The **pneumotaxic centre** antagonises the apneustic centre, resulting in the fine-tuning of the breathing rate (**f**).

The body exquisitely regulates the rate and depth of breathing in response to metabolic needs. Figure 3.12 lists the primary factors involved in ventilatory control. This is another example of **negative feedback control**, where, for example, an increase of carbon dioxide in venous blood tends to increase breathing rate which helps extract the carbon dioxide from pulmonary blood and reduce carbon dioxide in blood arriving back at the heart from the lungs.

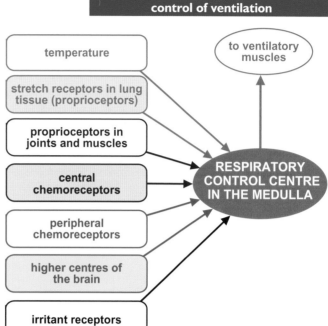

figure 3.12 – primary factors affecting control of ventilation

Chemical control

The **chemical** state of the blood largely regulates pulmonary ventilation at rest.

- **Central chemoreceptors** (located in the medulla) are major regulators, and **respond to increased concentration of carbon dioxide in the blood**. The partial pressure of CO_2 is termed pCO_2, and this regulation process tries to keep pCO_2 to below 5.3 kPa as well as controlling increased acidity (or decreased pH due to H^+ ions from carbonic acid formed in the blood plasma).

- **Peripheral chemoreceptors** (in the aortic and carotid bodies) provide an early warning system as they sense the constituents of blood as it passes them.

- Both central and peripheral chemoreceptors respond to **increased** pCO_2 and **decreased** pH and pO_2 (oxygen concentration in the blood).

These receptors send messages to the inspiratory centre which then stimulates respiratory muscles to increase **rate** (**f**) and **depth of breathing** (**TV**) as described above. For example, lack of oxygen at high altitude stimulates respiration which has nothing to do with exercise, but indicates how these receptors work. This chemical control, via the pneumotaxic and apneustic centres of the brain, adjusts ventilation to maintain arterial blood chemistry within narrow limits. This means that these brain centres attempt to keep blood oxygen to a maximum, and blood carbon dioxide to a minimum by causing the person to adjust breathing rate and depth.

Proprioceptors in joints and muscles

Proprioceptors (such as working muscle spindles) send signals to the RCC about the tension within and state of contraction of a muscle, and hence when a muscle is being used intensely. During physical activity increased stimulation will increase rate and depth of breathing via the inspiratory centre as described above.

Lung stretch receptors

A type of **proprioceptor,** these lung receptors are located within the walls of bronchi and bronchioles. When stimulated these receptors relay information, via the vagus nerves, to the RCC to inhibit the inspiratory centre, resulting in expiration via the expiratory centre. As expiration proceeds, the stretch receptors are no longer stimulated and the decreased inhibitory effect on the inhibitory centre allows the inspiratory centre to become active again, known as the **Hering-Breuer Reflex**. Its overriding effect is to prevent over-inflation of the lungs.

Temperature

Thermoreceptors (located in the hypothalamus region of the brain) respond to increases in body and blood temperatures. These receptors directly excite the neurones of the RCC and help control ventilation during prolonged exercise.

Irritant receptors

The activation of touch, thermal and pain receptors can also stimulate the RCC.

Higher centres of the brain

Through the **cerebral cortex** it is possible consciously to increase or decrease rate and depth of breathing. Swimmers and sports divers **hyperventilate** and **breath-hold** to improve physical performance. At the start of a swimming race athletes hyperventilate on the starting blocks to prolong breath-hold time during the swim. In short course racing, the breath-hold time can be the whole of the racing time. Snorkel divers hyperventilate to extend breath-hold time. During breath-hold time the pO_2 content of the blood can fall to critically low values before arterial pCO_2 increases to stimulate breathing.

Emotions acting through the limbic system can also affect the RCC.

The impact of exercise on the respiratory system and the consequences for long-term health

Aerobic exercise

Intense **aerobic** exercise (see figure 3.13) has the effect of forcing the person to breathe more deeply and more often (the **vital capacity** of the lung is fully utilised, and the breathing frequency (**f**) increases).

Therefore, as a result of long-term exercise, the following adaptations take place within the body which tend to make more efficient the transfer (from air breathed in) of oxygen to working muscle.

figure 3.13 – effect of exercise on respiratory systems

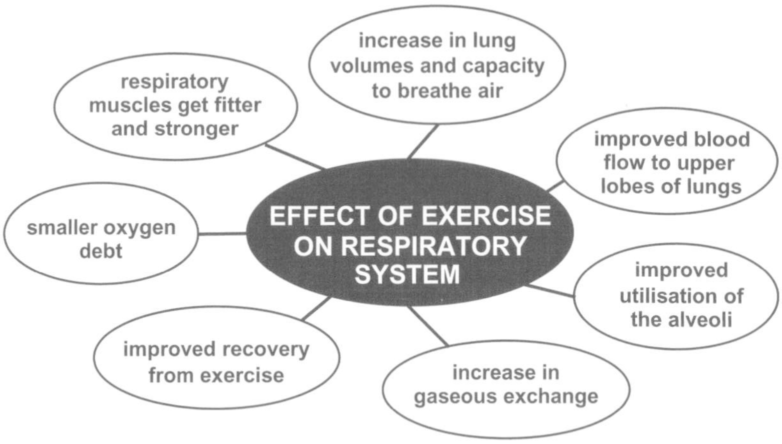

- respiratory muscles get fitter and stronger
- increase in lung volumes and capacity to breathe air
- improved blood flow to upper lobes of lungs
- smaller oxygen debt
- **EFFECT OF EXERCISE ON RESPIRATORY SYSTEM**
- improved utilisation of the alveoli
- improved recovery from exercise
- increase in gaseous exchange

- Long-term exercise has the effect of exercising the respiratory muscular system – namely, the diaphragm and intercostal muscles. If exercise is continued at least two to three times per week, these muscles will get fitter and stronger and more capable of working without cramps and conditions like stitches.
- The efficiency of the respiratory system will depend on the utilisation and capacity of the alveoli to take oxygen from air breathed in and transmit it to blood flowing through the alveolar capillary bed. Long-term physical activity increases blood flow to the upper lobes of the lungs to increase utilisation of lung alveoli, hence increases gaseous exchange and therefore $\dot{V}O_{2max}$ at high intensity aerobic workloads.
- At submaximal workloads $\dot{V}O_2$ will be less because of greater efficiency of oxygen uptake, and general improvements in lung function will occur such as increase in tidal volume (TV) and vital capacity (VC) at the expense of residual volume (RV).
- Increased efficiencies of the respiratory system will improve **recovery** from exercise and reduce **oxygen debt** during exercise.
- At submaximal workloads there is a slight decrease in the breathing rate (f – the frequency of breaths).
- During maximal workloads there is a big increase in breathing rate (f), hence much bigger values in minute ventilation are achieved.

Exam style questions

1) Describe the structures involved in gaseous exchange in the lungs and explain how gaseous exchange occurs within this tissue.
6 marks

2) a) The diagram in figure 3.14 (page 45) represents the lung volume changes based on a number of spirometer readings during various breathing actions. With reference to the trace, briefly explain resting tidal volume (TV), expiratory reserve volume (ERV), vital capacity (VC), and residual volume (RV).
4 marks

2) b) Using the information in the spirometer trace, state what happens to the following volumes during the exercise period: residual volume, inspiratory volume (IRV), and expiratory volume (ERV).
3 marks

c) Why does tidal volume change by only a small amount during the exercise period? **3 marks**

d) Identify two effects of regular aerobic training on lung volumes and capacities. **2 marks**

e) A student measured the volume of air that he or she ventilated at rest and during submaximal exercise. The results are shown in table 3.4 below.

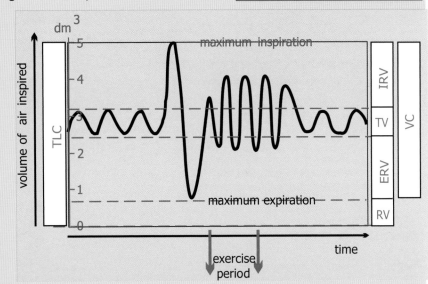

figure 3.14 – spirometer trace

Table 3.4 – **ventilation at rest and during submaximal exercise**

activity level	inhalation volume (TV)	breathing rate (f)	minute ventilation volume (V̇E)
at rest	500 ml	one every 6 seconds	A
submaximal exercise	800 ml	one every 2 seconds	B

2) e) (continued) Define what is meant by the term 'minute ventilation volume' and calculate the values for A and B, clearly showing the method used. **4 marks**

3) The binding of oxygen to haemoglobin depends on pO_2 in the blood and the affinity of haemoglobin with oxygen. The curves in figure 3.15 show how different concentrations of carbon dioxide affect the saturation of haemoglobin at varying partial pressures of oxygen.

a) Explain what is meant by partial pressure of oxygen (pO_2). **1 mark**

b) What are the values of percentage saturation of haemoglobin on the three curves when the partial pressure of oxygen is 5.0 kPa? **3 marks**

c) What are the implications of the carbon dioxide values for curves B and C for an athlete? **2 marks**

d) Why is the partial pressure of oxygen (pO_2) important to the process of gaseous exchange? **3 marks**

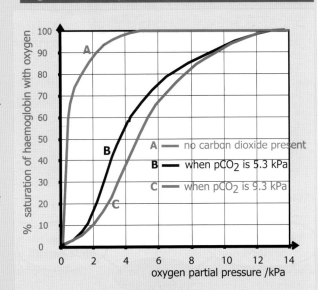

figure 3.15 – oxyhaemoglobin dissociation curve

A — no carbon dioxide present
B — when pCO_2 is 5.3 kPa
C — when pCO_2 is 9.3 kPa

4) A hockey player has a match in one hour's time.
Describe how inspiration occurs during this resting period.
During the hockey match, the player must increase the volume of gas exchanged in the lungs and muscles.
Explain the changes in the mechanics of breathing (inspiration and expiration) which facilitate this increase. **12 marks**

5) Identify the long-term adaptations an elite performer would expect to occur in the structure and functioning of the respiratory system as a result of an intense aerobic training programme. **12 marks**

6) A level. Describe the effect of exercise on pO_2, pCO_2 and pH and explain how ventilation might be increased during exercise. **15 marks**

Answers link: http://www.jroscoe.co.uk/downloads/as_a1_revise_pe_edexcel/EdexcelAS_A1_ch3_answers.pdf

CHAPTER 4 - *The cardiovascular system*

1.2.5 The structure of the heart

STUDENT NOTE

Your syllabus requires an understanding of the structure and function of the cardiovascular system.

figure 4.1 – heart structure

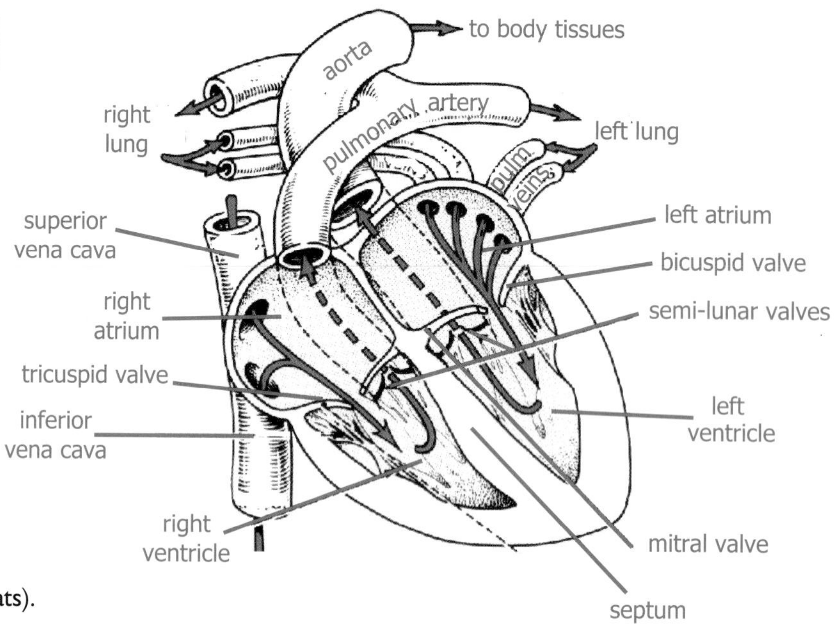

The heart (figure 4.1) is a muscular pump lying deep within the chest cavity and slightly to the left of the sternum.

Heart layers

The **heart** consists of **three** layers:

* The **outer** layer, known as the **pericardium**, is a double layered bag surrounding the heart. The fluid between the two layers reduces friction between the heart itself and the surrounding tissue as the heart moves (beats). This layer also maintains the heart's shape.

* The **second** layer is called the **myocardium** or striped cardiac muscle tissue consisting of united fibres (united because they are all in one mass) joined by intercalated discs. This muscle tissue is activated by the 'all-or-none law'. The **cardiac impulse** is transmitted throughout the entire myocardium at the same point in time, and hence this muscle tissue is **all** activated at once. When there is no cardiac impulse, none of the heart muscle can be activated. Since the heart generates its own impulse it is said to be **myogenic**. The **septum** consists of myocardial tissue (muscle) and divides the heart into two sections, each of which acts as a pump.

* The **third** layer is an inner glistening membrane called the **endocardium**. Its function is to prevent friction between heart muscle and flowing blood.

Heart chambers

The heart consists of **four** chambers:

* **Two** are at the top (**atria**). Both the right and left atria have thin walls.
* **Two** are at the bottom (**ventricles**). Both ventricles have thicker walls than the atria. The left ventricle wall is the thickest, since this ventricle pumps blood to the main body mass, whereas the **right ventricle** pumps blood to the **lungs only**.

Heart valves

Heart valves **prevent back-flow of blood**, with the (**cuspid**) **mitral** or **bicuspid** valve sited between the left atrium and the left ventricle, and the **tricuspid** valve sited between the right atrium and the right ventricle. The **semi-lunar** valves prevent back-flow of blood into the heart from the pulmonary artery and aorta, and only allow blood to flow in one direction through the heart. This means that when the heart muscle contracts, it only pumps the blood out to the lungs (pulmonary artery) or body (aorta), and not back the wrong way.

Blood vessels

Blood vessels attached to the heart are the **venae cavae** and the **pulmonary artery** on the right side, and the **pulmonary veins** and the **aorta** on the left side.

Coronary blood supply

The coronary blood supply consists of arteries (within the cardiac muscle itself) which supply glucose and oxygen (O_2) to myocardial tissue, and coronary veins, which transport carbon dioxide (CO_2) and other wastes from the heart muscle.

1.2.6 Cardiac responses to physical activity

How the heart works

The cardiac impulse

- The dynamic action of the heart (figure 4.2) is that of a dual-action pump in that both sides of the heart contract simultaneously, even though the functions of the two sides are different.

- Cardiac contractions are initiated by an electrical impulse (the **cardiac impulse**) that originates from the pacemaker or sinoatrial node (**SA node**). Because the heart generates its own impulses it is said to be **myogenic**.

- The electrical impulse travels down the atrial mycardium until it reaches the atrioventricular node (**AV node**) situated in the wall of the atrial septum. This is followed by the atrial walls contracting (atrial systole).

- The AV node conducts the impulse through the **bundle of His** to the branched network of **Purkinje fibres** located within the septum and the ventricular walls (both the bundle of His and the Purkinje fibres are modified cardiac muscle), causing both ventricles to contract (**ventricular systole**).

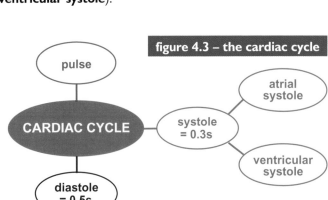

figure 4.2 – the cardiac impulse

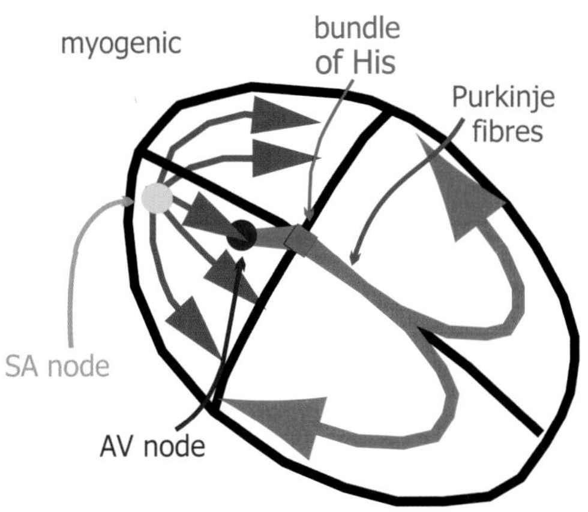

myogenic

bundle of His

Purkinje fibres

SA node

AV node

The heart's conducting system regulates the sequence of events that make up the cardiac cycle.

The cardiac cycle

The cardiac cycle (figure 4.3) is a sequence of events that make up one heart beat and lasts for about 0.8 seconds, thus occurring about 75 times per minute.

The cardiac cycle consists of a period of relaxation of the heart muscle, known as diastole (0.5 seconds), followed by a period of contraction of the heart muscle, known as systole (0.3 seconds). During systole the electrical impulse is initiated in a set-timed sequence.

figure 4.3 – the cardiac cycle

pulse

CARDIAC CYCLE

systole = 0.3s

atrial systole

ventricular systole

diastole = 0.5s

Cardiac diastole

During **diastole** (0.5 seconds), the relaxed heart muscle allows the chambers to fill with blood. This occurs with the cuspid valves open, and the semi-lunar valves closed.

Cardiac systole

During **atrial systole** (0.3 seconds), the **SA node** impulse causes a wave-like contraction over the atria forcing blood past the cuspid valves into the ventricles. The semi-lunar valves remain closed.

In **ventricular systole**, the impulse reaches the **AV node**, the cuspid valves close because the fluid pressure (of blood) in the ventricles is greater than in the atria, and rises further as the ventricles contract. The semi-lunar valves open (since now the fluid pressure in the ventricles is greater than in the main arteries) and blood is pushed out into the pulmonary artery (towards the lungs) and the aorta (around the body).

The **pulse** is a wave of pressure produced by the contraction of the left ventricle. This pressure wave transmits itself around the arterial system of the rest of the body. The frequency of the waves represents the number of beats per minute (heart rate).

Short-term cardiac responses to physical activity

See figure 4.4 for a summary of cardiac factors in short-term responses to exercise.

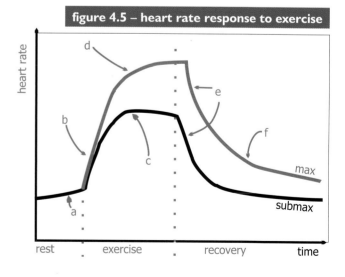

figure 4.4 – cardiac factors

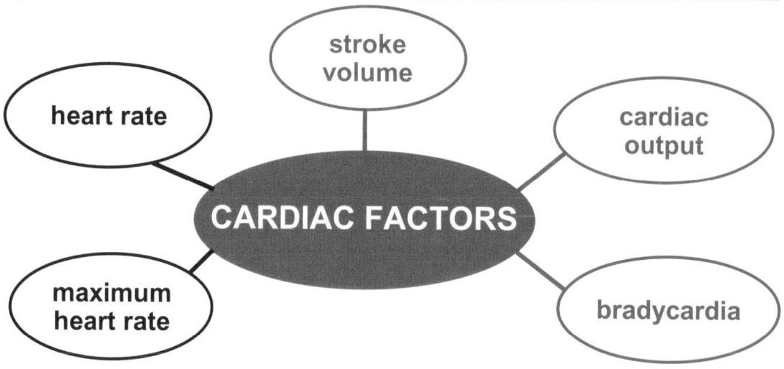

stroke volume

heart rate

cardiac output

CARDIAC FACTORS

maximum heart rate

bradycardia

- **Heart rate** (HR) is defined as '**the number of beats of the heart per minute (bpm)**'.

- The average resting HR for males is 70 bpm, and for females 72 bpm.

- At rest, the HR for a trained athlete = 60 bpm or lower (heart rates of less than 60 is **bradycardia**), and the HR for an untrained person = 70-90 bpm (average 80).

- **Maximum heart rate** can be calculated using the formula: $HR_{max} = 220 - age$.

  So, for a 20 year old, $HR_{max} = 220 - 20 = 200$ bpm. Usually, maximum heart rates for untrained people are slightly less than for highly trained people, an example would be 190 (untrained) to 200 (trained) in the calculation outlined below.

- **Heart Rate Reserve** (HRR) is the difference between resting heart rate and maximum heart rate and is often used as method of setting up individual training programmes (see page 106).

- **Stroke volume** (SV) is '**the volume of blood pumped by the left ventricle of the heart per beat**' and is determined by venous return and elasticity and contractility of the myocardium.

- For example, the SV for a trained athlete = 110 ml at rest, and the SV for an untrained person = 70 ml at rest.

  The SV for a trained endurance athlete during maximal exercise intensity = 190 ml, and for an untrained person, during his or her maximum exercise intensity SV = 110 ml.

- **Cardiac output** ($\dot{Q}$) is '**the volume of blood pumped by the left ventricle of the heart in one minute**', and is the product of stroke volume and heart rate: $\quad \mathbf{Q = SV \times HR}$

Example figures are:

For an untrained person at rest,	$\dot{Q} = 70 \times 80$	= 5.60 l/min (or dm³ min⁻¹).
For an untrained person during maximal exercise,	$\dot{Q} = 110 \times 190$	= 20.90 l/min (or dm³ min⁻¹).
For an endurance athlete at rest,	$\dot{Q} = 110 \times 51$	= 5.61 l/min (or dm³ min⁻¹).
For an endurance athlete during maximal exercise,	$\dot{Q} = 190 \times 200$	= 38 l/min (or dm³ min⁻¹).

Short-term changes in heart rate, stroke volume and cardiac output during different intensities of physical activity

Heart rate response to exercise

Referring to the graph in figure 4.5:

a = **Anticipatory rise** due to the hormonal action of adrenaline and noradrenaline. This happens because the person tends to get excited **before** the exercise starts, and hence heart rate rises slightly.

b = **Sharp rise** during anaerobic work due to proprioceptor sensory stimulation, and also due to continued release of hormones and action of the skeletal muscle pump (see page 54).

c = **Steady state** and some recovery of O_2 debt (aerobic).

d = **Continued high HR** due to maximal workloads which continue to stress anaerobic systems, producing lactic acid + CO_2 + K^+, which stimulate chemoreceptors. Additionally, intrinsic factors are also stimulated at maximal level (refer to page 50).

e = **Rapid recovery** due to cessation of proprioceptive stimuli, the skeletal muscle pump, and the withdrawal of hormones.

f = **Slow recovery**, clearance of metabolites such as lactic acid, as systems return to normal resting values.

figure 4.5 – heart rate response to exercise

heart rate

d

b

e

f

max

c

a

submax

rest   exercise   recovery   time

Stroke volume response to exercise

Referring to the graph in figure 4.6:

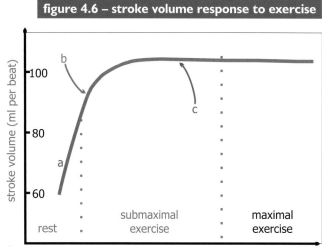

figure 4.6 – stroke volume response to exercise

a = An increase in stroke volume, from a resting value of 60 ml beat^{-1} to 85 ml beat^{-1} prior to the start of the exercise period, and is due to the release of hormones such as **adrenaline** and **noradrenaline**. This effect is known as the **anticipatory rise**.

b = An increase in stroke volume as exercise commences. This is primarily due an **increased venous return** and **increased myocardial contraction during ventricular systole** (**Starling's Law of the Heart**) which causes the heart muscle to contract more forcefully, from 85 ml beat^{-1} to more than 110 ml beat^{-1} during submaximal work.

c = As work intensity increases during maximal exercise, there is a slight decline in stroke volume. At this point heart rate will rise rapidly to sustain the continued increase in cardiac output to meet exercise demands.

STUDENT NOTE

Stroke volume increases to maximal values during submaximal work and does not increase further as work increases towards maximal effort. This is because once the heart is expanding and contracting utilising its fullest possible size, it obviously cannot get any bigger even though the energy needs of the body are greater. At this increased value, stroke volume is unable to increase any further since the overlap of the actin and myosin fibres during cardiac systole has reached maximum, and therefore stroke volume levels off.

Cardiac output response to exercise

Since **cardiac output** is the product of stroke volume and heart rate values $\dot{Q} = SV \times HR$, it will increase directly in line with exercise intensity.

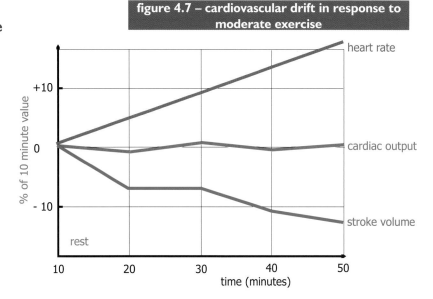

figure 4.7 – cardiovascular drift in response to moderate exercise

Cardiovascular drift (figure 4.7)

- With **prolonged aerobic exercise**, at a constant exercise intensity, such as marathon racing or **aerobic exercising** in a **hot environment**, stroke volume gradually decreases and heart rate increases, and hence cardiac output remains approximately constant. During this process arterial blood pressure declines.

- These responses are due to the need to transfer excess heat produced by active tissues from deep in the body (known as the core) to the skin where it has access to the outside environment.

- This heat is moved by the blood during **vasodilation** of blood vessels directly underneath the skin. Evaporation is the primary route for heat dissipation and so as fluid or sweat evaporates heat is lost. Loss of fluid results in a reduced plasma volume and subsequent decreased venous return and stroke volume.

- A **reduced stroke volume** initiates a compensatory **heart rate increase** to maintain a **nearly constant cardiac output** as exercise progresses. All these circulatory responses are collectively referred to as the **cardiovascular drift**. See figure 4.7.

- It is important for athletes to **rehydrate** with sports drinks (water containing a little sodium and glucose) during prolonged exercise periods or whilst performing aerobic exercise in a hot environment. This will minimise the loss of fluids and thus reduce the effects of the cardiovascular drift.

Regulation of heart rate

The cardiac control centre (in the medulla oblongata in the brain) regulates feedback that results in changes to heart rate from important **neural, hormonal** and **intrinsic** factors (figure 4.8).

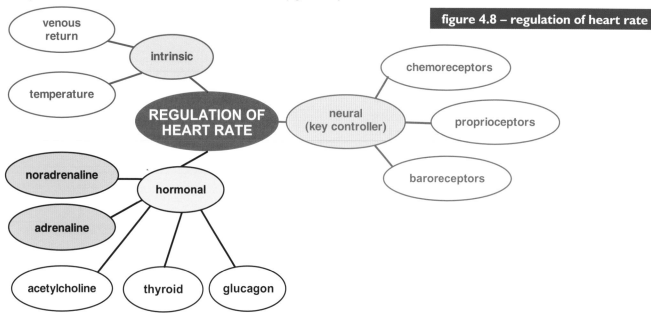

figure 4.8 – regulation of heart rate

Neural control factors

Neural control factors are the key controlling regulators and consist of:

- **Chemoreceptor reflexes** which involve receptors located in blood vessels such as the aortic arch and carotid sinuses. These reflexes detect chemical changes in blood O_2, CO_2, H^+ concentrations, and pH levels. Decrease in O_2 and pH levels, and increase in CO_2 and H^+ concentrations, all stimulate changes in heart rate via the cardiac accelerator nerve.
- **Proprioceptor reflexes** found in muscle spindles and Golgi tendons which respond to mechanical stimuli such as compression, bending or stretching of cells, detecting changes in movement. Increase in tension within cell structures will increase heart rate via the cardiac accelerator nerve.
- **Baroreceptor reflexes** which involve receptors located in blood vessels (such as the aortic arch and carotid sinuses). Their role is to detect changes in blood pressure. When blood pressure is too high the parasympathetic nerve releases acetylcholine, which decreases heart rate.

Hormonal factors

Hormones are released by the body in response to various stimuli. Those that affect heart rate are:

- **Noradrenaline** and **adrenaline** (the key hormonal regulators) which act to accelerate heart rate (tachycardia) and increase the strength of ventricular contraction which increases stroke volume.
- **Acetylcholine** which slows the heart (bradycardia) as described below.
- **Thyroid** hormone and **glucagon** which increase HR.
- **Increased glucagon** levels which assist in the breakdown of **glycogen to release glucose** into the circulatory system to fuel muscular contractions.

Intrinsic factors

Intrinsic factors account for changes in venous return:

- **Venous return** is 'the volume of blood returning to the heart during each cardiac cycle'. This changes as a result of the actions of the skeletal muscle and respiratory pumps, and the electrolyte balance (Na^+, K^+) in muscular tissue.
- **Myocardial temperature** also affects venous return, in that the speed of nerve impulse transmission increases with temperature, and this will increase heart rate.
- **Starling's Law of the Heart** states that cardiac output is equal to venous return. An increase in venous return stretches the ventricular walls more and results in an increased strength of contraction and therefore an increase in stroke volume.

Neural control

- **Neural impulses** (resulting from feedback from neural, hormonal and intrinsic control) override the inherent rhythm of the heartbeat. Signals originate in the **cardiac control centre** (**CCC**) in the medulla and travel via the antagonistic actions of the sympathetic and parasympathetic nervous systems, to the pacemaker or SA node.

Sympathetic influence

- The **sympathetic nervous system**, the **SNS** (via the cardiac accelerator nerve), releases the neurotransmitters adrenaline and noradrenaline onto the SA node to **speed up** heart rate.

Parasympathetic influence

- The **parasympathetic nervous system**, **PNS** (via the vagus nerve), releases the neurotransmitter acetylcholine onto the SA node to **slow down** heart rate.

Long-term adaptations of the heart and its control system due to aerobic exercise

Long-term responses of the heart (figure 4.9)

- **Regular aerobic training** results in **hypertrophy** of the cardiac muscle, meaning that the muscle becomes larger and stronger. This means that the heart pumps a larger volume of blood out per beat, hence the stroke volume is larger. This is termed **bradycardia** and has the consequence of producing a resting HR below 60 bpm. This in turn affects cardiac output, as illustrated in the equations above.
- At rest a bigger and stronger heart pumps more blood out per beat, even though the body's requirement for oxygenated blood would be approximately the same as for an untrained person. Hence resting heart rate decreases, with the net effect of an unchanged cardiac output. Highly trained sportspeople tend to have resting heart rates of well below 60 bpm.
- During **maximum exercise**, an increase in heart rate, coupled with an increase in stroke volume, results in an increase in cardiac output. As expected, cardiac output for the endurance athlete is more than double that of the untrained person due to **cardiac muscle hypertrophy**.
- During the **recovery period** following maximal exercise, heart rate will decrease more rapidly, and so will return to its resting level much more quickly for the endurance athlete when compared with an untrained person.
- Hence heart rate recovery is used as an **index of cardio-respiratory fitness**.

Long-term responses of the nervous control system

- **Endurance training** creates an imbalance between the two sets of nerves (the **PNS** and the **SNS**) in favour of parasympathetic dominance. This type of training is also known to decrease intrinsic firing rate of the SA node.
- These adaptations account for the significant **bradycardia** observed amongst highly conditioned endurance athletes.

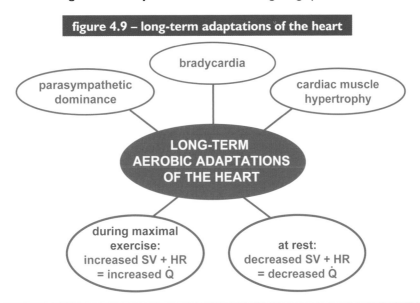

figure 4.9 – long-term adaptations of the heart

Vascular responses to physical activity

The blood circulation systems

There are two systems circulating blood from the heart as in figure 4.10.

The systemic circulatory system

This system consists of all the vessels which carry oxygenated blood away from the heart via the aorta, the arteries and arterioles and on to the capillaries embedded in the working tissues of the body. Then after giving up the oxygen (to the working tissues), the deoxygenated blood returns to the heart via venules, veins and the venae cavae.

The pulmonary circulatory system

This system consists of the pulmonary arteries that carry this deoxygenated blood from the right atrium of the heart to the lungs, where the blood is re-oxygenated from the air breathed into the lungs. Oxygenated blood is then returned to the heart via the pulmonary veins.

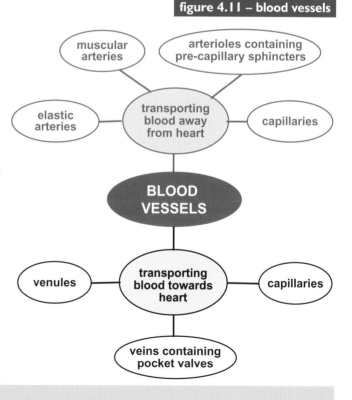

figure 4.10 – the circulatory systems

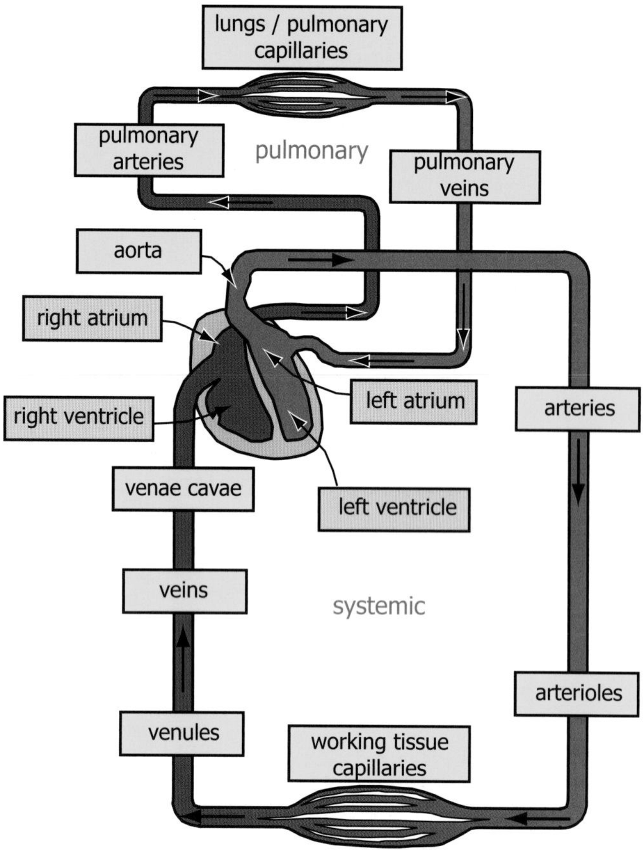

lungs / pulmonary capillaries

pulmonary arteries — pulmonary — pulmonary veins

aorta

right atrium

right ventricle — left atrium

venae cavae — left ventricle — arteries

veins — systemic

arterioles

venules — working tissue capillaries

figure 4.11 – blood vessels

muscular arteries — arterioles containing pre-capillary sphincters

elastic arteries — transporting blood away from heart — capillaries

BLOOD VESSELS

venules — transporting blood towards heart — capillaries

veins containing pocket valves

Blood vessel structure

Blood vessels (see table 4.1 page 53) have properties that help circulation and allow blood to perform many of its functions (see summary in figure 4.11).

Except for single-walled capillaries and venules, all blood vessels have 3 layers. The thickness and composition of the layers vary with blood vessel type and diameter. Smooth involuntary muscle, within the middle layer of blood vessel walls, regulates the diameter of blood vessels via **vasomotor** and **venomotor** control (described on page 54).

Question

Why does the human body need a double circulatory system?

Table 4.1 – **blood vessel structure and function**

type of blood vessel	vessel structure	vessel function / structure	vessel function	blood pressure in vessels
elastic arteries (aorta)	are thin-walled with large diameters.	middle layer (tunica media) contains a high proportion of elastic fibres and little smooth muscle.	during ventricular systole, these arteries extend with a rise in left ventricular pressure and recoil (contract) during ventricular diastole.	transport blood at high pressure away from the heart.
muscular arteries	thick-walled vessels with small diameters.	middle layer (tunica media) consists of some elastic fibres and lots of smooth muscle.	smooth muscle controls the shape of the central space or lumen via **vasoconstriction** and **vasodilation**.	transport blood at high pressure.
arterioles	reduce in size and muscular content as they get closer to the capillary bed.	smooth muscle (in the tunica media).	smooth muscle contracts (to reduce blood inflow) and relaxes (to increase blood inflow) to control inflow to their own capillary bed.	blood pressure reduces as vessel diameter reduces but total CSA of all vessels increases.
pre-capillary sphincters (contained within arterioles)	placed before capillary bed (within muscle or other tissue).		contract (to reduce blood inflow) and relax (to increase blood inflow) to control inflow to their own capillary bed.	
capillaries	tiny blood vessels whose walls are one cell thick, have semi-permeable walls or small spaces in the walls (tunica intima).	walls allow fluids rich in nutrients (O_2 & glucose) to be delivered to tissue cells, nutrients travel through the capillary walls into the tissue cells.	waste products (CO_2 and urea / lactate) are removed by travelling through the capillary walls from the tissue cells into the blood fluids. this is the opposite direction to the nutrients.	very low blood pressure as total vessel area reaches a maximum.
venules	walls consist of an inner wall (tunica intima), surrounded by a few smooth muscle cells.	positioned where several capillaries unite to collect outflow from a capillary bed at low pressure.	as venules approach the veins they develop a thin middle layer coat (tunica media).	blood pressure still very low as blood is transported towards the heart.
muscular veins	thin walled vessels contain less smooth muscle and fewer elastic fibres than arteries of same size.	have non-return valves, called pocket valves. positioned within the central space (or lumen) of these vessels.	sympathetic nerves causing **venoconstriction** activate the tunica media. The outer wall (tunica externa) is supported by collagen.	low blood pressure.
veins	thin middle layer supported by smooth muscle cells and collagen and elastic fibres. some large veins are valveless e.g. hepatic veins.	blood flows in the veins because of muscular action in the surrounding skeletal muscle - **skeletal muscle pump**.	contracting muscle squashes veins forcing blood forwards towards the heart. since blood cannot flow back away from the heart due to the pocket valves within each vein.	low pressure blood reservoirs moving stored blood into general circulation during exercise.
venae cavae	are valveless and contain more smooth muscle in the middle wall.	smooth muscle acts to constrict or dilate the vessel (venomotor control).	deliver blood to the right atrium of the heart.	low blood pressure.

STUDENT NOTE

CSA means cross sectional area, and represents the internal area of a blood vessel as viewed end-on. This approximately circular space is the space into which blood will flow. The further away from the heart, the bigger the total cross sectional area (CSA) of all the blood vessels carrying blood, hence the flow is slower (as the blood flows into a bigger space), and the blood pressure is lower (see figure 4.16 on page 56).

Venous return mechanism

The **venous return mechanism** (see figure 4.12) is the process by which blood returns to the right side of the heart. It depends on:

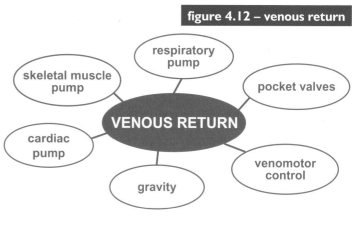

figure 4.12 – venous return

- **Gravity** that assists the flow of blood from body parts above the heart.

- The **skeletal muscle pump** in which contracting skeletal muscle squashes veins forcing blood forwards towards the heart (since blood cannot flow back away from the heart due to the pocket valves within each vein), as described above in table 4.1.

- The **respiratory pump** which relies upon the changes in pressure that occurs in the thoracic and abdominal cavities during inspiration and expiration. These pressure changes compress nearby veins and so assist blood flow back to the heart.

- **Valves (pocket valves)** which ensure that blood can only flow in one direction back towards the heart.

- **Venomotor control** which describes the limited capacity of veins to change their shape and therefore slightly increase venous return, due to **venoconstriction**. For a fuller description of this concept see page 55.

Hence the mechanism by which the bulk of blood returns to the heart during exercise is via the skeletal muscle pump, with the respiratory and cardiac pumps also helping.

How is blood flow controlled?

Changes in blood vessel diameter depend upon the metabolic needs of body tissues. The vasomotor centre, located in the medulla oblongata of the brain, controls blood pressure and blood flow. This is an example of **negative feedback control**, in which an **increase** of blood pressure as sensed by baroreceptors causes a **decrease** in the blood pressure by changing blood vessel diameter.

As cardiac output increases, sensory receptors such as **baroreceptors** (responding to changes in blood pressure) and **chemoreceptors** (responding to changes in chemical composition of the blood) are stimulated.

Vasomotor control (figure 4.13)

Vasomotor control is concerned with the ability of muscular **arteries** and **arterioles** to change their shape. **During exercise**, the sensory receptors, baroreceptors and chemoreceptors, are stimulated. The vasomotor centre receives this sensory information. From here sympathetic nerves carry impulses to the smooth muscle walls of arteries and arterioles.

Non-active tissue

Within **non-active tissues**, these impulses cause **vasoconstriction** (tightening or narrowing) in the arteries, arterioles, and to the **pre-capillary sphincters** located at the openings of capillaries to the inactive tissue. The effect of this constriction is to **restrict blood flow** into the capillary bed of the non-active tissue.

Active tissue

In contrast, within **active tissue**, sympathetic stimulation to the smooth walls of arteries and arterioles and pre-capillary sphincters **is reduced**, and the muscles in the arterial walls and pre-capillary sphincters **relax**. Therefore these vessels dilate or open wider (known as **vasodilation**) and the **pre-capillary sphincters** open up, resulting in **additional blood flow** into active muscles.

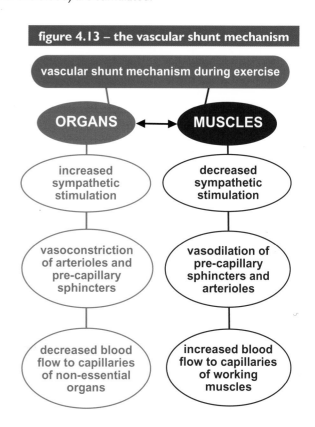

figure 4.13 – the vascular shunt mechanism

Capillary exchange and the vascular shunt

The flow of blood from an arteriole to a venule (that is through a capillary bed) is called the microcirculation. A **vascular shunt** (metarteriole-thoroughfare channel), is a short vessel that directly connects the arteriole and the venule at opposite ends of the bed (figure 4.14). When the **precapillary sphincters** are relaxed (open), blood flows through the true capillaries, and when the **precapillary sphincters** are contracted (closed), blood flows through the metarteriole thus bypassing the tissue cells.

Vascular shunt mechanism

Hence, **as exercise begins**, as a result of vasomotor control, blood flow is diverted into active skeletal muscle where it is needed. This redirection of blood flow is called the **vascular shunt mechanism** and is illustrated in figures 4.13, 4.14 and 4.15.

The vasomotor centre works in conjunction with the cardiac centre in maintaining blood pressure. Table 4.2 illustrates the redistribution of blood flow as exercise begins, away from the major organs of the body towards working muscle.

Table 4.2 – **comparison of the distribution of cardiac output at rest and during exercise**

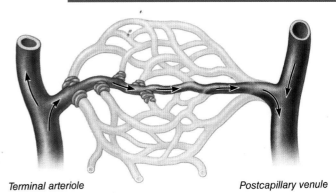

figure 4.14 – the vascular shunt metarteriole

Terminal arteriole   Postcapillary venule

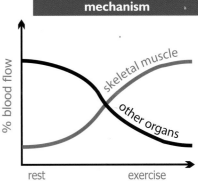

figure 4.15 – vascular shunt mechanism

redistribution of blood during exercise

| tissue | proportions of blood in various tissues | | | |
| | rest | | maximal exercise | |
	%	ml min⁻¹	%	ml min⁻¹
liver	27	1350	1	300
kidneys	22	1100	1	250
brain	14	700	3	750
heart	4	200	4	1000
muscle	20	1000	88	22000
skin	6	300	2	600
other	7	350	1	100
total	100	5000	100	25000

STUDENT NOTE

Note the five-fold increase in total rate of blood flow at maximal exercise, and the fact that the brain maintains approximately the same blood flow – otherwise if the rate of flow to the brain reduced substantially, the sportsperson would faint and fall to the ground!

Venomotor control

Venomotor control describes the limited capacity of veins to change their shape. This is the result of venomotor tone, whereby the veins' muscular coat receives stimulation from the sympathetic nervous system. The effect of limited **venoconstriction** of veins causes a small increase in blood velocity and hence **an increase** in venous return.

Transport of oxygen and carbon dioxide by the vascular system

Oxygen transport

Blood consists of 55% plasma (which transports dissolved nutrients, hormones and waste) and 45% corpuscles.

- **97%** of the **oxygen** carried by the blood is transported via **haemoglobin** in the **red** corpuscles, since haemoglobin readily attaches itself to O_2 when exposed to it in the alveoli within lung tissue. The remaining **3%** of the oxygen carried is dissolved in the blood plasma.
- **Exercise** causes a **small increase** in **pulmonary blood pressure, which distorts red blood corpuscles** within the alveolar capillary system, and this enables **10 times as much oxygen** to be picked up as at rest.
- The formula for the oxygenation of **haemoglobin** (Hb) is: $Hb + 4O_2 \rightarrow Hb(O_2)_4$, where one molecule of Hb combines with 4 molecules of O_2 to form a molecule of **oxyhaemoglobin** $Hb(O_2)_4$.

Oxygen transport

- The amount of oxygen transported by the blood is a function of cardiac output and the oxygen **content** of the blood.

- At rest, we use about **25%** of available oxygen. This leaves an unextracted 75% of the available oxygen in blood returned to the heart via venous return. This is called the **oxygen reserve**, which is immediately available for exercise when it begins.

- The remaining corpuscles within the blood are the **white** blood cells. These cells produce antibodies and regulate the body's immune system, and **platelets** responsible for blood clotting.

Carbon dioxide transport

Carbon Dioxide (CO_2) is produced by the **respiration** process in tissue cells, the oxidation of fuels in oxygen to produce energy, which in muscle cells enables the person to move, run or jump. CO_2 is transported in venous blood as:

- **Carbonic acid** (most of which dissociates into H^+ and HCO_3^-) (70%).

- **Carbaminohaemoglobin** (the combination of CO_2 with haemoglobin in a similar way that O_2 combines with Hb to form oxyhaemoglobin) (23%).

- **CO_2 dissolved in blood plasma** (7%).

Carbon dioxide is excreted from the lungs during expiration. This CO_2 has to be removed from the tissue cells since if it stays it forms carbonic acid (dissociated into H^+ and HCO_3^- as mentioned above), which in effect acts as a poison and will reduce a muscle cell to complete inactivity within a few seconds. Further notes on gas transport and exchange are to be found on page 38.

Hence it is very important to maintain an efficient blood transport system (carrying oxygen into, and carbon dioxide away from muscle) if a person is to be able to exercise and live healthily.

Blood pressure

Blood pressure is defined as '**the force per unit area exerted by the blood on the inside walls of blood vessels**' and so represents the driving force that moves blood through the circulatory system. It is the combination of cardiac output and peripheral resistance of blood vessels and is measured using a sphygmomanometer around the upper arm.

- **Systolic** pressure (the highest pressure) is generated by left ventricular contraction (systole) as blood is ejected into the aorta and main arteries.

- **Diastolic** pressure (the lowest pressure) is reached when the heart relaxes (diastole) and the aortic valves close due to pressure changes.

- Hence blood pressure is measured using these two pressures:

  <u>**systolic pressure**</u> **mmHg**
  diastolic pressure

Blood velocity

- You will notice from figure 4.16 that as blood flows through the network of blood vessels the blood velocity falls. This is because it encounters vessels which branch repeatedly, with a bigger space to flow into.

- This means that the vessels have a bigger total combined **cross sectional area** (**CSA** – see solid green line in figure 4.16) and hence the blood slows down (**blood velocity** falls – see the solid red line in figure 4.16). When blood reaches the capillaries, the **CSA** is a maximum (many tiny vessels) and therefore the blood flows very slowly.

- This process reverses as the blood flows back towards the heart. **CSA** reduces (see the green line in figure 4.16), and blood velocity increases until it almost matches the speed of blood leaving the heart.

- You have to note that the same volume of blood will return to the heart as leaves it (in any given period of time) – this is **Starling's Law of the Heart**.

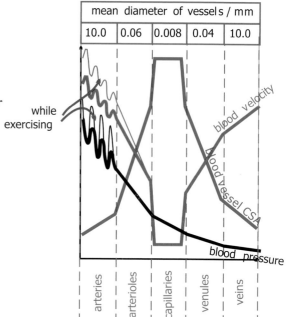

figure 4.16 – blood pressure / velocity / CSA of vessels

mean diameter of vessels / mm				
10.0	0.06	0.008	0.04	10.0

while exercising

blood velocity

blood vessel CSA

blood pressure

arteries | arterioles | capillaries | venules | veins

Blood pressure

- Blood pressure forces blood through arteries and arterioles, and as the **CSA** increases, the individual **diameters of blood vessels reduce**. This **increases** the **peripheral resistance** (the resistance - fluid friction drag - to flow of a fluid through a tube), and reduces the rate of flow through these vessels.

- Therefore, in comparison with the pressure forcing the blood into the system (by the pumping heart), the pressure forcing the blood along the tubular system of blood vessels is less at any particular point, and lowest near the end of the system – which is the capillary bed. Hence the blood pressure (represented by the black line in figure 4.16) falls as the blood travels from the heart to the capillary system. Therefore once the blood has flowed through the capillary beds the **pressure** forcing the flow onwards is **very low**.

- This means that unless action is taken, the blood will remain in the capillary beds at the furthest points from the heart, and before the veins and venules are reached. This is called **blood pooling** and is the main reason why an active cool-down is essential after intense exercise.

- Therefore in veins, **venous return** is forced by the action of the **skeletal muscle** and **respiratory** pumps, and the **cardiac** pump, which is the action of the heart itself beating as it forces blood out into the aorta, and draws blood in from the venae cavae. This follows from Starling's Law of the Heart as mentioned above.

During vigorous rhythmic exercise, the skeletal muscle and respiratory pumps are much bigger, therefore venous return is bigger and **blood flow** is higher. Also, as blood flow is increased and venous return is higher, the heart is stimulated to pump harder and more frequently. Hence the **systolic blood pressure** is increased - which in turn forces greater blood flow into the arteries at greater **blood velocity**. Note that diastolic pressure remains relatively unchanged in dynamic exercise as quoted in the values in table 4.3.

Table 4.3 – **blood pressure**

blood pressure in mmHg

	rest	dynamic exercise	static exercise
systolic	120	170	200
diastolic	80	88	120

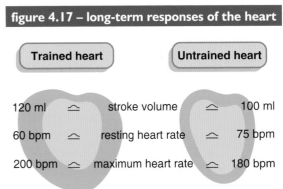

figure 4.17 – long-term responses of the heart

Trained heart		Untrained heart
120 ml	stroke volume	100 ml
60 bpm	resting heart rate	75 bpm
200 bpm	maximum heart rate	180 bpm

1.2.7 Long-term responses of the cardiovascular system due to exercise

The heart

The **long-term** adaptations to the **heart** produced by exercise are outlined on page 51, illustrated in figure 4.17, and include:

- Increase in **maximum heart rate**, as the myocardium (heart muscle) becomes fitter and able to contract more often per minute.
- **Bradycardia** or increase in size and strength of the heart muscle which causes:
  - Increase in stroke volume (**SV**).
  - A consequent decrease in **resting heart rate**.
- Increase in **blood supply** to the myocardium, therefore the heart is more efficient.

These adaptations enable more blood (and hence oxygen) to be pumped around the body during exercise.

Long term response of the vascular system to exercise

The **long-term** adaptations to the **vascular** system would be:

- Greater tolerance to blood lactate levels. The onset of blood lactate accumulation (**OBLA**) occurs at higher exercise intensity.
- Increase in **blood volume** and **haemoglobin** (Hb) count.

Long-term response of the vascular system to exercise

- Improved **capillarisation** around lung alveoli and skeletal muscle tissue.
- Therefore increase in $\dot{V}O_{2max}$.
- Increase in blood flow to working muscle tissue.
- Therefore increase in **a-$\bar{v}O_{2diff}$** (see page 49 for details of this concept).
- **Elasticity** of **blood vessels** (the muscular walls) increases, reducing blood pressure.
- Blood **lactate** is **less acidic** due to a more efficient aerobic system.

The consequences for long-term health are that oxygenated blood is able to reach the body's extremities more easily, and therefore service the limbs and reduce circulatory problems such as thrombosis. Cardiac functioning is more efficient reducing the risk of CHD.

1.2.8 Response of cardiovascular and cardio-respiratory systems to warm-up

Physiological value of warm-up

- Increase in body **temperature** and metabolism.
- Slightly **better blood flow** due to blood viscosity lower at higher temperature.
- Increase in heart rate and **cardiac output**.
- Increase in **volume of air** breathed per minute.
- **Capillaries dilate** with oxygenated blood.
- Increase in **blood pressure** forces blood more quickly through arteries.
- Secretion of **adrenaline** increases the metabolic rate (normal rate at which energy is produced by the whole body).
- **Blood shunting** will facilitate blood widening of the blood vessels via vasodilation within the active tissue, as a response to increase of body temperature and metabolism, and increase in local tissue O_2 availability, uptake and consumption (increased **a-$\bar{v}O_{2diff}$**).
- This facilitates oxygen delivery and use by active tissues because haemoglobin releases oxygen more readily at higher temperatures (Bohr effect).

1.2.9 An unhealthy lifestyle's effects on cardiovascular & cardio-respiratory systems

Figure 4.18 lists some of the concerns brought about by modern lifestyles.

Obesity

Obesity is a major problem in our affluent society linked with poor eating habits and lack of sufficient physical activity. Statistics show that obesity is widespread in all age groups, but there is a particular concern over young children and older people. The risks for children lie with poor health in the future.

The risks for older people are the facts of poor health now, with great danger of coronary heart disease (**CHD**) and poor mobility and the consequent lack of independence. Such factors for older people cause great expense to the nation, with the costs of health care and nursing support being very high.

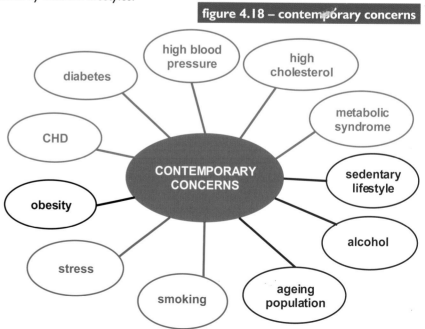

figure 4.18 – contemporary concerns

Obesity

Medical conditions linked with **obesity** and **inactivity** include coronary heart disease, diabetes, high blood pressure, high cholesterol and metabolic syndrome.

Obesity (figure 4.19) is defined as '**a surplus of adipose tissue resulting from excessive energy intake relative to energy expenditure**'.

The definition of obesity implies that the actual amount of body fat or its percentage of total weight can be estimated. The problem is that exact standards for allowable fat percentages have not been established. However, men with more than 25% body fat and women with more than 35% should be considered obese.

figure 4.19 – obesity and inactivity

Positive energy balance

This definition of obesity highlights the major cause of obesity, namely an obese person would have energy intake far greater than energy output, which would be the result of inactivity and too much dietary fat intake.

This relationship is expressed as:

ENERGY INTAKE > ENERGY EXPENDITURE

to create a **positive energy balance**, which means that more energy is eaten (figure 4.20) as food than energy is used via exercise.

Excess carbohydrate (CHO) from food is stored as glycogen. When glycogen stores are filled, CHO together with excess fat intake are converted to fatty acids and glycerol, and then are stored as triglycerides or **fat** in adipose tissue. This is situated around major organs such as the heart and stomach, underneath the skin, and in skeletal muscle. Upper body obesity poses the most significant risk to disease.

figure 4.20 – less food required?

Excessive weight gain is associated with certain health conditions such as **coronary heart disease** and **hypertension** (high blood pressure) with an increased risk of mortality and morbidity.

Controlling obesity

The only method of controlling obesity is to shift the energy relationship so that energy output exceeds energy intake – known as a **negative energy balance** and expressed as:

ENERGY INTAKE < ENERGY EXPENDITURE

This means that more energy is used via exercise than is eaten as food.

What is a good level of fat?

An **essential** (minimum requirement which would allow full body functions) body fat percentage for men is between 2% and 3% and for women between 8% and 12%. Normally **only** healthy elite athletes attain these percentages.

How is a person's body fatness related to good health?

Relative body fat is a major concern of athletes. Achieving a desired weight goal can lead to clinical eating disorders such as anorexia nervosa, which has occurred in some female endurance-based athletes. The restriction of food intake to levels well below energy expenditure causes anorexia nervosa.

The facts about obesity

The following facts about obesity should be noted:

* Over 30,000 deaths a year are caused by obesity – in England.
* 22% of the British adult population are obese.
* 75% of the British adult population are overweight.
* Child obesity has increased 3-fold in the last 20 years.

Coronary heart disease

As mentioned above, obese people have high risk factors of developing **coronary heart disease** (CHD). **CHD** is one of Britain's greatest killers and encompasses diseases such as **angina** and **heart attacks** or **coronary thrombosis**. Angina begins as a chest pain, which is due to ischemia. Ischemia is a condition in which there is a reduction in flow of blood and hence oxygen to the heart muscle itself. The first symptoms of **CHD** are usually noticed during physical exertion or excitement and the subsequent increase in heart rate. Heavy, cramp-like pains are experienced across the chest. Angina is normally treated and controlled with drugs and relaxation, but a person suffering from this condition has a higher risk of suffering from a **coronary thrombosis**.

Health risks from CHD can be reduced by regular aerobic exercise. This helps to maintain good coronary circulation (blood flow in the heart muscle itself), and strengthens and improves cardiac function, for example, resting heart rate is lowered.

Diabetes

Diabetes is a condition which occurs when a person's body cannot regulate glucose levels. Glucose is regulated by the release of the hormone insulin from the Isles of Langerhans situated in the pancreas. Too much glucose present in the bloodstream causes more insulin to be released to help remove it. If not enough glucose is present, the insulin available is reduced, and glucose levels are allowed to build up. The insulin enables the **transfer of glucose** from the blood into cells where it is needed for metabolism.

There are two types of diabetes:

* **Type 1 diabetes** usually occurs in younger people and is caused by the failure through disease of the mechanism for the production of insulin. This form of diabetes usually requires daily insulin injections for the rest of a person's life.
* **Type 2 diabetes** usually occurs in older people and is caused by age-related changes in the way the body reacts to insulin production.

Obesity is a major risk factor for type 2 diabetes.

Symptoms of type 2 diabetes are:

* Lack of circulation to the hands and feet.
* Extremes of thirst or hunger.
* Unexplained weight loss.
* Partial or total sight loss.

Regular aerobic exercise improves the regulation of blood glucose levels in the blood of type 2 diabetes sufferers.

High blood pressure

Hypertension (high blood pressure) is a condition that occurs when a person's blood pressure is continually high, equal to or greater than 140/90 mmHg. High blood pressure is another condition associated with **obesity** and also with hardening of the arteries (**arteriosclerosis**). Arteriosclerosis is an age-related condition whose effects can be lessened by exercise continuing into old-age. Hypertension is a major contributing factor in atherosclerosis, coronary heart disease (CHD), and strokes.

High cholesterol

figure 4.21 – abdominal obesity

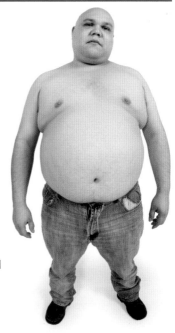

Cholesterol is a substance produced from fatty foods, particularly from a diet high in the saturated fats found exclusively in animal products. It is transported in the blood and to body tissues in the form of lipoproteins.

Two of the **lipoproteins** seem to have a relationship with the onset of coronary heart disease and have different amounts of cholesterol in their molecular make-up:

- **Low-density lipoprotein cholesterol** (LDL-C) contains high amounts of cholesterol and is known as '**bad cholesterol**'. If the digestive process does not remove this, it can lodge in the walls of arteries in the form of plaques causing the arteries to be narrower. This is a form of **atherosclerosis**.
    - Ideal level for blood LDL-C is less than 85 mg per decilitre of blood (mg/dl).
    - Risk level for blood LDL-C starts at above 110 mg/dl.
    - So the higher the level of LDL-C, the greater the risk of heart disease.

- **High-density lipoprotein cholesterol** (HDL-C) contains a high concentration of protein that is known as '**good cholesterol**'. It is thought that the HDL-C molecule helps prevent the process of atherosclerosis by blocking the movement of LDL-C into the arterial wall and by aiding the transport of cholesterol to the liver for removal by the body.
    - Ideal level for blood HDL-C is 70+ mg/dl.
    - Risk level for blood HDL-C starts at below 45 mg/dl.

Therefore, individuals with a high level of HDL-C seem to experience less coronary heart disease when compared to people who have high levels of LDL-C.

Exercise increases HDL-C and decreases LDL-C. Hence regular exercise helps keep arteries open and blood pressure (BP) lower than it otherwise would be. Blood pressure therefore tends to be more stable thus reducing hypertension.

The risk factors for high cholesterol are:
- Lack of exercise and or **obesity**, heredity, age.

Metabolic syndrome

Metabolic syndrome is a term used to link coronary artery disease, hypertension, abnormal blood lipids (fats), **type 2 diabetes** and abdominal **obesity** to **insulin resistance**. The syndrome refers to the fact that some people develop a resistance of their muscle cells to the action of insulin, and therefore not enough glucose finds its way into the cells to enable them to work properly.

Hence cells (particularly muscle cells) will not have enough glucose to function properly - and the person feels **exhausted**.

The risk factors for this syndrome are:
- Arterial plaque build-up.
- **Excessive fat deposits** in the abdominal region (figure 4.21).
- High blood triglycerides, low HDL cholesterol and high LDL cholesterol.
- Raised blood pressure.

figure 4.22 – healthy and unhealthy lifestyles

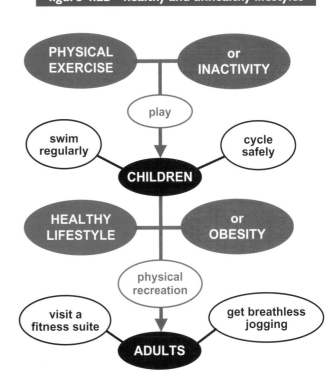

Roughly 20% of the population in the USA have this condition which makes type 2 diabetes worse, with the consequent risk of eyesight and circulation problems in older people.

Figure 4.22 illustrates healthy and unhealthy lifestyle pathway options. Most children like to be physically active. However, people become less active as they grow older, which can lead to diseases such as metabolic syndrome. Regular aerobic exercise reduces the risk of metabolic syndrome.

Sedentary lifestyles

The **sedentary** nature of modern life fails to give us the physical activity our bodies need for a long and active life.

Sedentary men and women are approximately twice as likely to suffer a fatal heart attack compared to their physically active friends.

Overall death rates from cancers, such as colon and breast cancer, are significantly higher among the sedentary population.

The **causes** of sedentary behaviour among adults and physical inactivity among children are:

- The increased availability of **transport**, for example, the car run to school in the mornings.
- Absence of the need to **walk** or **run**.
- The discouragement of vigorous play activities in the playground for children.
- The widening availability of **non-exercise** based recreational activities such as computer games.
- Limited physical education on the curriculum or extra-curriculum for children, with school fields being sold off or under-utilised.
- The actual increase in **leisure time**, which can mean less time spent being physically active at work or in physical recreations.
- The increase in white-collar (sedentary office based) working environments as opposed to the predominance of physically demanding blue-collar occupations of former times.

Avoidance of the sedentary lifestyle

To achieve the **benefits** of physical exercise and to work towards a level of **fitness** in the interests of a healthy lifestyle (figure 4.22 above), the recommendations are:

- **Regularity** of exercise.
- A degree of exercise **intensity** sufficient to increase the heart rate over a period.
- The intention of **sustaining** this improved condition, thus promoting **long-term health**.
- Giving the individual a more **balanced attitude** towards **personal fitness**.
- For example, a minimum of exercise three times per week of at least 20 minutes duration and raising the pulse and breathing rates to 70% of maximum.

Smoking

For smokers, the chemicals in tobacco adversely affect nearly every organ and system in the body. 40% of male smokers die before reaching retirement age, and pregnant women smokers increase the risk of harming the unborn child. Children born to smokers are on average smaller and take longer to reach maturity than children born to non-smokers. Such children tend to be later learning to read and tend to have disorders such as attention deficit disorder.

Women smokers increase the risk of cervical cancer, and once lung cancer or emphysema (for males and females) are diagnosed, death will be sooner rather than later.

Smoking worsens respiratory conditions such as colds, bronchitis, and passive smoking has all the same risks as first hand smoking. The net result is a reduced oxygen supply to lung alveoli.

Alcohol

- There can be damage to the mouth, throat or oesophagus (the possibility of cancer) and damage to the ciliated linings.
- **Cirrhosis of the liver**, alcohol hepatitis and an enlarged fatty liver.
- **Muscle atrophy**, pain and spasms.
- **Vascular issues** such as vasodilation within skin and hypertension.
- Stomach ulcers and cancer, and lung cancer.
- The nervous system is damaged, alcohol destroys brain cells producing slurred speech, and producing taste and smell deficiency.
- The **heart weakens** or heart muscle enlarges and there is an increased risk of heart attack.
- Damage to reproductive organs such as erectile dysfunction. Alcohol can harm foetal development.
- There is an increased incidence of **psychiatric disorders** such as alcoholism, depression with a link to suicide.

Recreational drugs

Drugs such as LSD, ecstacy, cannabis, speed, cocaine, crack cocaine, heroin and crystal meth plus many others can harm essential organs of life. Taking drugs can destroy family and social life, drive the users toward criminal behaviour to fund the habit, and destroy self-esteem and self respect through reliance on a drug.

Exam style questions

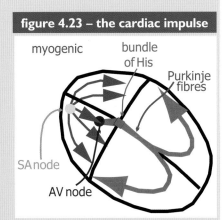

figure 4.23 – the cardiac impulse

1) Figure 4.23 shows a diagrammatic picture of the cardiac impulse. Using the information in this diagram, describe the flow of blood during the specific stages of the cardiac cycle in relation to the cardiac impulse. In your answer explain how the heart valves help control the direction of blood flow.   8 marks

2) $\dot{Q} = SV \times HR$. Explain the meaning of this equation and give typical resting values that you would expect in an endurance-based athlete.   6 marks

3) A fit 18 year old female student performs a 400m time trial in one minute.
   a)   Sketch and label a graph to show a typical heart rate response from a point 5 minutes before the start of the run, during the time trial, and over the 20 minute recovery period.   4 marks

   b)   Explain why heart rate takes some time to return to its resting value following the exercise period.   2 marks

   c)   Identify a hormone that is responsible for heart rate increases prior to and during an exercise period.   1 mark

   d)   Heart rate is regulated by neural, hormonal and intrinsic factors. How does the nervous system detect and respond to changes in heart rate during an exercise period?   4 marks

4) Jodie Swallow is a top class female British Triathlete, and has a resting heart rate of 36 bpm. Give reasons why such an athlete might have a low resting heart rate.   4 marks

5) Table 4.4 shows the rate of blood flow (in cm^3 per minute) to different parts of the body in a trained male athlete, at rest and while exercising at maximum effort on a cycle ergometer.

Table 4.4 – **estimated blood flow at rest and during maximum effort**

organ or system	estimated blood flow in cm^3 min^{-1}	
	at rest	during max effort
skeletal muscle	1000	26400
coronary vessels	250	1200
skin	500	750
kidneys	1000	300
liver & gut	1250	375
other organs	1000	975

Study the data carefully before answering the following questions.
   a)   The rate of blood flow to the 'entire body' increases significantly during exercise. Explain briefly how the heart achieves this.   2 marks

   b)   What percentage of the total blood flow is directed to the skeletal muscle at rest and during maximum effort? Show your calculations.   3 marks

   c)   How is blood flow to various regions of the body controlled?   4 marks

Exam style questions

6) a) What is meant by the concept 'venous return mechanism'?   2 marks

   b) Describe how it is aided during physical activity when a person is exercising in an upright position.   3 marks

   c) Explain the importance of the skeletal muscle pump mechanism during an active cool-down.   2 marks

   d) What effect does enhanced venous return have upon cardiac output and stroke volume?   3 marks

7) a) How is oxygen transported by the blood?   2 marks

   b) Identify the main method whereby carbon dioxide is transported in venous blood.   1 mark

   c) Explain how increased levels of carbon dioxide levels affect performance during physical activity.   3 marks

8) A simple equation for the calculation of blood pressure can be written as:
   Blood Pressure = Cardiac Output x Resistance to blood flow

   a) Identify **one** factor that affects resistance to the flow of blood within systemic blood vessels.   1 mark

   b) Blood pressure is quoted as two numbers. An example would be resting values of 120/80 mmHg. Explain what each of these numbers refer to.   2 marks

   c) How would these blood pressure values change during a game of football and a rugby scrum lasting 6 seconds? Give a reason for each of your answers.   3 marks

9) Table 4.5 identifies differences in total blood volume, plasma volume, and blood cell volume between untrained and highly trained endurance males (same age, height and body mass). Comment on the data that is presented in table 4.4 and suggest how the trained athlete would benefit from these increased volumes.   4 marks

Table 4.5 – **blood volumes in trained and untrained males**

subjects	total blood volume (dm³)	plasma volume (dm³)	blood cell volume (dm³)
trained male	7	4.2	2.8
untrained male	5.6	3.2	2.4

10) An unhealthy lifestyle is likely to lead to risky behaviours. Describe how smoking adversely affects the respiratory system.   6 marks

11) Identify three healthy lifestyle changes to reduce diabetes risk.   3 marks

12) A Level. Discuss the following statement: 'An unhealthy lifestyle has a detrimental effect on the cardiovascular and respiratory systems'.   15 marks

Answers link: http://www.jroscoe.co.uk/downloads/as_a1_revise_pe_edexcel/EdexcelAS_A1_ch4_answers.pdf

CHAPTER 5 - 1.3.1 The neuromuscular system

1.3.2 / 1.3.3 / 1.3.4 Muscle fibre types

Muscle fibres

Not all skeletal muscle fibres have identical functional capabilities. Some muscle fibres contract quickly and fatigue quickly (known as **fast twitch** muscle fibres) whereas others contract more slowly and are resistant to fatigue (known as **slow twitch or type I or Slow Oxidative (SO)** fibres). Fast twitch fibres are classified into 2 groups – **fast twitch type IIa or Fast-Oxidative-Glycolytic (FOG)** and **fast twitch type IIb or Fast-Glycolytic (FG)** muscle fibres also known as **type IIx**.

Table 5.1 - **major structural and functional differences** between **Slow-Oxidative (SO type I), Fast-Oxidative-Glycolytic (FOG type IIa) Fast-Glycolytic (FG type IIb)** muscle fibre types.

	SO – type I	FOG – type IIa	FG – type IIb or type IIx
structural differences			
colour	red	red to pink	white
fibre diameter	small	medium	large
fibres per motor unit	10-80	300-800	300-800
sarcoplasmic reticulum development	low	high	high
myoglobin content	high	high	low
capillary density	high	midway / high	low
mitochondrial density	many	midway	few
energy stores (phosphocreatine (PC) / glycogen / ATP content)	low	high	high
functional differences			
myosin ATPase activity	low	high	high
glycolytic enzyme activity	low	high	high
oxidative enzyme activity	high	midway	low
motor unit strength	low	high	high
recruitment order	first	second	third
contractile strength	low	high	high
contractile time	long	midway	short
fatigue resistance	low	midway	high
aerobic capacity	high	moderate	low
anaerobic capacity	low	high	high
primary function	maintaining posture / endurance-based activities	running / sprinting	high intensity rapid activity

STUDENT NOTE

The **metabolism** of the different types of cell or fibre differs depending on the different way in which ATP is regenerated following dissociation to produce energy. The fast twitch muscle fibres tend to be anaerobic and do not require oxygen for production of energy. They have high storage of phosphocreatine but low myoglobin content. The slow twitch muscle fibres tend to be aerobic and have low phosphocreatine but high myglobin content. The myoglobin (see page 39) contains an immediate source of oxygen which is transferred across the cell wall, from blood haemoglobin to the mitochondrion for abundant energy release.

Question

1) It can be deduced from the information summarised in Table 5.1 above that slow twitch fibres are best suited to aerobic (performed with a full and adequate supply of oxygen) types of exercise. On the other hand, fast twitch fibres are specifically adapted for high intensity and mainly anaerobic (performed without sufficient oxygen to cope with the energy demand) types of exercise. Describe some of the characteristics that support this deduction.

Short-term responses to exercise

Fibre type recruitment and force production

Fibre type usage (**recruitment**) is based on the intensity of exercise.

- **At low intensity, slow twitch** (ST or SO – slow oxidative) motor units are recruited first.
- **At higher intensity fast oxidative glycolytic** (FOG) type **IIa** motor units are recruited.
- **At greatest intensity fast glycolytic** (FG) type **IIb** motor units are recruited to produce powerful fast muscle contractions.

All available fibres are recruited for all high power activities as seen in the graph (see figure 5.1).

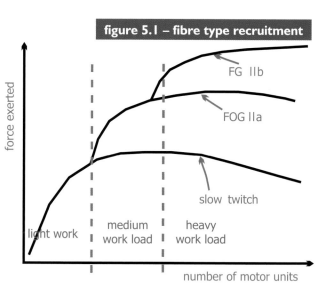

figure 5.1 – fibre type recruitment

Differences within individual muscles

The proportion of muscle fibre type differs within individual muscles. Most muscles have both fibre types, however the large postural muscles contain a high proportion of slow twitch fibres because postural muscles need to produce low forces over a long period of time.

The arms tend to consist of more fast twitch muscle fibres as they need to move quickly but over shorter periods of time. The percentage type of muscle fibres found in the legs determines whether the athlete is more suited to sprinting or endurance running.

Differences in fibre type distribution between different individuals

The average fibre type distribution within **sedentary** men and women and young children is between 45% and 55% slow twitch fibres, with fast twitch equally distributed between type IIa and IIb subdivisions. However individual variation is large.

Elite sprinters have a greater percentage of fast twitch muscle fibres, whereas elite long-distance runners have a higher percentage of slow twitch muscle fibres in their leg muscles. As might be expected, elite men and women show similar trends.

Table 5.2 - **differences in fibre type proportion between different sports and type of event**

	average % ST	range of % ST
males		
marathon	81	50 - 98
cross country skiers	64	52 - 75
cyclists	59	52 - 72
800m runners	52	40 - 62
untrained	47	42 - 76
shot putters	39	19 - 57
sprinters	40	20 - 53
females		
cross country skiers	59	47 - 74
cyclists	54	37 - 66
800m runners	62	44 - 73
untrained	53	30 - 72
shot putters	53	50 - 55
sprinters	32	28 - 52

Long-term adaptations as responses to exercise and training

Endurance training results in **type IIb** muscle fibres being converted to **type IIa**, and increases the aerobic capacity of **slow twitch** muscle fibres. This explains why long steady training results in loss of speed. The efficiency of the blood supply to these muscles will improve with endurance training, enabling slow twitch muscle to function more effectively.

High intensity anaerobic training causes increase in size of **fast twitch** muscle fibres (**hypertrophy**), and number of **fast twitch** type IIb fibres (**hyperplasia**). Refer to figure 5.2. Lack of high intensity training causes atrophy (loss of size and function) of fast twitch muscle. Therefore, a lot of high intensity training will make a muscle structure bigger and stronger and enabled to apply greater force than before training.

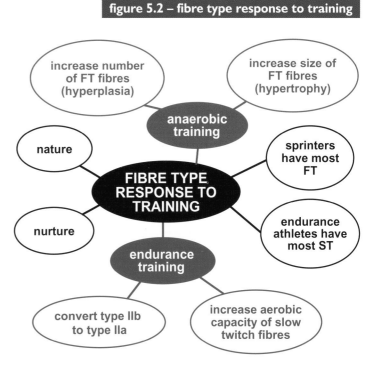

figure 5.2 – fibre type response to training

Nature or nurture?

- Proportions of fibre types are **genetically determined**, and this could account for specialisms of individuals such as whether a person becomes good at marathon running or weight lifting.

- On the other hand, researches have shown that a knowledge of a person's predominant fibre type is of limited value in predicting the outcome of specific exercise performances.

- This finding is not surprising because performance capacity is the end result of the blending of many physiological, biochemical, neurological and biomechanical 'support systems' – and is not simply determined by a single factor, such as muscle fibre type.

- Men have a greater tendency to be more muscular than women, due to the release of greater amounts of the hormone **testosterone** during adolescence and adulthood. But women can grow muscle in a similar way to men when exposed to high intensity training.

1.3.5 The anatomy of the neuromuscular system

Short-term responses of the neuromuscular system to exercise

Skeletal muscle is caused to contract by **nerve impulses** sent from the **cerebellum** in the brain. These electrical impulses are sent down a specialised nerve called a **motor neurone** (figure 5.3 page 68). At the muscle fibre end of the motor neurone, this nerve terminates at a **synaptic end bulb**. The synaptic end bulb is the end of the nerve fibre at the junction with the muscle fibre. The muscle fibre side of this junction (between nerve and muscle fibre) is called a neuro-muscular junction or **motor end plate** (see figures 5.5 on page 68, and 5.6 on page 69 for more details of this). A signal is transmitted between the motor end plate and a muscle fibre causing the muscle fibre to contract and exert force.

Further specialised nerves called sensory fibres relay information back to the cerebellum where information about the tension within the muscle and its rate of contraction is received.

The muscle motor unit

A motor neurone will terminate at several synapses (motor end plates) each linked to a number of muscle fibres. The block of muscle fibres and the nervous system which controls their contraction and relaxation is called a motor unit. A **motor unit** is therefore defined as '**a single block of muscle fibres and its neurone**'. Therefore when a motor neurone is stimulated, all fibres connected to that neurone are activated at once (the '**all or none law**'). A single neurone will control muscle fibres of the **same type**, either fast twitch **or** slow twitch. Figure 5.5 on page 68 shows a simplified diagram of a motor unit which is structurally enlarged in figure 5.3 also on page 68.

Structure of a motor neurone

See figure 5.3 for a diagrammatic view of a
motor neurone.
The **cell body** includes a nucleus and cytoplasm, but the
cell membrane is receptive to stimuli from other neurones.

Dendrites are highly branched processes which extend out from
the cell body and are specialised to receive stimuli from sensory
organs or from other neurones. The **axon** conducts nerve impulses
to other cells (nerve, muscle, gland cells).

Special structures include:

* **Myelin sheath** which electrically insulates the nerve.
* **Nodes of Ranvier**, which are gaps in the myelin sheath where
  the **action potential** jumps from node to node.
* **Axon terminal** which ends with a **synaptic end bulb** containing
  neurotransmitter substances.

These substances enable the **action potential** to be applied to
adjacent cells.

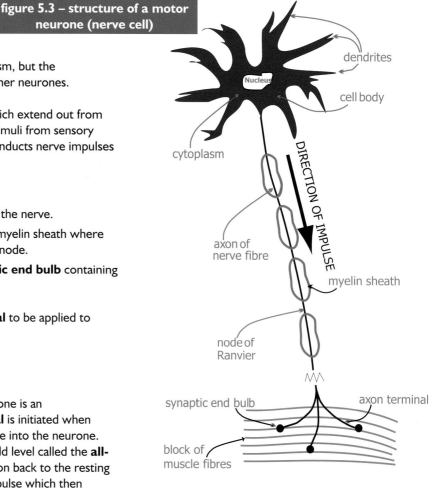

figure 5.3 – structure of a motor
neurone (nerve cell)

An action potential

Transmission of neural messages along a neurone is an
electrochemical process. An **action potential** is initiated when
sufficient numbers of sodium ions (Na^+) diffuse into the neurone.
This depolarises the axon to a critical threshold level called the **all-
or-none law**. This is followed by repolarisation back to the resting
potential. This process forms an electrical impulse which then
transmits itself down the neurone (see figure 5.4). In effect this electrical impulse is **conducted** down the axon. The **myelin
sheath** insulates the axon, and the action potential travels from node to node in a wave like action, since ion exchange only
occurs at the nodes of Ranvier.

The nerve action potential is followed by the muscle
action potential. A delay of 0.5 milliseconds occurs
due to release of transmitter substances (such as
acetylcholine from synaptic knobs) which initiate the
muscle action potential. The area of depolarisation
travels down a muscle cell passing the entrances to 'T'
vesicles which secrete calcium ions needed to initiate
muscle contraction.

Each different muscle fibre type (slow twitch or fast
twitch) is innervated by a separate and different type
of motor neurone.

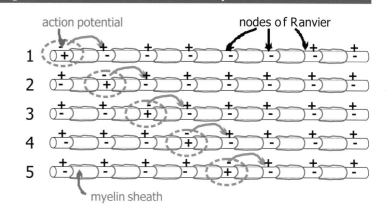

figure 5.4 – transmission of an action potential down an axon

The motor end plate

The function of the motor end plate is to transfer an impulse from the motor
neurones (see figure 5.5) to the muscle fibre block. This causes all muscle
fibres attached to this end plate to contract.

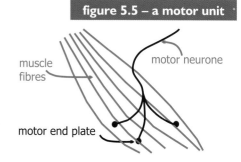

figure 5.5 – a motor unit

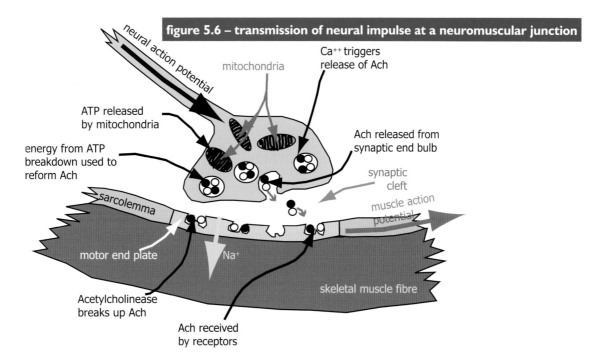

figure 5.6 – transmission of neural impulse at a neuromuscular junction

neural action potential

mitochondria

Ca++ triggers release of Ach

ATP released by mitochondria

energy from ATP breakdown used to reform Ach

Ach released from synaptic end bulb

synaptic cleft

sarcolemma

muscle action potential

motor end plate

Na+

skeletal muscle fibre

Acetylcholinease breaks up Ach

Ach received by receptors

Synapse

- A synapse is a junction where the axon of one neurone interacts with another neurone. Figure 5.6 outlines the process whereby the nerve impulse is transmitted from the neurone via the synapse to the muscle bed.

- This process involves the use of calcium ions (Ca^{++}) to trigger the release of a substance called acetylcholine (Ach) which then jumps into receptor sites in the motor end plate attached to the muscle fibre.

- This in turn triggers release of sodium ions (Na^+) which re-establish the action potential within the muscle fibre itself (and eventually cause it to contract and use energy).

1.3.6 Muscle fibre structure and physiology

There are three types of muscle tissue in the human body.

- **Involuntary** or smooth or visceral muscle, which is found within the walls of blood vessels (the tunica media) and the alimentary canal.

- **Cardiac** muscle, which forms the walls of the heart – the myocardium.

- **Skeletal** muscle, which is the muscle type concerned with human movement and activity.

Skeletal muscle tissue

Skeletal muscle (also called striated voluntary muscle because microscopic bands or striations can be seen) attaches to bone and is responsible for the following functions:

- **Producing** movement by exerting force on its origin and insertion.

- **Maintaining** body posture and changing body shape.

- **Generating** heat to keep us warm.

- **Storage** of glycogen for energy.

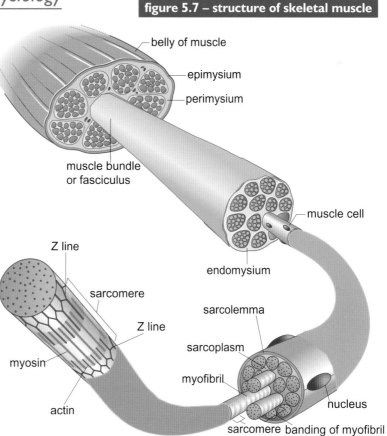

figure 5.7 – structure of skeletal muscle

belly of muscle

epimysium

perimysium

muscle bundle or fasciculus

muscle cell

endomysium

Z line

sarcomere

Z line

sarcolemma

sarcoplasm

myosin

myofibril

actin

nucleus

sarcomere banding of myofibril

Skeletal muscle tissue

Figure 5.7 on page 69 shows the basic structure of a muscle from the muscle belly down to the individual sarcomere. Each myofibril consists of filaments of actin (thin filaments) and myosin (thick filaments), the forces between which enable a muscle to shorten its length and hence contract and exert forces on its origin and insertion.

Muscle contraction

- Prior to muscle contraction, muscle tissue is in a **resting** or relaxed state (as illustrated in figure 5.8 a).
- The process of muscle contraction is initiated when a **neural action potential** (electrical impulse form the brain) travels via a **motor neurone** to the **motor end-plate**, which creates a **muscle action potential** (see page 68) over the muscle fibre's **sarcoplasm**, and inward along the **'T' tubules**. This process is known as **excitation**.
- This triggers the release of **Ca^{++}** ions from 'T' vesicles (located within SR - Sarcoplasmic Reticulum) into the sarcoplasm, where it binds to a **troponin** molecule on an actin filament (troponin is a globular protein with a high affinity for Ca^{++}).
- Then **tropomyosin** molecules (thread-like protein which winds around the surface of actin) on the thin **actin** filaments move, exposing actin's active sites, and energised **myosin cross-bridges** bind to actin's active sites.
- Hence their energy (released from ATP via the enzyme **myosin-ATPase**) is used to pull the thin **actin** filaments towards the centre of the sarcomere (called the power stroke), causing the H zone within the sarcomere to disappear as you go from figure 5.8 a to figure 5.8 b, from a **relaxed** to a **contracted** muscle state.
- This attach, detach, reattach of cross-bridges is called the **ratchet mechanism**.
- The cycle repeats itself - **recharges** - as long as ATP is available.

figure 5.8 – actin/myosin structure within the sarcomere

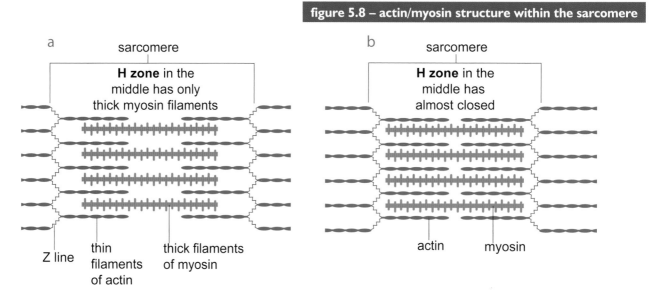

Hence during a muscle contraction, the **thin actin filaments** are drawn in between the **thicker myosin filaments** (this is called **Huxley's sliding theory of muscle contraction**). The greater the overlap of filaments the stronger the contraction.

Figure 5.8 shows the basic structure of actin/myosin filaments within the sarcomere in a **relaxed** and **contracted** state.

Motor neural firing patterns

In order to control muscle contraction, the cerebellum innervates one or more motor units. Each motor unit controls a number of fibres, so that either **all** the fibres attached to the motor unit are activated at the same time, or **none** of these fibres are activated. This is called the '**all-or-none law**'. Different fibre groups (attached to different motor units) are fired at different times. Each firing produces a fibre '**twitch**'.

figure 5.9 – force produced by a single fibre twitch

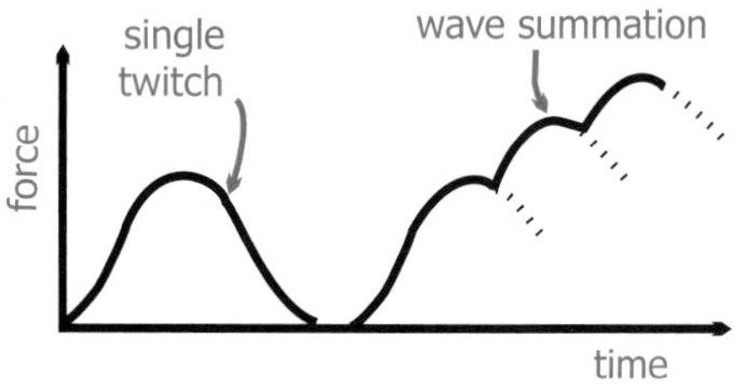

The force produced by a single fibre twitch follows the left hand graph in figure 5.9. Note that each twitch only lasts a short length of time, so that in order to prolong the force exerted by a twitch, the fibre group must be fired repeatedly. The build up of force in a single fibre is represented in the right hand graph in figure 5.9. When a fibre is fired repeatedly in this manner, the way in which the force builds up is called '**wave summation**'.

Multiple fibre twitches

In order to activate fibres across a whole muscle body to produce force in a controlled manner, different fibre groups are fired in succession. The total force across the space of a muscle is the sum of the effect of different fibre groups, and is shown in figure 5.10. This is called '**spatial summation**'.

In order to control very fine movements, it is necessary to be able to vary the total force produced by fibre twitches. **Gradation of contraction** refers to the ability of muscle to produce forces varying from very light to maximum force or tension.

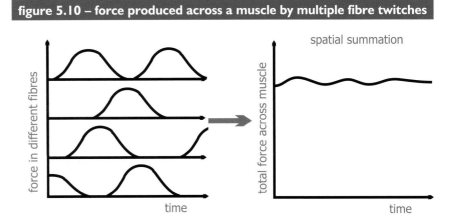

figure 5.10 – force produced across a muscle by multiple fibre twitches

This can be achieved in two ways:

- Increasing the frequency of stimulus (wave summation).
- Varying the number of motor units recruited.

For example in hockey, there would be fine control of movement required for a flick, as opposed to the maximum effort required for a full hit.

If there were no time for relaxation between motor unit firing, eventually (after a few seconds) there would be a complete lock up of muscle. This is called '**tetanine contraction**' and happens when a muscle is used at maximum for too long.

The cerebellum

The balance of fine and gross control is under the control of the **cerebellum**. In order to produce smooth coordinated movement, the cerebellum compares the intended movement with the actual movement (from sensors within the moving structure – the proprioceptors). If a difference is detected, the cerebellum sends impulses to the appropriate motor units in the spinal cord which would produce a correction. In sport, the cerebellum is involved in the learning of **fine motor skills** (as in archery) or **gross motor skills** (as in weight lifting).

Gross movements use leg and arm muscles having about 1000 muscle fibres associated with one motor unit, whereas fine movements (of the eyes and fingers for example) require muscles with far fewer (10-100) muscle fibres controlled by a single motor unit.

Control is achieved by increasing or decreasing the number of motor units in operation. Different motor units are activated in turn across a muscle and this gradation of contraction across a muscle enables very small forces to be maintained if required. The self-regulation of rhythmic movements between one muscle and its antagonist relies on control of movement which requires relaxation of antagonists during the dynamic activity of an agonist. This process is called '**reciprocal innervation**'.

The benefits of warm-up on the neuromuscular system

- Increased rate of response of **CNS** (Central Nervous System).
- Enables recruitment of additional fast twitch fibre motor units.
- Hence improved coordination of fast twitch fibre motor units.
- And increased strength of associated muscle actions.
- Practice and rehearsal of sports movements will enable retention of important skills ready for full effort.
- Practice and rehearsal of sports will reduce reciprocal innervation (the **antagonist response**) and enable more fluent performance.
- Hence increased coordination in response to the demands of competition.
- Increased neural activation will enable increase in strength (from the resting state).
- Reduced risk of injury, such as muscle tears.

1.3.7 Acute (short-term) response of the neuromuscular system to exercise

Skeletal muscle is caused to contract by **nerve impulses** sent from the **cerebellum** in the brain. These electrical impulses are sent down a specialised nerve called a **motor neurone** (figure 5.3 on page 68). At the muscle fibre end of the motor neurone, this nerve terminates at a **synaptic end bulb** - as shown in figure 5.3 on page 68.

The synaptic end bulb is the end of the nerve fibre at the junction with the muscle fibre. The muscle fibre side of this junction (between nerve and muscle fibre) is called a neuromuscular junction or **motor end plate** (see figures 5.5 and 5.6 on pages 68 and 69 repectively, for more details of this). A signal is transmitted between the motor end plate and a muscle fibre causing the muscle fibre to contract and exert force.

Further specialised nerves called sensory fibres relay information back to the cerebellum where information about the tension within the muscle and its rate of contraction is received.

1.3.8 Chronic adaptations (long-term) to muscle cells produced by exercise

Table 5.3 displays the adaptations to skeletal muscle cells produced by different types of exercise.

Table 5.3 – **adaptations produced by exercise**

adaptations to muscle cells produced by anaerobic exercise	adaptations to muscle cells produced by aerobic training
fast twitch muscle **hypertrophy** - increase in size by increased cross sectional area of a muscle.	**body fat** proportion is reduced by between 4% and 12%.
increase in the number of **myofibrils** within each muscle cell.	more **myoglobin** is created in muscle cells.
increase in the **sarcoplasmic** volume within each cell.	more and bigger **mitochondria** are created in muscle cells.
increase in the size and **strength** of the contractile proteins, **actin and myosin.** leading to increase in the **mass** of fast twitch fibres.	muscle cells have increased **oxidative enzymes** which increases aerobic cell activity.
increase in the **number** of fast twitch muscle fibres (**hyperplasia**). this means that the **proportion** of type II muscle fibre increases and the proportion of type I decreases.	increase in **utilisation** of **fat** in adipose tissue as an energy source.
increase in muscle **cell stores** of substances such as ATP, PC, and glycogen. increase in **anaerobic enzyme**s such as creatine kinase (CK), PFK, GPP, and LDH, which makes the muscle stronger and more powerful.	increase in **stores** of **glycogen** in muscle which enables more fuel to be available for aerobic work.
improved toleration of **lactate** in fast twitch fibres, and improved ability to remove lactate from muscle cell into blood - which enhances lactate thresholds and **reduces OBLA.**	**conversion** of type IIb to type IIa muscle fibres, so increasing the **proportion** of **aerobically** active muscle cells.
increased rate of response of **CNS** (Central Nervous System), **recruitment** of additional **fast twitch** fibre motor units, improved co-ordination of fast twitch fibre motor units.	better **recruitment** of **slow twitch** fibre motor units making muscle usage more efficient.
toughening of **proprioceptors** so that more force is required to stimulate inhibitory signals, an improved agonist antagonist response.	
reduction of **delayed onset muscle soreness (DOMS)**.	reduction of **delayed onset muscle soreness (DOMS)**.

OBLA = **Onset of Blood Lactate Accumulation**, see page 73.

figure 5.11 – muscle hypertrophy in a body builder

STUDENT NOTE

The increase in muscle mass caused by hypertrophy (see figure 5.11) will increase the proportion of muscle to body fat and help reduce obesity. Increased storage of ATP and phosphocreatine (PC) will increase the strength or efficiency of each fast twitch muscle fibre.

The long-term adaptations to muscle cells

Improved lactate handling enhances alactic/lactate and lactate/aerobic thresholds, and causes a delay in the onset of blood lactate accumulation (**OBLA**). These processes enable an improved capacity of alactic (ATP-PC) and lactic acid systems to resynthesise ATP, and hence to deliver energy more rapidly. Also there would be increases in maximum possible peak power, and the ability to maintain maximal power output for longer. There would be a decrease in delayed onset muscle soreness (**DOMS**), particularly following eccentric training.

The adaptations in which more muscle fibres are recruited within an activity will better utilise fast twitch muscle fibres at their existing level before hypertrophy occurs. Initial measured strength gains are almost exclusively via this process.

figure 5.11 – muscle hypertrophy in a body builder

figure 5.12 – a female bodybuilder with muscle hypertrophy

STUDENT NOTE

The adaptive response depends on an individual's fitness, cultural norms, gender, psychological preparedness and state of maturation. Given that anaerobic training will have the above effects, the outcomes will vary between individuals. Particularly, female athletes will acquire muscle hypertrophy if exposed to high intensity anaerobic exercise (figure 5.12).

Exam style questions

1) Identify and explain the function of the different regions of a motor neurone. — 6 marks

2) a) What is a motor unit? — 2 marks

   b) Explain how a motor unit transfers a neural impulse into muscular contraction. — 8 marks

   c) The result of an electric impulse reaching the muscle fibres is a maximal contraction of those fibres. Explain this statement and describe how the force exerted by the muscle can vary significantly. — 3 marks

   d) Why is it that muscle fibres attached to different motor units will not necessary contract at the same time? — 3 marks

3) Analyse how the characteristics of different skeletal muscle fibres help contribute to success in different sports. — 12 marks

4) Table 5.4 shows the percentage of slow twitch muscle fibres in three muscle groups of elite male (M) and female (F) athletes and non-athletes. The percentage of fast twitch muscle fibre is calculated as the difference between 100% and the percentage of slow twitch fibres.
(Data from research literature – source – 'Essentials of Exercise Physiology' 2e, McArdle, Katch and Katch)

Table 5.4 – percentage of slow twitch muscle fibres

athletic group	shoulder (deltoid)	calf (gastrocnemius)	thigh (vastus lateralis)
long distance runners		79% (M) 69% (F)	
canoeists	71% (M)		
triathletes	60% (M)	59% (M)	63% (M)
swimmers	67% (M) 69% (F)		
sprinters		24% (M) 27% (F)	
cyclists			57% (M) 51% (F)
weight lifters	53% (M)	44% (M)	
shot putters		38% (M)	
non-athletes			47% (M) 46% (F)

a) Compare and account for the differences in percentage distribution of slow twitch muscle fibres with respect to long distance runners and sprinters. 3 marks

b) Calculate the percentage of fast twitch muscle fibres for the long distance runners and sprinters. 2 marks

c) Data collected for male triathletes shows a fairly even distribution of slow twitch muscle fibres across all three muscle groups. Discuss two possible reasons for this trend. 3 marks

d) For shot putters, only the calf muscle is given a value in the table. What percentage distribution of slow twitch muscle fibres would you expect in the deltoid muscle for shot putters? Give a reason to support your answer. 2 marks

5) Briefly describe the structure of a skeletal muscle fibre, and explain how it contracts when stimulated. 7 marks

6) Identify the physiological adaptations that occur within sleletal muscle tissue as a result of anaerobic training. 7 marks

7) Describe three changes that occur in muscle cells as a result of endurance training. 3 marks

8) Describe some of the factors which determine muscle speed and tension characteristics. 4 marks

9) Skeletal muscle contains both slow and fast twitch muscle fibres but the proportion of each depends upon the function of a muscle as a whole. Table 5.1, page 65 lists some of the differences between slow and fast twitch muscle fibres.

a) Suggest why the muscles concerned in maintaining the trunk posture of the body of the sprinter might be expected to have a larger percentage of slow twitch muscle fibres.
Using table 5.1 explain why fast twitch muscle fibres may build up an oxygen debt during a 400m sprint. 5 marks

b) Account for the difference in the speed of contraction between slow and fast twitch muscle fibre types.
Fast twitch muscle fibres are divided into two types, IIa and IIb. Identify the major functional characteristic between these sub groups.
In what sporting activities would the adaptation of fast twitch type IIb to type IIa fibres be relevant to a sportsperson? 6 marks

10) An understanding of the functional structure of muscle cells is an important basis for an understanding of physical activity. Discuss this statement. 12 marks for AS
15 marks for A level

Answers link: http://www.jroscoe.co.uk/downloads/as_a1_revise_pe_edexcel/EdexcelAS_A1_ch5_answers.pdf

EXERCISE PHYSIOLOGY & APPLIED MOVEMENT ANALYSIS

CHAPTER 6 - *Diet and Nutrition*

2.1.1 Nutrition and weight management

A **balanced diet** is (figures 6.1 and 6.2) the combination and proportions of carbohydrates (CHO), fats, proteins, roughage, water and essential minerals and vitamins which best provide for a sportsperson's nutritional requirements. Table 6.1 gives the details of each food type and its contribution to life.

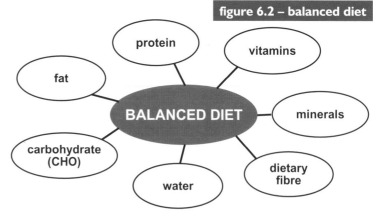

figure 6.1 – a balanced diet?

figure 6.2 – balanced diet

Table 6.1 – **summary of dietary content**

type of food / sources	function as a food fuel - how it is used	energy content (kJ g⁻¹)	percentage in a balanced diet
carbohydrate (CHO) sugars, rice, potatoes, pasta	**main energy supply**, absorbed as glucose in small intestine, transported around body as blood glucose. available for immediate energy. excess stored as muscle and liver glycogen and as fat.	17	60 %
fats butter, oil, pastry, fried food	**secondary energy supply**, absorbed as fatty acids and glycerol in the small intestine, stored as triglycerides in adipose tissue. **triglycerides** conveyed to the liver via the circulatory system. in the liver they are converted to **glucose**, available as delayed (20 minutes delay) energy source for long duration low intensity **aerobic** exercise.	39	20-25 %
proteins meat, eggs, milk, cheese, nuts	absorbed as **amino acids** in the small intestine, used for growth and repair by all tissues. used as an energy source when body is depleted of CHO and fat. excess protein not needed for tissue repair is broken down and used as an energy supply.		10-15 %
vitamins	organic substances needed for crucial functions in almost all bodily functions. regulate metabolism and facilitate energy release. have important functions in bone formation and tissue synthesis.		small amounts essential
minerals	**calcium** provides structure in bones and teeth. **iron** is needed for red blood cell production. **other minerals** assist in synthesising glycogen, fat and protein.		small amounts essential
dietary fibre wholegrain cereals, vegetables	non-starch, structural polysaccharide including cellulose, only available from plant sources. gives **bulk** to food residues in the intestines. aids **gastrointestinal** functioning.		large amounts necessary 20 to 40 grams per day
water	constitutes 72% of **muscle weight** and around 50% of adipose tissue, provides the body's transport and reactive medium. **transports** nutrients and leaves the body in urine and faeces. **lubricates** joints, keeping bony surfaces from grinding against each other. provides **structure** and form to the body, some sports drinks are designed to meet both energy and fluid needs of athletes.		large amounts necessary up to 5 litres per day

2.1.2 The need for a balanced diet

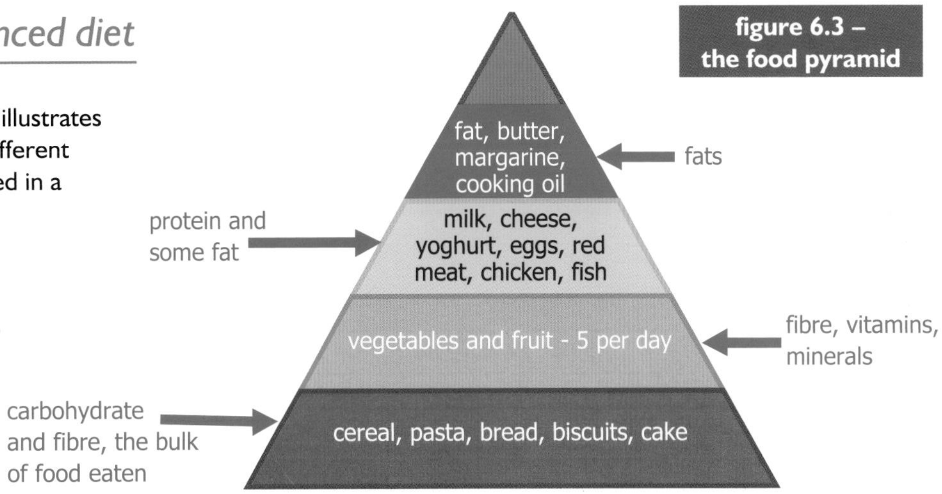

The food pyramid shown in figure 6.3 illustrates the approximate proportions of the different food groups which should be consumed in a balanced diet.

The foods in the lower part of the pyramid should form the main part of a balanced diet, while those at the top should be eaten in smaller quantities.

figure 6.3 – the food pyramid

fat, butter, margarine, cooking oil — fats

protein and some fat → milk, cheese, yoghurt, eggs, red meat, chicken, fish

vegetables and fruit - 5 per day → fibre, vitamins, minerals

carbohydrate and fibre, the bulk of food eaten → cereal, pasta, bread, biscuits, cake

Energy balance

When energy input is equal to energy output a **neutral energy balance** is achieved, as a result of which a person's weight remains constant. This concept can be expressed as:

ENERGY INTAKE = ENERGY EXPENDITURE

This means that there would be no tendency for this person to add adipose tissue to his or her body structure.

Positive energy balance

This definition of obesity highlights the major cause of obesity, namely an obese person would have energy intake far greater than energy output, which would be the result of inactivity and too much dietary fat intake.

This relationship is expressed as:

ENERGY INTAKE > ENERGY EXPENDITURE

to create a **positive energy balance**, which means that more energy is eaten as food than energy is used via exercise.

Excess carbohydrate (CHO) from food is stored as glycogen. When glycogen stores are filled, CHO together with excess fat intake are converted to fatty acids and glycerol, and then are stored as triglycerides or **fat** in adipose tissue. This is situated around major organs such as the heart and stomach, underneath the skin, and in skeletal muscle. Upper body obesity poses the most significant risk to disease.

Excessive weight gain is associated with certain health conditions such as **coronary heart disease** and **hypertension** (high blood pressure) with an increased risk of mortality and morbidity.

Controlling obesity

The only method of controlling obesity is to shift the energy relationship so that energy output exceeds energy intake – known as a **negative energy balance** and expressed as:

ENERGY INTAKE < ENERGY EXPENDITURE

This means that more energy is used via exercise than is eaten as food.

Questions

1) Define the term 'a balanced diet'.

2) Define the term 'energy balance'.

3) How can an understanding of the food classifications, illustrated in figure 6.3, assist in the maintenance an optimal weight for a sports performer?

4) How can energy balance assist in controlling obesity?

Achieving optimal weight for activities

The following table 6.2 shows how the body fat content for people of various age groups depends on whether they are fit or not. The data takes us up to 40 years of age.

Table 6.2 – **example data of relative body fat values for untrained and trained males and females**

| age group | relative body fat (%) | | | |
| | untrained | | trained | |
	females	males	females	males
15-19	20-24	13-16	12-20	7-13
20-29	22-25	15-20	10-18	6-12
30-39	24-30	18-26	12-20	8-14

The achievement of optimal body mass will require manipulation of the **energy balance**. When energy intake and expenditure are balanced (**energy intake = energy expenditure**), an athlete's body mass will be stable, with no tendency to add to or subtract from stored adipose tissue.

Dietary requirements for exercise

Table 6.3 – **a comparison of daily energy intake for athletes**

activity	daily energy intake kJ – females	daily energy intake kJ – males
Tour de France		25000
triathlon	10000	20000
rowing	12600	14700
swimming	8400	15500
hockey	9200	13400
soccer	9600	14700
running	9200	13000
gymnastics	6000	9000
body building	5900	14500

figure 6.4 – endurance cyclists consume huge amounts of energy

Within rather broad bands, a balanced diet from a regular food intake provides the nutrient requirements for active individuals (as observed in the Food Pyramid figure 6.3 on page 77). However, dietary requirements depend on the **intensity** and **duration** of the exercise period. This means developing a diet that is tailor-made to suit the needs of the individual.

Carbohydrate requirements

Glycogen is the most important and most valuable food for any type of exercise. Physically active individuals should obtain between 60% and 70% of daily energy intake from carbohydrates – particularly unrefined, low glycemic foods such as fresh acidic fruits (apples, pears, oranges) and most vegetables. The longer the duration of the activity, the greater the % of CHO intake.

In activity lasting longer than 90 minutes, as in the case of marathon running, dietary manipulation techniques, such as **carbo-loading**, will increase muscle glycogen stores to above normal levels. Carbo-loading is a process where extra carbohydrate is taken in after a short period of carbohydrate starvation (see page 82 for further details).

Carbohydrate requirements

For rapid carbohydrate **replenishment** after exercise, carbohydrate foods with a high glycemic index are recommended, for example, foods such as bananas, brown rice, pasta, raisins or wholemeal bread. Food should be eaten within two hours of completing the physical activity. This is because eating these foods will be more efficient in increasing blood glucose concentrations and hence stimulating the greater insulin release needed to convert glucose to glycogen. Optimal glycogen replenishment will benefit individuals involved in regular intense physical activity, such as playing in tournaments that span over a period of days.

Protein requirements

Physically active individuals need more protein than inactive people do (between 1.2-1.4 grams per kg body mass per day). Additional protein intake is needed to compensate for increased muscle breakdown that occurs during and after intense exercise. Protein is also needed to build new muscle cells (known as muscle hypertrophy).

In strength and power-based activities, additional protein intake is recommended (between 1.4-1.8 grams per kg body mass per day).

Fat requirements

Fat intake should be restricted, unless additional body mass is required, as is the case for extreme performers such as sumo wrestlers.
Unsaturated fats are preferable to saturated fats.

Vitamin and mineral requirements

Getting the right balance of vitamins and minerals can be sourced from the daily-recommended intake of fresh fruit and vegetables.

When and what should you eat before an exercise period?

- Food should be eaten between 3-4 hours prior to the competition so that it is well digested and absorbed into the bloodstream.
- The meal needs to be high in carbohydrates, low in fat and moderate in fibre to aid the digestive process.
- An example meal could be pasta bake with spinach, a banana and a still flavoured drink.

2.1.3 Hydration and electrolyte balance

Fluid intake has almost become an obsession with modern sportsmen and women. Modern athletes frequently use **isotonic sports drinks**, such as Isostar and Red Bull, just prior to competition to maintain rehydration and alertness respectively.

Exercise is thirsty work. Fluid loss during exercise depends on the intensity and duration of the exercise, temperature and humidity, body size and fitness levels. The longer and more intense the exercise period, for example in a long distance race, the more the need to drink before, during and after the event.

Bearing in mind that water comprises 60% of total body mass, it is important that **water balance** is maintained during exercise. **At rest**, water loss occurs via evaporation from the skin (sweat) and excretion with the majority lost as urine. Water intake will depend on climate and body mass. The modern fashion of carrying water bottles for ready consumption reflects modern concerns about water balance.

Questions

1) What are the three main groups of food?

2) Provide recommendations for carbohydrate, fat and protein intake for a cross-country skier and a ski jumper.

Hydration during exercise

During exercise, more water is produced during tissue respiration along with heat energy as a by-product of the metabolic process. In order to prevent the body from heating up too much, water is transported to the skin where **sweating** occurs. The loss of water from the skin by **evaporation** causes the skin to fall in temperature, and hence reduces the effect of heat production in muscle. But far more water is lost as sweat than is produced by tissue respiration, the amount of sweat being determined by external temperature, body mass and metabolic rate. There is increased water loss via expired air due to increased breathing, but the kidneys decrease urine flow in an attempt to decrease dehydration. The total effect is that the body loses more water than is produced or retained, and this must be replaced if exercise is to continue at a maximal rate.

Loss of water

* Also, the loss of water raises the osmotic pressure in body fluids because the electrolytes become more concentrated in these body fluids.

* The thirst mechanism does not exactly match the body's hydration state, so more fluid should be consumed than thirst dictates.

* Only by **replenishing water** content can the electrolytes return to normal concentrations.

In extreme exercise situations (for example during a marathon, figure 6.5) 6-10% of body water content is lost, hence the need for water intake during exercise. This means that during 1 hour's exercise an average person could expect to lose around 1 litre of fluid, and even more in hot conditions. This could represent as much as 2 litres an hour in warm or humid conditions.

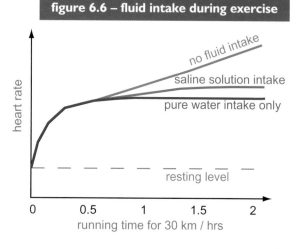

figure 6.5 – Paula Radcliffe could be taking in water throughout a marathon

figure 6.6 – fluid intake during exercise

Dehydration and loss of performance

Excessive loss of fluid impairs performance as blood plasma volume decreases and body temperature rises. The graph in figure 6.6 shows how heart rate is affected by fluid intake during prolonged exercise. Heart rate rise without fluid intake is explained earlier, but the graph also shows how heart rate is kept constant - if suitable water is taken during the exercise.

The potential benefits of sports drinks

Sports drinks are designed to supplement energy, fluid and protein needs of the athlete.

When taken during exercise, **hypotonic** sports drinks are designed to quickly replace fluids lost through sweating as they are low in carbohydrates at around 4% glucose. They are very popular with athletes who need fluid without much carbohydrate. **Isotonic** sport drinks contain concentrations of salt and glucose (between 5-7%) that match the same levels of concentration as in the blood to maximise fluid intake and absorption. Both hypotonic and isotonic sports drinks are an important source of energy during exercise as they reduce the risk of dehydration.

During recovery, **hypertonic** drinks contain much higher levels of glucose - up to 20%. This highly concentrated drink is used to replenish depleted glycogen stores and should be drunk as soon as the exercise period has been completed.

Questions

1) How does dehydration affect heart rate, body temperature and exercise performance?

2) Explain the importance of hydration to an active athlete.

3) How is body water balance maintained during prolonged aerobic exercise?

4) Distinguish between isotonic and hypertonic sports drinks?

5) What are the potential benefits of sports drinks?

2.1.4 - 2.1.5 The role and use of supplementation

Almost all modern sportspeople use sports supplements (figure 6.7) as part of their diet. Such supplements are aimed at filling the gaps in diet caused by inappropriate dietary content, or at enhancing features of food or drink taken which would be required to enhance sporting requirements for such a diet.

Creatine supplementation

Creatine is a substance found in skeletal muscle and which is stored as **phosphocreatine** (PC). Creatine (usually as Creatine Monohydrate) supplementation, together with large amounts of CHO, increases PC levels to enhance the ATP-PC system of ATP resynthesis, thereby delaying the alactic/lactic threshold (see page 73). This is a **legal ergogenic aid**.

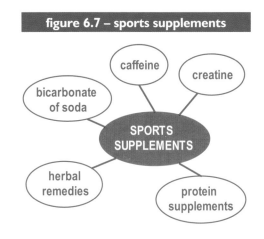

figure 6.7 – sports supplements

caffeine
creatine
bicarbonate of soda
SPORTS SUPPLEMENTS
herbal remedies
protein supplements

Sportspeople use creatine in a way which will help improve anaerobic power and lengthen the time over which they can apply maximal power. It is not a muscle development 'drug', and eating lots of raw white meat (as in fish) would have the same effect. This is because white muscle cells (those not containing lots of myoglobin, which is red in colour and is present in large quantities in slow twitch muscle cells) are predominantly fast twitch in nature and contain creatine in relatively large quantities.

Power athletes, such as the pole vaulter lifting weights in figure 6.8, use in their competitive event a little bit of the ATP-PC system and mostly ATP storage. But almost all the training will be serviced by the ATP-PC system, and therefore creatine supplementation will help the training process.

Creatine supplementation can cause muscle cramps, can be responsible for athlete weight gain, and can cause heat-related disorders such as dehydration and renal stress.

figure 6.8 – power athletes benefit?

Protein supplementation

Many athletes regularly consume sports drinks that are designed to supplement the energy, fluid and protein needs of the athlete. Protein supplements, such as **whey protein**, are used to increase total protein content of an athletic diet. Sportspeople need more protein than the untrained person to enable muscle hypertrophy and muscle repair following hard training. This particularly applies to sports requiring large muscle mass, as in weight lifting and gymnastics.

Within the section on the Athlete's diet on page 84, a protein shake is recommended as an important protein supplement for a female 800 metre athlete, particularly following a high intensity training session.

- A controversial area of research is whether there is need for protein supplementation. This is particularly if the athlete is already consuming a balanced diet that meets all his or her nutritional requirements. If this is the case protein supplementation becomes a very expensive form of energy food.
- Most protein supplements are legal, but can cause liver and kidney damage if taken in excess.
- **Glutamine** is an **amino acid** forming part of **skeletal muscle** and **immune cells**. Supplementation after exercise therefore reinforces the immune system and **reduces the risk of infection** and therefore enhances the process of glycogen synthesis in recovering muscles. Glutamine supplementation is widely used by athletes.

Questions

1) What is creatine?

2) What type of athlete would benefit from taking a creatine monohydrate supplement?

3) Identify the advantages and disadvantages of using a creatine monohydrate supplementation?

Herbal remedies

Herbal remedies are derived from plant extracts and are part of the practice of homeopathy and are in the form of tablets, oils or creams and liquids. Intake of a broad range of herbal supplements for ergogenic purposes has expanded considerably over the past decade. Examples include:

- **Ginseng**, which is reported to increase mental alertness, boosts energy levels and the immune system, increases $\dot{V}O_{2max}$, and reduces OBLA. The controversial use of ginseng was popularised by Chinese women endurance athletes in the 1990s. Little evidence exists to support the effectiveness of ginseng as an ergogenic aid.
- **Glucosamine** is known to reduce joint inflammation and stiffness.
- **Arnica** is used to reduce inflammation, bruising and pain.
- **Camomile** is known to reduce stress, support the immune system, promote tissue repair and assist sleeping.

Many herbal remedies for common conditions such as colds, flu and bronchitis are used to avoid restrictions imposed by doping regulations. This is because there are substances commonly used in the pharmaceutical versions of such remedies, such as codeine or ephedrine, which are against doping regulations. However, care needs to be taken when using herbal remedies since some herbal remedies contain substances on the doping register.

Bicarbonate use

Bicarbonate loading is a process whereby a performer ingests bicarbonate prior to a competition. An athlete can increase plasma bicarbonate levels that provide additional **buffering capacity**, thus allowing higher concentrations of lactate in the blood. Theoretically, this could delay the onset of fatigue in all-out anaerobic activity such as a 400 metre race. Bicarbonate loading can cause cramping, vomiting, bloating and diarrhoea.

Caffeine

By drinking a large black coffee one hour prior to activity, caffeine can produce significant increase in specific power output for all fibre types during both anaerobic and aerobic exercise, thus improving fatigue resistance during the performance. Consuming too much caffeine leads to a drop in performance for endurance events, such as a marathon race.

- Caffeine **stimulates** the central nervous system thereby reducing reaction times.
- Caffeine acts as a **diuretic**, which can lead to dehydration and heat related conditions.
- Caffeine used to be illegal in large quantities, but the rules changed in 2002, making this **legal** again!
- Caffeine is also used to promote **fat metabolism** and hence to reduce adipose tissue in the elite sportsperson.
- Consuming caffeine before prolonged exercise increases fat metabolism thus **sparing** precious **glycogen reserves** for later.
- Caffeine produces a state of **nervousness**, and can disrupt normal sleeping patterns therefore contributing to fatigue.
- Abrupt ceasing of caffeine intake can lead to severe headaches.

Alcohol

Alcohol is a relaxant in quite small quantities. It is absorbed into the body as an alternative to water therefore causes dehydration. Quite small quantities of alcohol can cause a drastic loss of performance. Alcohol is a **legal** ergogenic aid - but anyone using it as such must be aware of the consequences!

figure 6.9 – carboloading

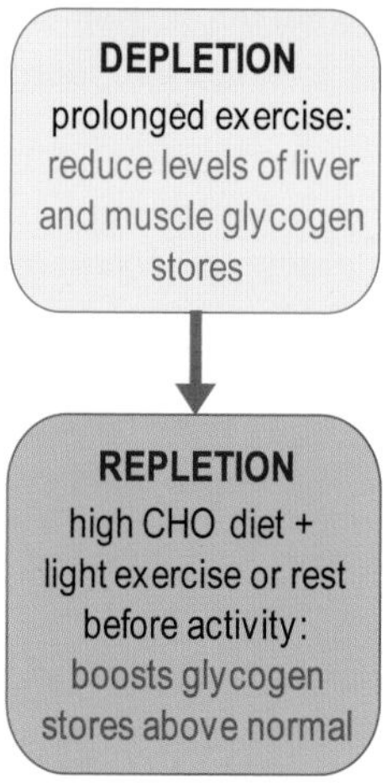

DEPLETION
prolonged exercise: reduce levels of liver and muscle glycogen stores

↓

REPLETION
high CHO diet + light exercise or rest before activity: boosts glycogen stores above normal

2.1.6 Strategies for optimising food fuel intake

Carbo-loading

Carbo-loading aims to raise muscle glycogen stores above their normal resting levels prior to endurance competitions with over 90 minutes continuous activity. This process is suitable for activities with low anaerobic and high aerobic components.

Figure 6.9 outlines the **depletion-repletion** model upon which carbo-loading is based. It is suitable for any activities lasting longer than 15-20 minutes. Note that a two-day high CHO diet beforehand provides the best CHO boost for an endurance event.

Carbo-loading - glycogen supercompensation

The graph in figure 6.10 (see page 83) shows how the muscle glycogen level returns to above normal values when the **depletion-repletion** process is undertaken as outlined in the previous paragraph. In effect the body reacts to a loss of glycogen by vigorously replacing it to a level above normal. This is a normal reaction to **biological stress**.

Pre-competition nutrition

Should consist of:
- Fluids for hydration.
- Light complex CHO such as pasta or wholemeal bread at least 3 hours before activity.
- Fruit (banana) contains complex CHO.
- Small amounts of glucose.

The effect is to provide the slow release of blood glucose and reduce hunger sensations.

Post-competition or training nutrition

Should consist of:
- **Hypertonic** sports drink immediately after exercise has finished.
- This begins **replenishment of blood glucose** and **glycogen** stores.
- A **high CHO** meal within 15 minutes of exercise ending (or as soon as possible) continues glycogen replenishment.

The importance of high glycogen content in muscle before a marathon race

The graph in figure 6.11 shows that a runner's time would increase by around 10 minutes in a 2 hour run if muscle glycogen started at 50% of its maximum possible. The effect of reduced muscle glycogen begins to be felt at the 1 hour mark. Hence the importance of glycogen loading to endurance sportspeople.

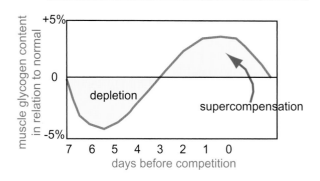

figure 6.10 – glycogen supercompensation

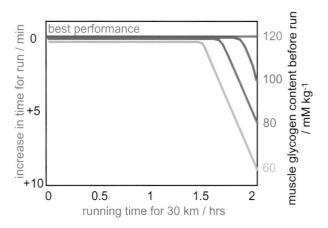

figure 6.11 – effect of glycogen store on endurance running times

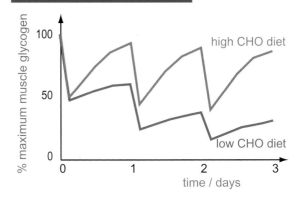

figure 6.12 – the athlete's diet

Nutritional dietary manipulation during training

The graph in figure 6.12 shows the influence of dietary carbohydrate on **muscle glycogen** stores. In this training situation, repeated daily exercise of 2 hours is followed by either a high CHO or low CHO diet.

STUDENT NOTE

Note the difference that high CHO makes to the energy available to the sportsperson, and a major possible reason for exhaustion for those 'on a diet'!

Questions

1) Figure 6.12 shows the influence of dietary carbohydrate on muscle glycogen stores. Give examples of types of food that are high in carbohydrates.

2) What is meant by the terms depletion and repletion within the concept of carbo-loading?

3) What are the benefits of taking a sports drink immediately after exercise?

Case study of an elite athlete

So how does an elite athlete assess whether their diet meets the demands of their training and competition programmes? A qualified nutritionist normally undertakes a nutritional assessment of the athlete's current diet:

- The athlete will undertake a detailed dietary log containing all food eaten (including food portions) during a selected period of time.
- He or she will answer a questionnaire about food habits and training issues, such as symptoms of fatigue that may be due to poor nutrition.
- Analysis of training and competition demands.
- Body mass assessment to work out BMR.
- Body composition to assess ideal body weight (many female endurance athletes suffer from anorexia nervosa).

Additional assessments may include:
- Blood samples to test for iron deficiency anaemia. Female athletes are particularly vulnerable to low haematocrit levels.
- DEXA scan (DEXA stands for 'dual energy x-ray absorptiometry') to measure bone density. In general, the more dense the bone, the stronger it is, and the less likely it is to break. Dietary calcium is needed to maintain bone density levels.

Once a dietary assessment has been completed, a tailor-made diet can be created that meets the specific energy and dietary requirements of the athlete.

Summary of the nutritional recommendations for an elite female 800 metre athlete

Body fat and weight are fine – any slight increase in body weight must be muscle gain and not fat (her body fat was measured at 9%).

The food choices in table 6.4 below aim to keep body fat low. Low GI (glycaemic index) carbohydrate intake should be considered, and a focus on protein-type foods supplemented by fresh vegetables and fruit. Notice also that snacks between the 3 main meals aim to top up the ever-depleting energy reserves and so aid recovery following training sessions.

Table 6.4 – **dietary suggestions for elite endurance runner**

	dietary suggestions for elite endurance runner
1	**breakfast** – include some protein (yoghurt, eggs) and carbohydrate (cereal, porridge and wholegrain toast)
2	**mid morning snack** – banana and water, cordial are fine
3	**lunch** is not enough - need cooked meal such as pasta or rice or potato dish with some form of meat, fish, salad + yoghurt and fresh fruit, in place of sandwiches
4	**afternoon snack** – suggest a protein shake
5	immediately after training go for a Yazzoo or Smoothie or protein shake
6	cooked **evening meal** with meat, fresh vegetables, yoghurt, fresh fruit, water
7	**light night-time snack** such as Carb Sense bar or porridge, muesli, water
8	more fluid should be consumed than thirst dictates
9	increase CHO intake 36 hours prior to competition date
10	need daily **supplements**: glucosamine and chondroitin for joints, 1 x multivitamin a day, 1 x 100mg of omega-3 fatty acid a day

Vegetarian athletes should give careful consideration to selecting plant foods that provide a good balance of the essential amino acids (such as beans, lentils, quorn, soya and tofu), sufficient calories and adequate sources of vitamin A, riboflavin, vitamin B12 (dairy products), vitamin D, calcium, zinc and iron (dark green leafy vegetables).

Exam style questions

1) Figure 6.13 shows the daily energy intake (kjoules) of elite male and female endurance, strength and team sport athletes.

   a) Account for the differences in the daily intake for males and females. **2 marks**

   b) Give reasons why cyclists competing in the Tour de France require a daily intake of up to 25000 kjoules. **3 marks**

   c) Why do female body builders have the lowest daily energy intake compared with other female sportspeople? **2 marks**

   d) How can a negative energy balance ultimately compromise an athlete's potential to train and compete? **3 marks**

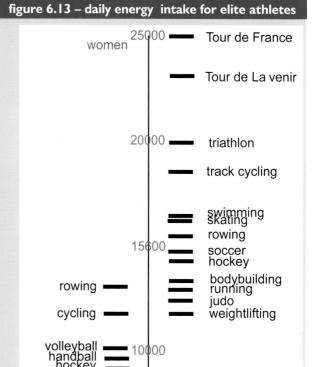

figure 6.13 – daily energy intake for elite athletes

2) The ideal precompetition meal should maximise muscle and liver glycogen storage and provide glucose for intestinal absorption during exercise. How can these goals be achieved? **4 marks**

3) An athlete is competing in a decathlon (consisting of 10 track and field events) over a period of two days.

   a) What nutritional advice would you give this athlete during and between the events in order to achieve an optimal performance. **6 marks**

   b) At the end of day one, how could this athlete replenish his glycogen reserves? **4 marks**

4) Identify some of the benefits of taking commercially prepared liquid meals. **3 marks**

5) Table 6.5 provides information on exercise intensity and duration. Information on the appropriate fuel foods for action has been omitted.

Table 6.5 – **fuel and exercise**

exercise intensity	exercise duration	fuel used
maximal sprint	short	
low to moderate	moderate - up to 2 hours, eg jogging	
severe	prolonged - eg cycling	

   a) Complete the third column to show which fuel foods supply the glycogen needed as exercise intensity and duration change. **3 marks**

   b) Why is carbohydrate a much faster fuel (energy) source when compared with fat utilisation? **2 marks**

   c) High-fat diets, as an ergogenic strategy for sports performance, have been used by athletes for endurance and ultra-endurance sports. Discuss. **6 marks**

Exam style questions

6) What are the benefits of adding a small amount of sodium to a rehydration beverage? What is the effect of hyperhydration on sodium function within the human body?   3 marks

7) Why is water considered an important nutrient to the human body, and why might a person who is exercising need extra amounts of it?   4 marks

8) a) Discuss how a balanced diet could be manipulated to increase an athlete's glucose reserves prior to a marathon race.
6 marks

   b) Carbohydrates are used as an energy source during both aerobic and anaerobic conditions. It is therefore beneficial that an elite athlete's stores of carbohydrate are at a maximum before competition day. Discuss the advantages and disadvantages of glycogen loading.   4 marks

   c) How can an athlete's diet aid the recovery process?   2 marks

9) Give a brief outline and comment upon the following techniques, which may be employed in the belief that they will enhance sport performance:

   a) Whey protein.
   b) Ginseng.
   c) Bicarbonate loading.
   d) Caffeine.   12 marks

10) What is an ergogenic aid? Discuss the role which nutritional supplements play in improving performance.   12 marks

11) The dietary requirements of a power athlete and an endurance-based athlete have similarities and differences. Discuss.
12 marks

12) A level. Give a brief outline and comment critically upon the effects of glycogen loading on the enhancement of sport performance.   15 marks

13) How can an elite athlete assess whether his or her diet meets the demands of their training and competitive programmes?   4 marks

Answers link: http://www.jroscoe.co.uk/downloads/as_a1_revise_pe_edexcel/EdexcelAS_A1_ch6_answers.pdf

CHAPTER 7 - 2.2.1 Preparation and training methods

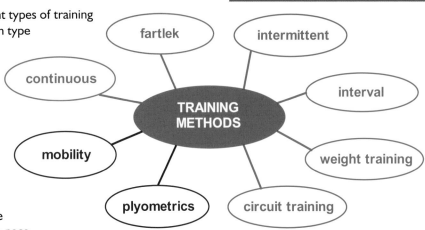

figure 7.1 – training methods

As listed in figure 7.1 there are several different types of training that can be used to improve fitness levels. Each type is summarised in table 7.1 on page 89, with examples of sessions and advantages and disadvantages of the different methods.

Continuous training

Involves continuous activity in which there is **no rest or break** and is normally associated with developing aerobic capacity ($\dot{V}O_{2max}$).

The **duration** of the training session should be at least 20 minutes and upwards. Adjusting the pace or effort of the activity can vary the exercise **intensity** (recommended between 60-75% of maximum heart rate) from long, slow distance training to high-intensity endurance training. **Frequency** of sessions should be at least 3 times per week to benefit from aerobic adaptations.

Fartlek

Fartlek or speed play is a form of continuous training during which the **speed or intensity of the activity is varied** so that both aerobic and anaerobic energy systems and recovery can be stressed.

Intermittent or interval training

This type of training is characterised by periods of **alternating exercise** and **rest**, providing a very versatile training method that enables the individual to perform considerably more work and with greater physiological benefits.
Variables include:

- **Duration** of the exercise period.
- **Intensity** of the exercise period.
- Number of **repetitions** within a set.
- Number of **sets** within a session.
- Duration of the rest intervals (rest relief) or **recovery**.

The exercise **type** and **loading**, number of **repetitions** and **sets**, and length of **rest relief** govern the **adaptive response** produced, thus enabling the individual to select the required intensity of work to stress the relevant energy system:

- **ATP-PC intervals** are characterised by high intensity effort (80-100% of maximum effort) lasting between 3-10 seconds and no more than 2 minutes recovery. Increases ATP-PC stores.
- **Lactic acid intervals** are characterised by medium to high intensity effort (60-80% of maximum effort) lasting between 15-90 seconds with variable recovery depending on exercise duration. Increases blood buffering capacity or increased lactate tolerance.
- **Aerobic intervals** are characterised by low intensity effort (below 50% of maximum effort) lasting beyond 20 minutes with short recovery. Increases aerobic capacity or $\dot{V}O_{2max}$.

Weight training

Weight training is a form of interval training and can be used to develop or stress several components of fitness such as strength and strength endurance depending on the resistance, number of repetitions, sets and rest relief. (see table 7.1 page 89).

Exercises are normally classed in four groups:

- **Shoulders and arms**: bench press, pull downs, curls.
- **Trunk and back**: back hyperextensions, sit ups.
- **Legs**: squats, leg press, calf raises.
- **All-body exercises**: power clean, snatch, dead lift.

Circuit training

A type of interval training that provides all-round body fitness, characterised by a number of exercises or stations performed in succession so that different body parts are exercised successively. The training is normally organised to work for a set time period at each station.

Plyometric training

A type of power training **involving eccentric-to-concentric actions at 100% effort** designed to improve elastic strength and power.

Plyometric leg training occurs when, on landing, the muscle performs an eccentric contraction (lengthens under tension) performed quickly so that the loaded agonist muscle stretches slightly prior to concentric action. This stimulates adaptation within the neuromuscular system as muscle spindles cause a **stretch reflex** to produce a more powerful concentric muscle contraction. The throwing and catching of medicine balls is a way of developing elastic shoulder strength.

In figure 7.2, two athletes are throwing a medicine ball back and forth. The catch phase of this movement is eccentric for the trunk musculature and the shoulders, with the throw movement being concentric in the same muscle groups. Normally this exercise is done too slowly to activate the stretch reflex, but a rapid rebound movement could have the desired effect.

figure 7.2 – catch and throw as eccentric then concentric exercise – similar to plyometrics

In figure 7.3, the athlete is performing two-footed jumping (bunny jumps), which would have to be performed quickly to activate the stretch reflex in time with the concentric phase of the jump.

figure 7.3 – bounding and jumping can be plyometric

Flexibility training

figure 7.4 – mobility training is essential

Flexibility or mobility training is discussed below under the heading of flexibility and stretching on page 112.

The aim of this type of training is to improve (or maintain) the range of motion over which muscles can act and joints can operate (figure 7.4). This works on the **stress-overload principle** by forcing the contractile tissues such as muscle tissue to operate at full stretch. Mobility work is best done at the end of an anaerobic training session, during cool-down. This is because the muscular system is usually more relaxed at this time, with muscle temperatures slightly higher than during the warm-up.

Table 7.1 – **training methods examples, advantages and disadvantages**

training method	examples	advantages	disadvantages
continuous training	**alternative activities:** 30 km bike ride. 3 km run. 30 minute swim.	trains cardiovascular and muscular endurance, needs no specialist equipment, highly suitable for fat burning metabolism / weight loss, time efficient. can be sport-specific, can be assessed using methods such as the Borg scale and exercising heart rate, less chance of injury because of lower intensity workloads.	can lead to tedium. may not be sport-specific, for example usefulness for fencers?
fartlek	**continuous activity:** 10 minutes jogging. 6 x 20 seconds fast striding with 60 seconds walk recovery. 5 minutes jogging. 2 uphill runs, jog down recovery. 5 minutes jogging.	beneficial to games players where the demands of the game are constantly changing. develops both aerobic and anaerobic capacities.	
intermittent / interval training	**endurance interval training for a 5000m runner:** **session 1:** 4 x 1500m @ 80% pace with 5 min rest relief (recovery period). **session 2:** 20 x 400m in 65 seconds (s) with 20 s rest relief. **session 3:** 3 x (8 x 200m) with 30 s rest relief between reps and 5 min rest relief between sets.	versatile training method since it can be used in almost any activity (sport specific). effective in establishing levels of required fitness for both anaerobic and aerobic activities. individual able to perform more work during session due to rest periods or intervals between sets.	can lead to over-training and chronic injury (chronic repetitive trauma), because of the repetitive nature and higher training intensity. takes more time to complete session because of rest periods.
weight training	**example:** athlete selects 2 exercises from each group, (shoulders & arms / trunk & back / legs / all body) working at 85% of 1RM. 4 sets of 5 repetitions 2 minutes recovery / rest relief between sets. this session stresses the ATP-PC energy system & so will enhance the ATP muscle stores and create **muscle hypertrophy.**	can be sport-specific. trains cardiovascular, muscular strength and strength endurance. easy to measure improvements from previous sessions.	needs access to equipment. issues of safety using equipment. can cause chronic injuries through repetitive impact.
circuit training	**8 station circuit:** each circuit performed 3 times: star jumps, rope climb, v-sit-ups, alternate dumbbell press, shuttle runs, chinnies, step ups, bench dips. performer works for 60 seconds at each station on 1st circuit, 30 seconds at each station on 2nd circuit and 15 seconds at each station on final circuit.	can be sport specific. trains cardiovascular, muscular strength and strength endurance. enables a large number of participants to train together. easy to measure improvements from previous sessions – for example counting the number of repetitions achieved in the time period. time efficient.	needs access to equipment. can cause chronic injuries through repetitive impact.
plyometrics	**jumping example:** depth jumping from a box and rebounding quickly from impact point, 2 foot bounds over a flight of hurdles, bounding exercises. 3-5 sets of 3-10 repetitions with medium recovery (1-3 minutes).	maximises muscular development by improving power / elastic strength. can be very sport specific, for example in explosive take-off as when jumping and bounding in events such as triple jumping.	because of the repetitive nature, can cause chronic repetitive trauma injuries such as achilles tendinosis, patellar tendinosis and shin splints. because of vigorous nature of exercise, can cause acute injuries such as sudden ruptures of muscle, tendons and ligaments particularly to vulnerable knee and ankle joints (such as a sprained ankle).
mobility or flexibility training	**dedicated session after intense specific training session:** choose 10 exercises covering all joints / body areas. 4 sets of 10 seconds hold at each exercise.	helps prevent potential injury. sport specific mobility training can improve performance, for example extreme spinal flexibility is needed by elite high jumpers when performing the flight phase of the fosbury flop, or elite gymnasts performing floor or beam moves.	can lead to hyper-flexibility and reduce effectiveness of muscle strength. extreme range of motion isn't necessary in many sports activities – how flexible must long distance runners be? since they don't raise their knees very high or extend their hips very far!

2.2.2, 2.2.3, 2.2.4 Fitness tests and their results

Energy sources

We derive our energy from food, namely carbohydrates (CHO), fats, and to a lesser extent proteins.

The energy derived from carbohydrates, fats and proteins is stored in bodily tissues in the form of a high energy compound called **adenosine triphosphate** (ATP).

Adenosine triphosphate (ATP) and its resynthesis

figure 7.5 – all muscle action uses ATP

ATP is the compound which stores energy and is therefore the energy currency linked to **intensity** and **duration** of physical activity. ATP exists in every living tissue and its breakdown gives energy for all life functions - this includes the action of the liver and the brain for example, as well as the contraction of muscle tissue. All muscular activity requires the availability and breakdown of ATP (figure 7.5).

The energy stored within ATP is only available as long as ATP is retained within the cells using it. In muscle cells during intense (flat-out) exercise, the stored ATP only lasts about 2 seconds. Therefore the ATP must be replaced as soon as possible so that exercise can continue. There are **three** processes by which this can happen:

- The **ATP-PC** system (also called the alactic anaerobic system).
- The **lactic acid** system (which is also anaerobic).
- The **aerobic** system.

Resynthesis of ATP from ADP uses the reaction: **energy + ADP + P$_i$ → ATP**

This is an **endothermic** reaction since energy is **given** to the molecule to enable the reaction to happen. This energy will be derived from **food fuels**.

Energy continuum

This describes the process by which ATP is regenerated via the different energy systems depending on the **intensity** and **duration** of exercise. Although **all** the systems contribute to ATP regeneration during any activity, one or other of the energy systems usually provides the major contribution for a given activity. Table 7.2 shows approximate proportions of ATP resynthesised via aerobic and anaerobic pathways for some sporting activities.

Table 7.2 – **percentage contribution of the aerobic and anaerobic energy systems to different sports**

sport or event	aerobic %	anaerobic (all) %
100m sprint	0	100
200m sprint	10	90
100m swim	20	80
boxing	30	70
800m run	40	60
hockey	50	50
2000m rowing	60	40
4000m cycle pursuit	70	30
3000m run	80	20
cross country run	90	10
marathon	100	0

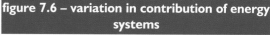

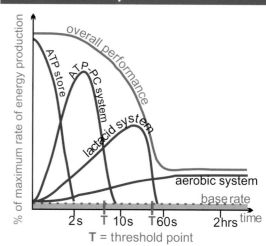

figure 7.6 – variation in contribution of energy systems

The graph in figure 7.6 shows how the different energy systems contribute resynthesis of ATP during flat-out exercise. Obviously, at reduced intensity of exercise, the contributions will be slightly different. But note that **all systems** are contributing from the start of exercise, only it takes some time for the lactic acid and aerobic systems to get going.

Functional thresholds

The concept of a **threshold** applies to the time at which one particular system of ATP regeneration takes over from another as the major regenerator of ATP during flat out exercise - marked as **T** in figure 7.6 page 90.

- For example, **ATP muscle stores** are depleted **within 2 seconds**, and towards the end of this period the ATP-PC system has risen enough to be able to provide the ATP necessary for the exercise.
- **Peak anaerobic power** is attained within the first 5 seconds of flat-out exercise, but depletion of PC occurs between 7 and 9 seconds.
- At this point, the lactic acid system has risen enough to be able to provide the ATP required for the next 40 seconds or so.

Hence the **threshold** between **ATP-PC and lactic acid** systems **T** occurs between 7 and 9 seconds after the start of an exercise period.

A **second threshold point** occurs at about 50 (the second **T** on graph 7.6 page 90) seconds and is between the lactic acid and aerobic systems reflecting a switch of ATP resynthesis from a predominantly **anaerobic mode** to a predominantly **aerobic mode**.

Long-term training effects - thresholds

It is found that thresholds are **delayed** by training, so that the trained individual has a greater capacity for ATP-PC, has a greater lactic acid toleration, and more efficient ATP regeneration than the untrained person.

Fitness testing and the reasons for testing

Fitness testing is a valuable tool that can be used in the planning of a training programme.

Reasons for testing are broad and are summarised in figure 7.7.

Tests:

- Tend to provide **objective measures** about the individual's current state of fitness or health.
- Attempt to highlight the **strengths** and **weaknesses** of the sportsperson.
- Attempt to evaluate the **effects** of a **training programme**.
- Can be used for **talent** identification.
- Can **motivate** an individual as he or she strives to reach his or her best test scores.
- Add **variety** to training programme.
- Can be **specific** to the individual's sport.

figure 7.7 – reasons for fitness testing

Specific test protocols

Sport specific tests should be appropriate for the subject's age, sex and current fitness. Also, sport specific tests recognise the **specificity** of the test activity, and therefore ensure the variables tested are relevant to the sport. Examples of the specific nature of tests are:

- Use of a flume pool for swimmers.
- Paddle ergometers for swimmers.
- Cycle ergometers for cyclists.
- Treadmill tests for endurance runners.
- Vertical jumps tests for high jumpers.
- Skipping tests for boxers.

Laboratory and field testing

Tests can be classified as laboratory or field tests based on:

- The setting.
- The equipment needed.
- The degree of control maintained during the test, and the application of the results (how the results are used, to modify training intensities for example)
- Most of the fitness tests listed on the following slides will be familiar to both teaching staff and students.
- For less familiar tests, such as the **Yo-Yo** test, a brief description has been included.

- A test is classified as a **laboratory test** when it can only be performed within the confines of the laboratory.
- And requires the testing equipment found within the laboratory, such as a **gas analyser** (in which quantities of oxygen consumed and carbon dioxide exhaled are measured) worn within a laboratory setting by the testing subject (see figure 7.8).

figure 7.8 – a gas analyser worn during a lab test

Sport Development Centre, Loughborough University

Field tests are frequently used to assess a variety of fitness components including:

- Muscular strength.
- Muscular endurance.
- Anaerobic and aerobic fitness.
- Flexibility.
- Body composition.

Table 7.3 – **the advantages and disadvantages of laboratory and field tests**

	advantages	disadvantages
laboratory tests	an attempt is made during the test to maintain a high degree of control over the conditions: temperature. the performer's diet. amount of rest. warm-up prior to the test. and the protocol - time intervals, specific treadmill speeds or cycle ergometer power levels. to be useful, research requires tests to be highly reliable and valid.	laboratory testing is very expensive and time consuming as it is done on a one-to-one basis. takes place in an artificial environment that differs from the more desired specific sports environment. and so can influence results. requires frequent testing. and travel to laboratory.
field tests	field tests were developed to test large groups of people outside a laboratory setting. as accurately and economically as possible. provide a cheap and popular method as screening tests. for example the NCF multi-stage shuttle run test which is a predicted $\dot{V}O_{2max}$ test.	not as reliable as laboratory tests since it is difficult to control variables such as height of bench or weather conditions. more open to human errors, such as inaccurate counting of recovery heart rate.

Principles of maximal and submaximal tests

Maximal tests

Maximal means that the subject makes an '**all-out**' **effort** or undertakes a test to **exhaustion**.

In **anaerobic** work **1RM** represents **one repetition maximum** which is the maximum possible weight which can be lifted at a certain specific exercise movement. Performing a 1RM represents a maximal test. Other examples of maximal **anaerobic** tests are 30 metre sprint, the Sergeant jump (described in table 7.4) and the Wingate 30 second cycle ergometer test.

A maximal **aerobic** test would be a test to exhaustion, such as the NCF multi-stage shuttle run test, or Cooper's 12 minute run or walk test.

Disadvantages of maximal tests

The main difficulty is in ensuring the subject is **exerting** maximum effort, and the possible dangers of **over-exertion** and **injury**. This issue is dependent on the level of **motivation** (arousal levels) of the performer.

Table 7.4 – **examples of standardised maximal tests**

test	fitness component	description	advantages	disadvantages
30m sprint	**speed**	a flat-out timed 30m sprint.	easily performed. high correlation with peak anaerobic power.	timing errors. differences in footwear (trainers / spikes). different surfaces (grass / rubber track).
Sergeant jump	**power**	two-foot standing take-off, measure between standing two armed reach and highest single hand jumped reach.	easy to administer. high correlation with peak anaerobic power.	skill factor. height differences between performers.
balancing on a beam	**static balance**	time how long balance can be maintained on the bar on an upturned gym bench.	easy to administer.	depends on motivation.
repeat anaerobic sprint test (RAST)	**speed** **speed** **endurance**	6 x 35 metre sprints with 10 seconds recovery Power = m x d ^{2} ÷ t ^{3} where m = body mass d = distance run t = time.	correlates well with sprint test and Wingate cycle test.	timing errors as 30m sprint above.
NCF multi-stage shuttle run	**predicted $\dot{V}O_{2max}$ cardiovascular endurance**	10m shuttle run in time to increasingly rapid timed pulse.	large groups can take part at any one time. everyone can run. cheap equipment.	need for measured runs between bleeps and slick turns. relies on subject motivation. gives a predicted $\dot{V}O_{2max}$.
Yo-Yo intermittent recovery test	**predicted $\dot{V}O_{2max}$ cardiovascular endurance**	see next page for description of this test.	large groups can take part at any one time. test level 1 average performer. level 2 elite performer.	relies on subject motivation.

Table 7.5 – **examples of standardised maximal tests**

test	fitness component	description	advantages	disadvantages
Cunningham and Faulkner inclined treadmill test	**anaerobic capacity**	treadmill set at a speed of 8 miles/hour and an incline of 11.3°. subject is timed and runs to exhaustion (normally between 40-50s).	simple test to conduct.	requires specialist expensive equipment (treadmill). only one person at a time.
Margaria Kalaman stair test	**power**	flat out run up stairs measure height run (h), weight of runner (W), time of run (t), power = (W x h) / t.	simple to conduct.	availability of steps with clear run-up. errors in hand-timing.
maximal accumulated oxygen deficit method (MAOD)	**anaerobic capacity**	the subject performs submaximal treadmill (or cycle ergometer) efforts connected to gas analyser to measure O_2 uptake.	reliability very high.	test validity tenuous. expensive protocol (treadmill). one person at a time. variable protocol.
Cooper's 12 min run, walk test	**cardiovascular endurance**	distance travelled in 12min running or walking.	simple test to conduct.	dependent on type of running shoe, weather and surface.

Yo-Yo Intermittent Tests

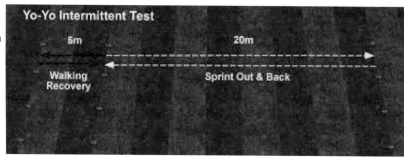

figure 7.9 – layout of a Yo-Yo test

Are similar in protocol to the multi-stage fitness test. There are 2 versions – subject runs 20m when instructed by the CD recording (see figure 7.9). Then turns and runs back to the starting point.

Followed by an active recovery period of 5 and 10 seconds respectively for the endurance (test 1) and recovery (test 2) versions of the test.

Assessment – the athlete's score is the total distance before subject is unable to keep up with the recording:

        Level 1 takes between 6-20 minutes.
        Level 2 takes between 2-10 minutes.

Formula for estimating $\dot{V}O_{2max}$ (ml/min/kg) from the Yo-Yo IR1 and IR2 test results (Bangsbo et al. 2008):

Yo-Yo IR1 test:

$\dot{V}O_{2max}$ (ml/min/kg)	= IR1 distance (m) × 0.0084 + 36.4
(sample results)	
distance run	= 1200m
$\dot{V}O_{2max}$ (ml/min/kg)	= 1200 × 0.0084 + 36.4 = 46.56

Yo-Yo IR2 test:

$\dot{V}O_{2max}$ (ml/min/kg)	= IR2 distance (m) × 0.0136 + 45.3
(sample results)	
distance run	= 2500m
$\dot{V}O_{2max}$ (ml/min/kg)	= 2500 × 0.0136 + 45.3 = 79.3.

The value here will be the $\dot{V}O_{2max}$. This test relies on the performer's ability to sustain the vigorous activity for as long as possible, and therefore is an indicator of aerobic fitness.

The MAOD details

Take 10 x 4 minutes submaximal exercise at different exercise intensities (set by the slope of the treadmill or torque on the cycle ergometer), a graph is plotted of exercise intensity against $\dot{V}O_2$ – extrapolation will give the supra max $\dot{V}O_{2max}$ The last bout is at high intensity and performed to fatigue.

The value here will be the $\dot{V}O_{2max}$.

MAOD calculates as the difference between the predicted supramaximal oxygen consumption and oxygen consumption measures during a 2-3 minute all-out treadmill (or cycle ergometer) run to fatigue.

Weights – the one-repetition maximum method

Strength can be defined as '**the maximal force that a muscle or muscle group can generate**', and can be assessed using a 1-repetition maximum test or the **1RM** test.

Weight lifting is a good method to assess 1RM maximal muscular strength.
* Since 1RM represents the highest successful lift.
* That can be achieved for one complete repetition of an exercise.
* Having failed at the final lift.

Once the 1RM's values are known, it is then possible to calculate a percentage of the maximum that can be used to establish both anaerobic and aerobic training programmes.

Table 7.6 sets out the approximate values of loading, sets and repetitions needed to stress the different energy systems available to provide energy to contracting muscle. Values are approximate because different exercises will require slightly different set regimes, and individuals will vary as to how efficient they are at utilisation of the systems.

Table 7.6 – **how to use the 1RM method**

	alactic anaerobic energy system	lactic anaerobic energy system	aerobic energy system
when is it used?	flat out exercise up to 8 seconds	flat out exercise between 10-60 seconds	any slow exercise while breathing freely
training load as % of 1RM	80% - 100%	60% - 80%	below 50%
repetitions	less than 3	5 to 12	15 to 30
sets	3 to 5	3 to 5	3
recovery	full recovery	restricted recovery	no recovery

With strength gains achieved as a result of regular systematic training, it is important to retest 1RM values at regular intervals (say once a month) so that percentage training values can be adjusted accordingly.

Submaximal tests

Submaximal means that the subject exercises **below** maximum effort. Data collected from submaximal tests can be extrapolated to **estimate** maximal capacities. Examples of **submaximal aerobic** tests are the PWC-170 test, the Queen's College step test described below, and the Fitech step test.

Submaximal tests are often favoured over maximal tests because there is less stress on the performer and greater reliability of results.

Disadvantages of submaximal tests

Submaximal tests depend on **projection or extrapolation** being made to an unknown maximum, and therefore small inaccuracies and uncontrolled variables can result in large discrepancies in the estimation of the actual maximal values as a result of magnification of results.

Table 7.7 – **examples of standard submaximal tests**

test	fitness component	description	advantages	disadvantages
PWC-170 test	**aerobic fitness**	two 6 minute cycle ergometer rides at predicted heart rates. used to extrapolate power output.	popular and inexpensive cycle ergometer test.	predicted test by extrapolation. fitness levels influence interpretation of results.
Queen's College step test	**predicted $\dot{V}O_{2max}$ cardiovascular endurance**	3 minutes of stepping at a set cadence. $\dot{V}O_{2max}$ predicted from HR recovery.	easy to administer. cheap equipment.	length of leg levers affects results, depends on stepping technique and rhythm. only produces a predicted $\dot{V}O_{2max}$.
body conductivity test	**body composition**	subject inputs height, weight, age and gender. then stands on scales and reads off body mass and % body fat.	very easy to administer.	results depend on skin moisture. % body fat predicted from standardised tables for weight / age/height/gender.
sit and reach test	**flexibility**	subject sits on floor and measures how far he or she can reach past feet.	very easy to administer.	specific to hamstring / hips flexibility. other joints would need a different exercise.

Results table for the Queen's College step test

Methodology:
Calculate the recovery HR (rHR) in beats per minute by multiplying the 15 second count by 4.
Approximate predicted $\dot{V}O_{2max}$ (P $\dot{V}O_{2max}$) in ml/min/kg can be estimated from table 7.8 below:

Table 7.8 – **Queen's College step test result table**

% ranking	rHR female	P $\dot{V}O_{2max}$ female	rHR male	P $\dot{V}O_{2max}$ male
100	128	42.2	120	60.9
90	148	38.5	128	57.6
80	156	37.0	140	52.5
70	160	36.3	148	49.2
60	163	37.5	152	47.5
50	166	35.1	156	45.8
40	170	34.4	162	43.3
30	172	34.0	166	41.6
20	180	32.6	172	39.1
10	184	31.8	178	36.6

Agility tests - the Illinois agility test

- A space 10 metres in length is marked out, and four obstacles 3.3m apart placed as shown in Figure 7.10.
- The subject lies prone, head to start line, hands beside shoulders. On the command 'go' the course is run as fast as possible, with the time taken. The fitness rating (Table 7.9 page 97).

Question

Using the information in Table 7.8, suggest reasons why the predicted $\dot{V}O_{2max}$ for females is lower than that of males.

Table 7.9 – **Agility run rating - times are in seconds**

males time	females time	rating
<15.2	<17.0	excellent
16.1 - 15.21	17.0 - 17.9	good
18.1 - 16.22	18.0 - 21.7	average
18.3 - 18.2	21.8 - 23.0	fair
>18.3	>23.0	poor

figure 7.10 – the Illinois agility test

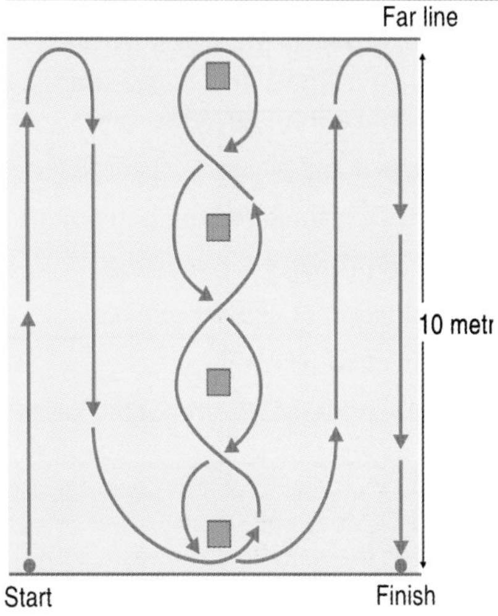

Your PAR-Q 'Physical Activity Readiness Questionnaire'

You should **administer to yourself** a questionnaire which establishes on **medical** grounds, whether you should undertake demanding fitness tests or not.

Limitations of fitness tests

- Many tests (see figure 7.11) are not sport **specific** and so do not replicate the specific movement patterns required for the chosen event.
- Many tests are **predictive** because they do not use direct measures and therefore can be inaccurate.
- Many tests do not take into account the sporting **environment**.

figure 7.11 – limitations of fitness tests

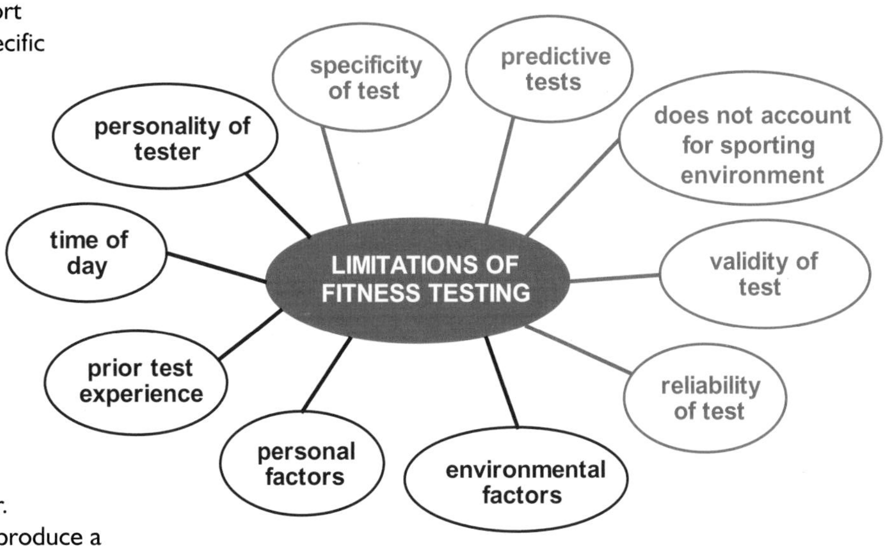

Making a test valid

The concept of **validity** is built around the question '**does each test measure what it aims to measure?**' A test may be valid **for one purpose** but not another. For example, the Wingate cycle test may produce a measure of strength endurance but not aerobic capacity.

Making a test reliable

The concept of reliability is built around the **accuracy** of the test results. How **dependable** are the test scores? Will we get **the same result** if the measurement is repeated? This is the **consistency** of test results from one occasion to another. For example, a measurement of body composition gives a measure of 19% body fat, but the same apparatus gives a measure of 17% the next day. Errors may be introduced because of differences in skin moisture and body water content. Therefore the same conditions should be adopted on each occasion if possible.

Factors which could affect test results are:

- Environmental factors (weather, temperature, noise, crowd, test surface).
- Personal factors (health, diet, mood).
- Prior test experience (have you done the test before and will this affect your results?).
- Time of day.
- Personality of the tester.

Question

Distinguish between the terms validity and reliability.

Standardising test protocols

A test protocol is the way in which a test is conducted. This implies that a test produces **measurable definite results**, and hence **human error and opinion** must not be allowed to influence results. Therefore a test protocol must attempt to **eliminate inaccuracies** using:

- **Efficient** and accurate recording equipment.
- Correct techniques and equipment.
- Use of protocol for **scoring**.
- Elimination of **crowd effects**.
- Controlled warm-up.
- Same conditions for repeated tests.

> **STUDENT NOTE**
>
> Some of the standardised tests aimed at measuring these fitness components are mentioned below and are briefly described on pages 93 and 94.

2.2.5 Components of fitness

Fitness is the ability to meet the demands of the environment.

This section breaks the concept of fitness down into components, and discusses how to perform exercises which will enhance these components.

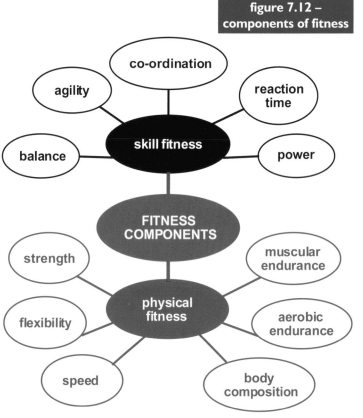

figure 7.12 – components of fitness

Fitness consists of (see figure 7.12):

- **Physical components** – which are anatomically and physiologically based, and assess a person's physical performance capacities. They include strength, flexibility, speed, body composition, aerobic endurance and muscular endurance.
- **Skill components** – which consist of neuromuscular components of fitness that are skill-related and include the capacity to repeat a particular exercise. These include balance, agility, coordination, reaction time and power.

Components of physical fitness

Muscular endurance

Muscular endurance can be defined as '**the ability of a muscle or muscle group to sustain repeated contractions over time sufficient enough to cause muscular fatigue**'.

- Muscular endurance relies on the ability of the body to produce energy under aerobic and anaerobic conditions.
- This type of exercise stresses slow twitch muscle fibres and fast twitch muscle fibres type IIa – both muscle fibre types are fatigue resistant.
- Simple tests that evaluate local muscular endurance include the Multi-stage abdominal test and maximum chin test i.e. the total number of chin-ups completed to exhaustion or within one minute.

Questions

1) Distinguish between the physical components of fitness and the skill components of fitness.

2) What is the difference between muscular endurance and strength?

3) Define what is meant by aerobic endurance (see page 99).

Aerobic endurance

This component is also known as **cardio-respiratory** or **cardio-vascular endurance** or **stamina**, and can be defined as '**the ability to provide and sustain vigorous total body activity aerobically**'.

- Aerobic endurance involves the ability of the cardiovascular and respiratory systems to take in and transport oxygen to large muscle groups working dynamically.

- Aerobic endurance (figure 7.13) enables moderate to high intensity exercise to be undertaken for prolonged periods of time as in the case of marathon running.

- A key component of aerobic endurance is aerobic power or **maximum oxygen uptake**.

- A $\dot{V}O_{2max}$ test assesses the maximum amount of oxygen that a person can consume per minute during a progressive exercise test to exhaustion.

- $\dot{V}O_{2max}$ is assessed directly when using closed-circuit spirometry.

- Simple **predicted** $\dot{V}O_{2max}$ tests are used as indicators of aerobic fitness, **aerobic capacity** or stamina, and include the Physical work capacity test (PWC170), the Cooper run/walk test, the Multi-stage shuttle run test, the Yo-Yo run test, and the Queen's College step test.

- Elite marathon athletes run at optimal percentages of their $\dot{V}O_{2max}$ in order to achieve world class performances.

- Percentage of **slow twitch fibres**, and **mitochondria** and **myoglobin** concentrations are some of the factors that affect stamina.

Strength

Strength is defined as '**the maximum force exerted by a specific muscle or muscle group during a single maximal muscle contraction – or one repetition maximum (1RM)**'.

- **Static strength** is exerted without change of muscle length, for example holding a weight at arms length, or pushing hard in a stationary rugby scrum thus creating an isometric muscle contraction.

- **Dynamic** or **explosive strength** is the maximal strength exerted during a movement or exercise in which muscle length changes. Most sports use this type of maximal strength. This is the sort of strength weight lifters use in competition when performing an Olympic lift (figure 7.14), the most usual in sports situations, such as throwing and sprinting. Most sports activities require flat out movements such as sprinting and therefore require dynamic strength.

- A sub-category of dynamic strength is **elastic or plyometric strength** or the ability to apply as large a force as possible using an eccentric muscle contraction (in which the active muscles get longer) **followed** by a concentric muscle contraction (in which the active muscles get shorter). Examples of plyometric movements include rebound jumping and high jump take-off (illustrated on page 88).

- Strength can be assessed with the use of **dynamometers**.

- Strength exercises stress **fast twitch muscle fibres type IIb** (also known as **type IIx**) which are able to generate high forces rapidly. Long-term, this type of exercise results in **muscle hypertrophy** (enlargement of individual muscle fibres).

Speed

Speed is defined as '**the maximum rate at which a person is able to move his or her body**'.

- In physical terms, speed is the **distance moved per second**.

- In physical performance it refers to the **speed of coordinated joint actions** and whole-body movements and is the ultimate test in a 30m sprint.

- Speedy movements stress **fast twitch muscle fibres type IIb** (**type IIx**) which are able to generate high forces rapidly and which long-term will result in muscle hypertrophy.

Flexibility

Flexibility is defined as '**the ability to move a joint through its complete range of movement**'.

* Flexibility concerns the **stretching** of muscles and tissues such as ligaments and tendons around skeletal joints (figure 7.15).
* The degree of movement is determined by the joint type.
* A standardised test is the sit and reach trunk flexion test.
* A gymnast needs great flexibility to achieve desired movement patterns.

Body composition

Body composition is a concept describing '**the relative percentage of muscle, fat and bone**'.

* Body composition analysis is a suitable tool for the assessment of a person's state of fitness.
* Body composition is **measured** using:
  * Skinfold measurements using the Jackson-Pollock (J-P) nomogram.
  * Body composition scales using bioelectrical impedance analysis.
  * Underwater weighing.
* Body composition can be **improved** (which usually means that body **fat** will be reduced) using:
  * A **balanced diet**.
  * Consideration of **energy balance**.
  * A **weight control programme**.

Components of skill fitness

Power

Power is defined as '**the ability to use strength quickly (strength x speed)**'.

* Power is measured in joules per second or **watts**.
* Power is visible in activities that require **explosive strength**, for example, throwing a heavy object such as a shot, or a long jumper during take-off.
* Standard tests include the **vertical jump test** (also known as the **Sergeant test**), the **Margaria Kalaman stair test** and the **standing broad jump test**.
* Power exercises stress **fast twitch muscle fibres type IIb** which are able to generate high forces rapidly, and in the long-term result in muscle hypertrophy.

Reaction time

Reaction time is defined as '**the time taken to initiate a response to a given stimulus**'.

* The stimulus may be **visual**, for example a batsman responding to the release of the ball from the bowler.
* Or **aural** as in the reaction time between the starter firing the gun and the athlete moving out of the starting blocks.
* The response time taken represents the amount of time it takes a person to move once he or she realises the need to act.
* Reaction time can be assessed using computer software or the stick drop test.

Agility

Agility is defined as '**the physical ability that enables a person to quickly change body position in a precise manner**'.

* Agility is a combination of balance, coordination, speed and flexibility.
* Rugby players need great agility as they weave in and out and around opposition.
* How quickly can you complete the Illinois agility run – a standardised test that assesses speed and agility?

Coordination

Coordination is defined as '**the ability to perform smooth and accurate motor tasks, often involving the use of senses**'.

* Good coordination is observed in elite gymnasts (figure 7.16) such as those performances associated with former World champion Beth Tweddle.

* Assess your own coordination skills by trying to juggle with 3 tennis balls.

Balance

Balance is defined as '**the ability to retain the centre of mass of a sportsperson's body above the base of support**'.

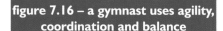

figure 7.16 – a gymnast uses agility, coordination and balance

* It is the awareness of the body's position in space and depends upon the **coordination** between the inner ear, brain, skeleton and muscles.

* Balance can be **static** where a position is held as in a handstand.

* Or **dynamic** - the ability to maintain balance under changing conditions of body movement, shape and orientation. For example, the changing balance required during a pole vault performance.

* Balance can be assessed by using the Standard Stork test, in which a person is asked to stand on one leg with eyes shut for as long as possible. The time before falling is a measure of static balance.

Exam style questions

1) a) Define the term functional thresholds.   2 marks

   b) Using figure 7.6 on page 90 name the two threshold points that occur on this graph.   2 marks

2) a) Distinguish between continuous training and interval training giving examples for each training method.   4 marks

   b) Continuous training is one of the least used methods of training by top performers. Suggest how this training method can benefit a performer.   2 marks

3) Fartlek training is a type of training that is used to develop aerobic capacity. What does the term fartlek mean? Illustrate your answer by outlining the training principles used to create a typical fartlek training session.   3 marks

4) a) Plyometric training is a type of power training, which involves performing exercises with maximum power and speed. Describe the main concepts of plyometric training, illustrating your answer with an example of an exercise. Identify the type of sports performer who would most benefit from this training method.   6 marks

   b) Discuss the advantages and disadvantages of plyometric training.   4 marks

   c) Why does muscle soreness (DOMS) often occur following a plyometric training session and how could muscle soreness be reduced?   4 marks

5) a) Define 'one repetition maximum' (1RM) and explain how it can be used to measure training intensity.   3 marks

   b) Suggest three ways in which you could increase workload during a weight training session.   3 marks

Exam style questions

6) a) Describe a valid and reliable field test used to estimate a person's $\dot{V}O_{2max}$.   3 marks

    b) Give one advantage and one disadvantage for the test you have selected.   2 marks

    c) Why are submaximal tests often favoured over maximal tests?   2 marks

    d) Explain why fitness testing is necessary for both coach and the athlete.   4 marks

7) The aim of Cooper's 12-minute run or walk test is to run as far as possible in 12 minutes.

    a) What aspect of physical fitness does the 12-minute run or walk measure?   1 mark

    b) Briefly outline the strengths and limitations of this maximal test as a test for aerobic capacity.   4 marks

    c) Identify some of the external variables that could influence the validity and reliability of this test if the test was performed outdoors on a school field.   3 marks

8) Explain, using examples, why the Illinois agility run test may be of more value to a games player than a 30 metre sprint test.   4 marks

9) Name tests that can be used to measure the following different types of strength: strength endurance, explosive or elastic strength, and dynamic strength.   3 marks

10) The table below gives a summary of resistance strength training guidelines for an aerobic athlete. Complete the table below by filing in the guidelines for an anaerobic athlete.   5 marks

	Aerobic athlete	Anaerobic athlete
repetitions	10+ reps	
number of sets	3-5 sets	
rest relief	1:2 (30-60 secs)	
intensity	low to moderate (50-70% of 1RM)	
frequency	3-5 per week	
specificity	aerobic system	

11) Briefly describe the following strength training methods: multi-gym, weights, plyometrics, and circuit training.   8 marks

12) a) Briefly describe the Repeat Anaerobic Sprint test (RAST) and identify the fitness components it measures.   4 marks

    b) How are maximum power, minimum power, average power and fatigue index calculated?   4 marks

    c) Identify a target group who would benefit from using this test as part of their training programme.   1 mark

13) How can an understanding of the components of fitness assist a sport's performer to achieve a level of fitness required for his or her individual sport.   12 marks for AS and 15 marks for A level

Answers link: http://www.jroscoe.co.uk/downloads/as_a1_revise_pe_edexcel/EdexcelAS_A1_ch7_answers.pdf

CHAPTER 8 - *Principles and methods of training*

2.2.6 Principles of training

The aims and objectives of training are to improve performance, skill, game ability and motor and physical fitness. Repeated days of training can be considered as positive stress because training improves one's capacity for energy production, tolerance of physical stress and exercise performance. A well-designed training programme follows a set of guidelines called '**principles of training**' (figure 8.1).

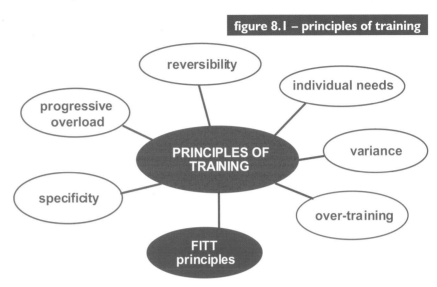

figure 8.1 – principles of training

Specificity

Specificity is defined as '**the relevance of the choice of exercise to the activity to be improved**'.

Choices to be made involve energy demands, strength, power, endurance and skill. This notion is thought to be very important for high performance in a chosen sport. For example, the shot put event requires speed and power developed by stressing the ATP-PC anaerobic energy system. So, in order to put the shot successfully, the shot putter needs to work on explosive muscular power in training. Hence the training programme must **stress** the **physiological systems** that are critical for optimal performance in the given sport in order to achieve the required specific training adaptations. Similarly, the marathon runner requires endurance which must be obtained by stressing the aerobic energy system. Hence his or her training programme must be largely based on lengthy endurance-based runs.

Progressive overload

Overload is defined as '**training activities that are harder, more intense and or lengthier than the normal physical activity undertaken by an individual**'.

Progression can be achieved (figure 8.2) by increasing the frequency, intensity or duration of the activity. These terms are also referred to using the acronym '**FITT principles**' described below. **Overload** places physiological systems under **stress** and the human body responds by becoming more capable of coping with this stress. This training principle applies to muscular endurance as well as to strength and power training.

figure 8.2 – overload

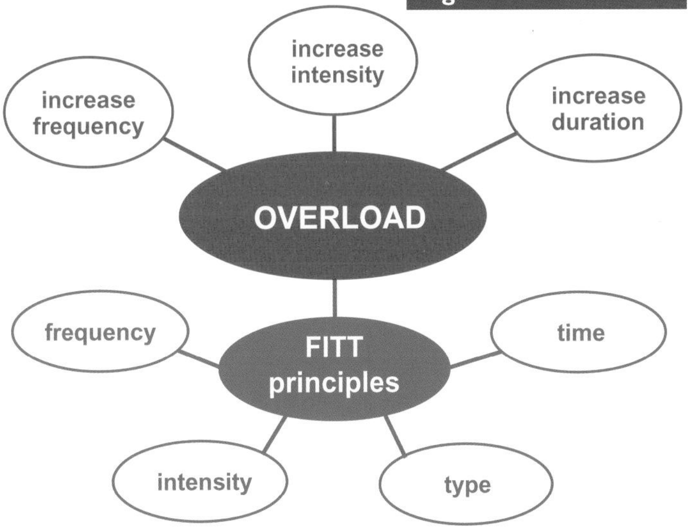

The major variables used for increasing or decreasing intensity are:

- Sets.
- Repetitions.
- Resistance.
- Rest relief or recovery period.

For example, an athlete performs bench press: 5 sets of 6 repetitions at 85% of 1RM (1 repetition maximum as described above on page 89), and 2 minutes recovery between sets. This exercise would stress the anaerobic fast twitch fibres type IIb of the muscles: anterior deltoid, pectoralis major and triceps brachii.

FITT principles of training

F (frequency) = how often do we train? How often we train will determine the physiological adaptations achieved. For example, the elite professional sportsperson may be required to train twice a day and thereby achieve optimal physiological adaptations and improvements in performance. On the other hand, a person who just wants to stay fit by attending three aerobic classes a week at their local leisure centre, may notice minor physiological changes such as easier breathing and less tendency to be out of breath when digging the garden.

I (intensity) = how hard do we train? For the elite athlete, training intensity will vary depending on the training emphasis in relation to the periodised year. **Periodisation** is a concept centred around a cyclical load design principle. In this case the training intensity is increased and decreased according to a set pattern, the first two weeks of a cycle may be easy, and the last two weeks very hard. As a general rule, the closer to the competitive phase the harder the workouts. The person who just wants to keep fit for everyday living may be content with 3 exercise bouts (walking, swimming or cycling) per week for about 30 minutes each at a level at which he or she can hold a conversation with a training partner.

figure 8.3 – athlete wins a marathon

T (type) = what type of training do we do? Type of training relates to the principle of specificity above. Types of training include:

- Continuous.
- Intermittent.
- Circuit.
- Weights.
- Plyometrics.
- Mobility.

(see page 87 and onwards for explanations of these and other types of training)

figure 8.4 – recreational cyclist on a 40 min ride

T (time) = how long do we train for or what is the duration of the activity? The intensity of training and exercise type often determines the duration of the activity. For example an aerobic, bodyweight reducing training programme should last for a minimum 30 minutes because of the time it takes for fat burning metabolism to commence. A plyometric workout may only last for 10 minutes before fatigue sets in, whereas an ultra distance runner may be unlimited by time during a long-distance run.

Progression

Progression is defined as '**a state of moving onwards, which implies an increase in training load as time goes on**'.

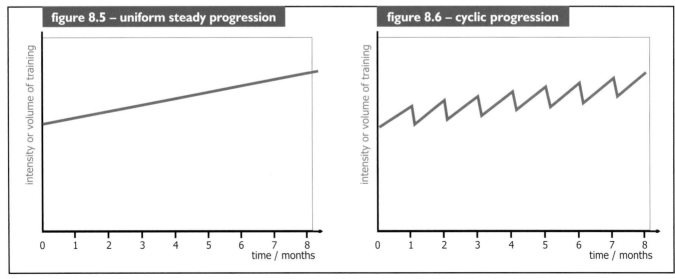

figure 8.5 – uniform steady progression

figure 8.6 – cyclic progression

The principle of progression involves the **gradual application** of the overload principle. You should note that progression could occur without overload, but that if overload does not happen, then you cannot obtain the necessary adaptations to body systems such as the muscular system, which would cause improvement in (for example) endurance or strength.

Progressive overload

The key point about progression is that the sportsperson should be performing at a higher level after the training period than before. In figure 8.5 page 104, progression is steady and over a period of eight months, training intensity increases, and hopefully overload is sufficient to provide long-term adaptations which would lead to improved performance. In figure 8.6 also page 104, training intensity progresses much more steeply than in figure 8.5 for a month before dropping down to a level above the previous starting point. Then training intensity progresses again for another month and so on. The outcome is a cyclic progression with a bigger overload (rather than steady slow progression) at the end of each cycle, hence **progressive overload**.

Over-training

Over-training is explained as '**when the intensity of training and or volume of training are increased to extreme levels, and there is a lack of recovery within or between training sessions leading to an associated decline in physiological function**'. This situation can lead to extreme **muscle fatigue** and **loss of performance**.

Successful training programmes will include **moderation**, which implies that note is taken of the sportsperson's state of physical health, and when signs of deteriorating performance are detected, training loads will be reduced and recovery times increased until feelings of tiredness are reduced.

Individual needs

Every athlete is different and so each of the elements shown in figure 8.1 page 103 needs to be tailor-made to meet his or her individual needs. This is linked to the specific nature of choice of sport (whether or not the sport demands anaerobic or aerobic activity), the age and gender of the performer and so-on.

Reversibility

Reversibility is also known as **regression** and is defined as '**when training loads are reduced or removed completely, the state of fitness or performance returns to a normal untrained state**'. This is often summed up as '**use it or lose it**'.

This principle explains why performance deteriorates when training stops or intensity of training is reduced. With reversibility, physiological systems revert or **regress** to their normal untrained state eventually. This will not happen immediately, but research has shown that the process begins within 5 days of ceasing training. Interestingly, it is found that adaptations established by longer periods of training remain for longer after training stops, than those produced by a short period of training. In figure 8.7, training and performance are improving up to the fourth month of the period shown. At this point, a minor injury occurs, and the sportsperson cannot train for the following four months. During this second four month period, performance falls as fitness and strength falls.

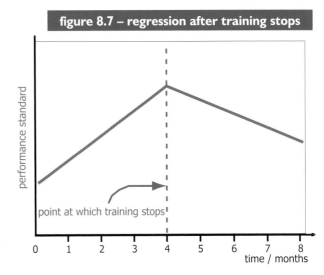

figure 8.7 – regression after training stops

point at which training stops

Variance

Training exercises, drills, or games which are **the same** (with the same outcomes and feelings) week in and week out, will eventually result in a lowering of motivation as the feelings of mastery of the activity are reduced. In other words, the person becomes used to the outcomes of the activity and his or her drive to continue with the same activity reduces.

Tedium is defined as '**training that lacks variety and causes boredom**'. This can be overcome by setting goals for sessions which **vary** (even though the activity itself may be the same), or by completely changing the activity while retaining the same goals (for example goals to improve strength or endurance).

Changing activities in training with the specific aim of reducing tedium is called **variance**, and is a crucial feature of a successful training programme.

2.2.7, 2.2.8 Measuring and calculating working intensity

Intensity of training can be measured scientifically using lactate testing or by calculating the respiratory exchange ratio. Field methods of measurement include **Karvonen's** training heart rate, weights lifted, heart rate response, and a **Rating of Perceived Exertion** (**RPE**) using the Borg scale.

It is possible to calculate working intensities by using a variety of methods. Table 8.1 compares three methods for rating training intensity.

Table 8.1 – **classification of exercise intensity based on 20 to 60 min of endurance activity, comparing heart rate maximum, Karvonen's maximum heart rate reserve and Borg's Rating of Perceived Exertion (RPE)**

classification of intensity	relative intensity by HR_{max}	relative intensity by $\dot{V}O_{2max}$ or HR_{max} reserve - Karvonen method	rating of perceived exertion Borg Scale RPE
very light	<35%	<30%	<9
light	35 - 59%	30 - 49%	10 - 11
moderate	60 - 79%	50 - 74%	12 - 13
heavy	80 - 89%	75 - 84%	14 - 16
very heavy	>89%	>84%	>16

(From Table 19.3 Wilmore, Costill, Kenney: 'Physiology of Exercise 4e', 2008, Human Kinetics)

Heart Rate Maximum method

To calculate the relative intensity using this method you have to work out the simple percentage of maximum heart rate (HR_{max}). This requires knowledge of the heart rate in near maximal exercise conditions. HR_{max} and percentage of HR_{max} can be estimated as follows:

$$HR_{max} = 220 - age \text{ (of the performer)}$$

For a 17 year old this would be:
$$HR_{max} = 220 - 17$$
$$HR_{max} = 203 \text{ bpm}$$

Assuming our 17 year old wanted to work at a moderate intensity of between 60% and 79% of HR_{max}, his or her target heart rate zone will be between:

60% of 203   = 122 bpm,
and 79% of 203 = 160 bpm.

The nearer to 160 bpm the harder the exercise intensity.

This simple method does not take into account differences in fitness levels.

Karvonen method

This HR method takes into account individual levels of fitness, as resting heart rate is required to work out an individual's training heart rate zone. Note that in table 8.1 above the percentage values for HR_{max} reserve are slightly lower than in the HR_{max} column. This is because the Karvonen method incorporates resting heart rate values and therefore is a more reliable method.

A training heart rate can be established by using the concept of **maximal heart rate reserve**.

Maximal heart rate (**HR_{max}**) is calculated (as above) using $HR_{max} = 220 - age$.

Our 17 year old would have a maximum heart rate of 203 bpm as in the previous example, and has a resting heart rate of 65 bpm.

Karvonen method

Maximal heart rate reserve ($HR_{max}R$) is worked out using:

$$HR_{max}R = HR_{max} - HR_{rest}$$

where HR_{rest} is the resting heart rate of the performer, and for our 17 year old:

$$HR_{max}R = 203 - 65 = 138$$

Thus a training heart rate (**THR** – the heart rate at which optimal aerobic training effects can take place during continuous training) can be calculated by taking a percentage of the maximal heart rate reserve and adding it to the resting heart rate:

$$THR = HR_{rest} + \text{(required percentage)} \times HR_{max}R$$
$$= HR_{rest} + \text{(required percentage)} \times (HR_{max} - HR_{rest})$$

So to work out the target heart rate for **moderate** exercise for the 17 year old of between 50% and 74% of $HR_{max}R$:

$$THR_{50\%} = HR_{rest} + 0.50(HR_{max}R)$$
$$= 65 + 0.50 \times 138$$
$$= 134 \text{ bpm.}$$

and

$$THR_{74\%} = HR_{rest} + 0.74(HR_{max}R)$$
$$= 65 + 0.74 \times 138$$
$$= 167 \text{ bpm.}$$

This gives a THR_{50-74} of between 134 bpm and 167 bpm which is approximately the range of heart rates corresponding to between 50% and 74% of the $\dot{V}O_2$ as shown in table 8.1 above.

An aerobic training zone of between 50% and 74% of maximal heart rate reserve (moderate intensity) should be used to ensure a training response when designing aerobic training programmes for most athletes. Progression through the range of training heart rate percentages can be planned as the athlete improves his or her aerobic fitness.

Borg Scale method

The Borg rating of perceived exertion (**RPE**) scale requires a person to **subjectively** rate the difficulty of the training, using a numerical scale that is related to exercise intensity as illustrated in table 8.1 above. This means that the person wishing to estimate his or her exertion, would guess at the rating on a scale between zero and 20. The score of zero corresponds to being asleep, and the score of 20 corresponds to absolutely flat out intensity which would bring about complete collapse in under 30 seconds.

Since exercise levels corresponding to higher levels of energy expenditure and physiological strain produce higher RPE ratings, this is an easy and effective method of measuring exercise intensity.

Weights – the one-repetition maximum (1RM) method

Strength can be defined as '**the maximal force that a muscle or muscle group can generate**', and can be assessed using a 1-repetition maximum test or the **1RM** test. The details of this method are set out in the fitness testing section on page 95.

2.2.9 Contemporary technologies used to monitor fitness and performance

The following are examples where technology has been used and is being developed for use in fitness assessment.

Pedometer - fitness activity tracker

- A **pedometer** is a wrist worn device used to detect footfall.
- What a pedometer actually detects is the **impact** between foot and the ground, which causes the whole body to decelerate and accelerate.
- Therefore it is an **inertial device** detecting change in position, and its purpose is to count the number of footfalls during a race, training session or activity.
- Contemporary pedometers track footfall, distance run and energy output using GPS technology.
- A coach will use this information to assess **stride length** or total energy output.

Force plates

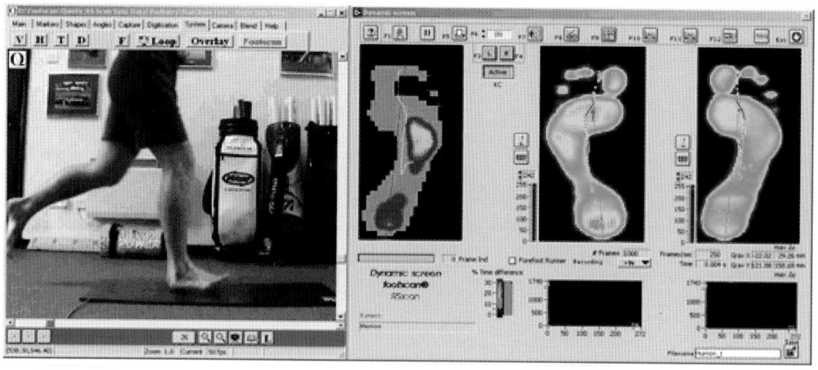

- A **force plate** is inserted into the ground at the take off area for a long jump or high jump, or in the space in a track immediately after a sprint start. This enables the patterns of force (figure 8.8) made by a foot striking the plate to be determined.
- This information (combined with video of the same footfall) can tell a coach the precise way in which the foot is active during its strike with the ground, and enables him or her to assess whether **changes in foot posture** are required.

figure 8.8 – force plate output

Heart rate monitors

- The HR monitor is fairly old technology, which can be strapped to the torso or worn as a watch-like device on the wrist or arm.
- Heart rate can be observed by the performer during training or competition to ensure that HR operates within a predetermined training zone. For elite performers, training intensities need to be accurately measured and match the variations in training intensity required during each phase of the periodised year (discussed in section 2.2.10 on pages 110 and 111).

Heart rate monitors are less accurate with anaerobic higher intensity activity and sudden short efforts.

Today's heart rate monitors are very sophisticated. For example, Garmin (figure 8.9) have a range of water resistant watches that, in addition to setting heart rate zones, offer the following features:

figure 8.9 – GPS, HR technology

- GPS tracking technology and associated mobile apps can calculate training intensities in relation to performer's age, height, weight and gender.
- Accurately track calorie burn, distance run and time splits.
- Store data facilities to compare data and plot performance graphs.

GPsports

GPS technology has been used to assess distances moved and speeds of players in premiership soccer and rugby. A device is worn throughout a game, the data is received remotely and software is able to print out and map the **movements of the player** (see page 145). The advantage of this system is that it provides real-time monitoring of **distance**, **speed**, **acceleration** and **heart rate** in order to assess training loads. The modern heat rate monitors almost duplicate this technology.
Source: www.Gpsports.com

Power meters

This technology is more appropriate for rowers and cyclists and offers a very accurate but expensive method of measuring training intensity by using a strain gauge. Knowing the power output is a quantitative, repeatable way of assessing how hard a performer is working and when it is time to rest between bouts of exercise.
From a coaching perspective, the flip side is that with power data you can also accurately determine the specific performance requirements of a given event or discipline.

Fitness machines

CYBEX machines are computerised cycle ergometer, treadmill, stepper and cross trainer machines, which can monitor **heart rate** and give information about **aerobic performance**.
Source: www.cybexintl.co.uk

Laser sensor equipment and positional software

This laser based system assesses **speed** of a performer, and can be used to measure speed during an activity such as long jump, triple jump, ski racer, cyclist and formula one racing car.
Source: www.manitgroup.com/jenoptik/laserpatrol.htm

Isokinetic strength training machines

These are expensive, computerised, workload-controlled, strength assessment laboratory machines that provide very accurate and controlled assessment of the rate of force development, force of contraction and at different angles of hinge joints (such as the knee and elbow). Ideal for maximal strength and muscle endurance testing.

For example, the **Lido isokinetic machine** can be used to compare the strength ratio between the agonist and antagonist muscles, such as the quadriceps femoris and hamstring muscle groups. The strength ratio between these muscle groups should be 2:1 for optimal performance and fitness, otherwise potential muscle pulls and tears could occur, particularly the weaker hamstring group.

Video analysis and software

Edited video commentary on a performance provides auditory cues or explanations from the coach. This can be in digital or MP3 format and accompany video footage.
Using software such as **Quintic** (figure 8.10) and **Dartfish**, a coach can highlight technical aspects of play/performance using a variety of drawing tools or playback facilities over the actual video footage. These clips can be repeated over and over again to reinforce the positive aspects of the performance and/or the ones that need improvement. Over time, the coach and performer can assess if technical improvements have been made.

figure 8.10 – video software

figure 8.11 – bike design in the wind tunnel

Wind tunnels

Wind tunnels are increasingly being used to assess the aerodynamics (improved flow of fluid - air or water - reducing drag or fluid friction) of bikes (figure 8.11), cycle helmets, and cyclist overall profile. This is done by blasting air past the stationary object in a tunnel, and using smoke to illustrate the layers of flow of the air. The task is to avoid vortex generation in the air flow, since smooth (laminar) flow generates less drag.

Factors investigated include:
* Wheel spokes and profiles.
* Width of handlebars.
* Riding posture, and hand position on the bars.
* Type of cloth and design of clothing.
* Forward cross-sectional area of frame and brackets.

Technology and drag

The computer programmes show how adjustments to shape can be made **before** construction, reducing expense and making more systematic the shape-making process. In addition to the cycling applications above, this is for:
* Kayaking and rowing.
* Bobsleigh, luge and skeleton.
* Speed skating (helmets, costumes and body angles).

Further application of the same technology is to **increase the drag effect** in order to improve propulsion in water based activities. This applies to:
* Improved patterns of pulling (hand and foot/leg positions and activity) in swimming.
* Shape of blades in rowing and canoeing.

2.2.10 Periodisation

Periodisation is a method of training which varies training intensity cyclically, organised in periods and cycles of training. Such cycles of training take place long-term, over time spans of months and years.

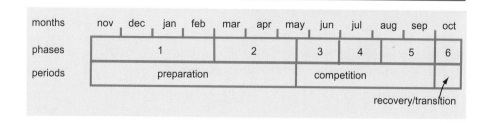

figure 8.12 – a single periodised year

Each period within a training plan will have a specific aim or objective within the overall training plan, for example:

* **Period 1** may be aimed at basic conditioning.
* **Period 2** may be aimed at strength development.
* **Period 3** may be aimed at speed development.

The time intervals within this training method can be defined as follows:

* A **period** is a basic year subdivision between 1 and 6 months.
* A **macrocycle** is a phase lasting between 4 and 26 weeks.
* A **mesocycle** is a phase lasting 2 to 4 weeks which would be part of a macrocycle.
* A **microcycle** is a phase lasting 1 week or less, and is the basic repetitive cycle of activities.

* Sometimes **daily cycles** of up to 3 sessions may be required for elite performers.

Figure 8.12 shows how periods and cycles can be laid out for a whole year. Note that an elite athlete may need a four or five year periodised programme to peak for an Olympic Games.

Planning a periodised training programme

* You will need to utilise the principles of training, decide on general activities, and then decide on specific activities.
* You will need to break down activities into relevance to different energy systems and ensure that this fits the energy system profile for your sport.
* You will next decide on time allocations (**duration**), and decide on the volume of work in a session (**intensity**).

* See figure 8.13 for an example breakdown of training intensity over the days of a microcycle (in this case 7 days long, one week).
* Note that elite athletes who don't need to plan round the working week (most people would have to fit in with school, college or work), often use 5, 6 or 8 day micro cycles to fit in with the time needed to recover from intense training.

* Decide on how many times in the microcycle you would like to train (**frequency**).
* Set out sets and repetitions within an activity (**repetition**).
* Ensure that **warm-up** and **cool-down** are included.
* Make notes on **progression** for future microcycles.
* Ensure that appropriate rest and **rest relief** is indicated.

figure 8.13 – variation in training intensity during a microcycle

Planning mesocycles

* You need to establish your **maximum training intensity** using fitness tests - this is your initial **100%** training intensity.
* Then decide on a **starting point** below this (for example, 80%).
* Then plan a **progressive intensity** mesocycle taking you up to 100% in say 4 weeks (figure 8.14).
* Next plan the subsequent 4-week **cycle** taking you up to 110%.
* With subsequent 4-week cycles taking you up to your planned goal for the year.

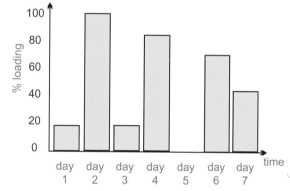

figure 8.14 – training intensity by mesocycle

Alternative methods of periodisation

- The example in figure 8.12 on page 110 is a single periodised year (just one competitive period). The same sort of arrangements can be made for two competitive periods - called a **double periodised year**.

- Figure 8.15 shows the possible layout for a **double periodised** year, the blue vertical line shows the end of the first competitive period.

- At this point the second half of the year (period) begins and the process of structure towards the second competitive period starts. Research has shown that this sort of programme can initiate greater progress in various indicators of fitness (strength, speed, endurance).

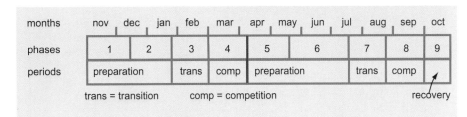

figure 8.15 – a double periodised year

months	nov	dec	jan	feb	mar	apr	may	jun	jul	aug	sep	oct
phases	1	2	3	4	5	6	7	8	9			
periods	preparation			trans	comp	preparation				trans	comp	

trans = transition   comp = competition   recovery

Tapering and peaking

- The periodisation method of training enables the coach to vary training intensity and quantity, so that a performer can **peak** for a major games such as the Olympics.
- This peaking usually involves **tapering**, which means that training intensity gradually reduces over a period of up to 14 days beforehand, which enables the athlete to be fresh and full of energy for the big event.

Peaking is partly psychological. How a performer feels about him or herself, and how confidence is flowing, are often as important as the state of fitness or strength.

See page 89 for details of various training programmes.

Questions

1) An 18 year old rugby player is doing pre-season fitness training.

    a)   Calculate her heart rate training zone for moderate-intensity physical activity.

    b)   Calculate the heart rate training zone for moderate-intensity physical activity and for vigorous-intensity physical activity for a 40 year old female.

2) What is the difference between a single and double periodised year?

3) Define macrocycle, mesocycle and microcycle.

4) a)   The figure below shows a curve that represents the intensity of training over a single periodised year. Draw in a further two curves that represent volume of work and technique.

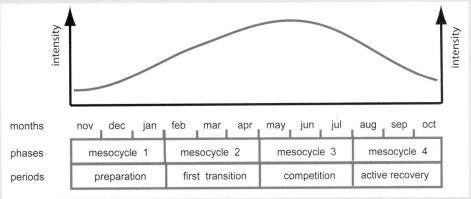

months	nov	dec	jan	feb	mar	apr	may	jun	jul	aug	sep	oct
phases	mesocycle 1			mesocycle 2			mesocycle 3			mesocycle 4		
periods	preparation			first transition			competition			active recovery		

   b)   The competitive phase lets the performer peak for competition. Using the intensity curve explain how strength development changes over the periodised year. Gives examples of work volume in terms of sets, repetitions, and percentages of 1RM.

2.2.11 Methods of training linked to activities

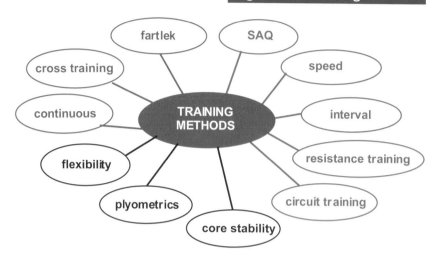

figure 8.16 – training methods

Most of the methods in figure 8.16 have been outlined in detail in table 7.1 on page 89.

Flexibility – Stretching

- The **aim** of flexibility training is to improve (or maintain) the **range of motion** over which muscles can act and joints can operate. In simple language this can be expressed as how far you can reach, bend and turn.
- **Joint flexibility** depends on the distensibility of the joint capsule, adequate warm-up, muscle viscosity and the compliance of ligaments and tendons.
- **Gender**, **ageing** and **body composition** affect flexibility, females are generally more flexible, older people are less flexible, and obese people tend to be less flexible (mostly because the extra mass gets in the way!).
- Flexibility is improved by stressing all these components. The effect produced is based on the **stress-overload** principle by forcing the contractile tissues such as muscle tissue to operate at full stretch.
- Mobility work is best done at the end of an anaerobic training session, during cool-down. This is because the muscular system is usually more relaxed at this time, with muscle temperatures slightly higher than during the warm-up.

Types of stretching and flexibility exercises

figure 8.17 – flexibility/stretching

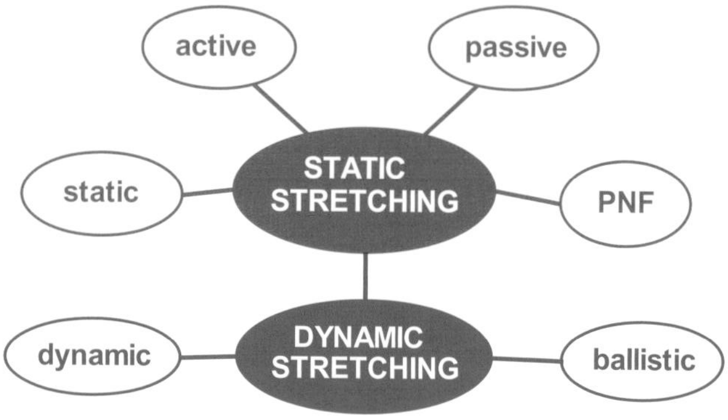

There are **two** main types of stretching (figure 8.17):
- **Static**.
- **Dynamic**.

Static stretching

Static stretching refers to stretching exercises that are performed **without movement**. In other words, the individual gets into a stretch position and **holds** the stretch for a specific amount of time.

Static stretching is performed by placing the body in a position **whereby the muscle to be stretched is under tension**. At this point the position is held to allow the muscle to lengthen. This is a very safe and effective form of stretching with a limited threat of injury. See figure 8.18 on page 113 as an example of a static stretch.

Active stretching

Active stretching is **slow stretching** in which flexibility is achieved **without assistance**. This form of stretching involves using only the strength of the opposing muscles (antagonist) to generate a held stretch (held for 10-15 seconds) within the agonist. The contraction of the opposing muscles helps to relax the stretched muscles. See figure 8.19 page 113 as an example of an active stretch. Active stretching is a very effective form of conditioning.

Passive stretching

Passive stretching is similar to static stretching, however a **partner** or **apparatus** can be used to help further stretch the muscles or joints. Figure 8.20 is an example of a passive stretch in which the floor is assisting the position.

Dynamic stretching

Dynamic stretching refers to stretching exercises that are performed with **movement** and are classified depending on the vigorousness of the bounce.

Dynamic stretching uses a **controlled**, **soft bounce** or gentle **swinging movement**, that moves a particular body part to the limit of its range of movement and is a preferred method over ballistic stretching.

figure 8.18 – hold this static stretch

Ballistic stretching

figure 8.19 – active stretch

- **Ballistic stretching** involves **aggressive**, **dynamic** or **rapid**, **bouncing** or **swinging** movements during which the contraction of the agonist forces the antagonist to relax. Ballistic stretching fails to allow the stretched muscle time to adapt to the stretched position and instead may cause the muscle to tighten up by repeatedly triggering the stretch reflex.

- Ballistic stretching should be **used towards the end of a warm-up** because the muscle temperatures are slightly higher than at the start of the warm-up phase.

figure 8.20 – passive stretch

- Ballistic stretching is considered to be an outdated form of stretching because of its vigorous nature and risk of muscle tear injury. Activities such as trampolining rely on ballistic stretching during routine work such as a ten-bounce routine. Figure 8.21 shows a side-to-side swinging movement aimed at stretching the lower trunk muscles.

figure 8.21 – ballistic stretch

Questions

Describe the following types of flexibility, stretching methods:

a)   Static.

b)   Dynamic.

c)   Ballistic.

d)   Proprioceptive neuromuscular facilitation (PNF).

Proprioceptive Neuromuscular Facilitation (PNF)

figure 8.22 – PNF

PNF is a progression on passive stretching, whereby after a stretch is held, the muscle is contracted **isometrically** for **between 6-10 seconds**. It then **relaxes** and is **contracted** again, usually going further the second time. This is known as the **CRAC** method (Contract-Relax-Antagonist-Contract).

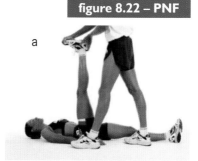

This method is best described in **three** stages:
Stage 1:
* The athlete and partner assume the position for the stretch (figure 8.22a), then the partner extends the body limb until the muscle is stretched and tension is felt.
Stage 2:
* The athlete then contracts the stretched muscle **isometrically** for 5-6 seconds and the partner must inhibit all movement (figure 8.22b).
Stage 3:
* The muscle group is relaxed, then immediately and cautiously pushed past its normal range of movement (figure 8.22c) for about 6 seconds.

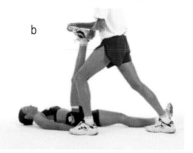

Allow 30 seconds recovery before repeating the procedure 2-4 times.

The aim of PNF is to **toughen** up or inhibit proprioceptors (such as **muscle spindles and Golgi tendons**) in the relaxation of muscle tissue.

This is a **long-term** adaptation.

Cross training

The term 'cross training' includes modern machines which simulate cross country skiing, and also the notion that a trainer will benefit from doing training in other activities not the specific sporting activity wthin which excellence is achieved. This tactic wthin a training programme adds variance to the activities undertaken and enables refreshment of motivation and 'fun'.

Resistance training with the use of mechanical specialist equipment

Resistance training equipment such as weight training **machines** or pulley machines (with stacks or hydraulics), are designed to add extra resistance to the performer through a range of motion. Many of these devices are designed to mimic the sports movement, which make the movement **specific** to the sport and so provide an alternative method of training.

Resistance aids form an integral part of land-based training drills for elite athletes such as swimmers, rowers and canoeists, as well as providing specialist equipment for individual athletes and team players.

A comprehensive range of specialised resistance training equipment is available such as pulleys, speed chutes, strength tubes and sledges.

Swim ergometers

Operates on a pulley system and **simulates swimming actions** on land. This pulley provides the tools necessary to develop aerobic endurance and anaerobic power for swimming without getting wet. An example of a type of swimbench is the expensive Vasa ergometer which is equipped with an electronic monitor that provides instant feedback on performance, including time, distance, pace, stroke rate, force, and power in watts. It features variable wind resistance that can be adjusted.

Rowing ergometers

The Concept II ergo rower is a specialist resistance training machine that has been used for this type of sport in the training and preparation of athletes for many years. More recently, indoor rowing has grown from a tool for off-the-water training for the serious rower to a sport in its own right.

Latex tubing or therabands

A cheaper alternative is for the athlete to use extendable latex tubes, which consist of tubes or strips made of rubber with varying degrees of thickness and strength. This type of resistance training is known as **stretchcord resistance training** and the idea is to pull on the tube for the selected movement pattern.

Parachutes

Otherwise known as **speed chutes**, this type of resistance training device is towed behind a running athlete to provide resistance to forward motion. It is designed to improve maximal speed, start acceleration and speed endurance, and is used in a variety of sports where speed is an essential physical fitness component.

Towing sledges

A **towing sledge** is a training device, which includes a powder coated steel sledge and belt attached to a shoulder harness as shown in figure 8.23. The user is required to add weights to the sledge to vary the training load or intensity.

Sledge resistance training is thought to improve speed, acceleration and leg strength. However some studies have shown that during flat-out work there is an immediate extension of the knee joint at the beginning of the support phase on the ground. This means that a concentric contraction is applied early thereby eliminating the important eccentric contraction phase of the initial ground contact. This may be a significant disadvantage in the context of improving the sprinter's ability at maximum speed.

These examples of resistance aids can help reduce the tedium of training by adding variance to the training regime.

figure 8.23 – sledge resistance

Assistance speed training - towing or downhill

The idea here is that the athlete should attempt to run faster than normal, and get used to a faster cadence and a bigger stride length than normal. This can be done either by running downhill or being towed by some sort of vehicle.

In the towing case, the performer would wear a jacket similar to the one shown in figure 8.23 (worn the other way round!), and a bungee or towing cord attached to the front of the jacket.

This method will add variance to the total training load experienced by an athlete. The only disadvantage of this method is that 'normal' running action and timing is practised at an unusual rate, thereby affecting the neuromuscular patterns involved.

Speed Agility Quickness (SAQ) training

A large number of exercises have been developed uiner this heading in an attempt to improve coordination and agility at speed. The variety of movements can be tailored to meet any sporting activity.

The exercises are done with precision and speed of foot placement, and use ladders or small hurdles (figure 8.24).

Example 1.
As in figure 8.25, the athlete moves between two lines 0.5 metres apart, plant feet as in a running motion. L then R on first line - L then R on second line, then back to first line L then R, and repeat. Feet are planted as quickly as possible - with a count to 50 foot plants or 20 second duration.

figure 8.24 – SAQ in a exercise ladder

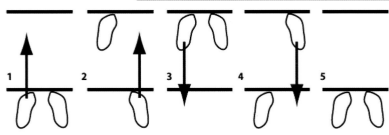

figure 8.25 – SAQ example 1 - foot speed

Speed Agility Quickness (SAQ) training

Example 2.
The athlete stands with his or her back to a bank of hurdles (figure 8.26).
He or she steps backwards over hurdles, reaching high and wide – with alternate legs.

figure 8.26 – SAQ example 2

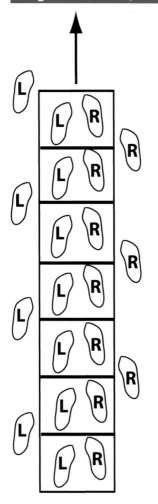

figure 8.27 – SAQ example 3

Example 3.
The athlete performs an alternate double step in single step out - using ladder laid on floor (figure 8.27). Left then right foot stepped into a rung space, then left foot stepped out alongside the ladder, then right then left foot stepped into the rung, and right foot stepped out alongside the ladder.

The advantages of SAQ methods are that they develop neuromuscular patterns which can link into specific sport requirements, and they give an extra agility element to performers whose main requirement is endurance or strength.
The disadvantages are that a lot of time is required for full involvement of these exercises (they need a lot of practice), and that precision and focus are required to perform movements accurately at speed.

Functional (Core) stability

During training, the function of the nervous system is developed. The brain learns movements by developing motor programmes which tell the person what to do almost automatically when faced with a physical task, without having to relearn the mechanics of the task each time.

figure 8.28 – examples of specialist core activities

Conditioning using repetitive movements improves the feedback of proprioceptors (such as muscle spindles and Golgi tendon organs) to muscles, so that movements are more certain and less likely to have errors which might lead to injury. This is at a subconscious level, since a person would not have to think about a movement to perform it successfully.

This is why modern sports training includes balance and core activities (figure 8.28), so that the neuromuscular system which establishes posture and balance is better developed, and hence injury risk reduced.

2.2.12 Peparation for altitude, heat and humidity

Altitude training

The effects of altitude on the respiratory system

The higher the altitude, the more that aerobic performance is affected by the lack of oxygen pressure in the air.

When you exercise at higher altitudes (see figure 8.29) you will have to work harder to achieve the same sea level performance, because your aerobic system will be taxed that much harder.

figure 8.29 – effects of altitude

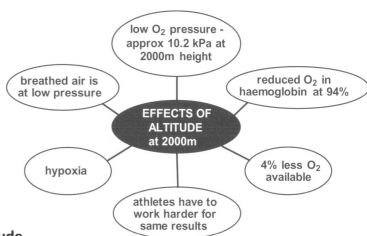

low O$_2$ pressure - approx 10.2 kPa at 2000m height

breathed air is at low pressure

reduced O$_2$ in haemoglobin at 94%

EFFECTS OF ALTITUDE at 2000m

hypoxia

4% less O$_2$ available

athletes have to work harder for same results

Adaptations to respiratory systems at altitude

During the first Global Games to be held at altitude (2240m) at the Mexico Olympic Games in 1968, African athletes who lived at altitude won all the track events at 1500m and over, with the World record holders (who were sea level dwellers) running a lot slower than their best.

*   What happens is that residents at altitude are found to have between 12% and 50% more haemoglobin per unit of blood than sea level residents.
*   Also, sea level residents who travel to altitude are found to **adapt** by producing more Hb at a rate of between 1% and 2% per week.

*   This is done by **increased manufacture of red blood cells** (erythropoietin production).
*   Also, there is a **reduction in plasma volume**, a slower long-term adaptation to living at altitude.

*   The effect of these **two** factors is to increase the haemoglobin **concentration** in the blood flowing to active tissue, and hence the oxygen-carrying capacity of the blood.

This is why endurance athletes (long distance runners, cyclists or triathletes) nowadays try to spend a period of time before competitions living and training at altitude – before returning to sea level, where the extra oxygen carrying capacity of their blood would help improve the intensity and duration of aerobic activity.

Further adaptations occur within tissue cells (see figure 8.30) when low pressure air (and hence oxygen) is breathed:

figure 8.30 – altitude training

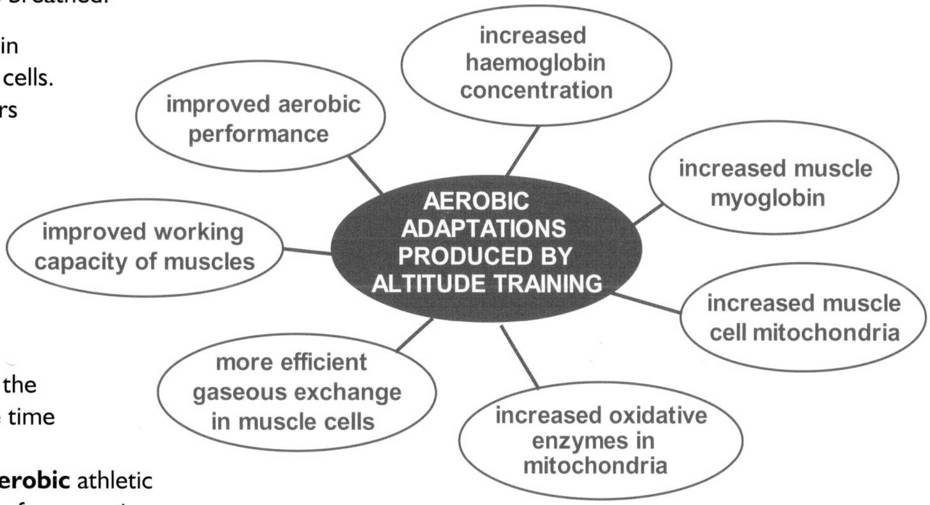

*   There is an increase of up to 16% in **myoglobin** content within muscle cells.
*   There is also an increase in numbers of **mitochondria** and **oxidative enzymes** (such as **pyruvate dehydrogenase**) within the **mitochondria** to improve the working capacity of muscles.

*   This happens because the efficiency of gaseous exchange improves **within muscle cells** for the sea level dweller that spends some time at altitude.
*   Hence he or she would improve **aerobic** athletic performance and oxygen recovery after exercise.

increased haemoglobin concentration

improved aerobic performance

increased muscle myoglobin

AEROBIC ADAPTATIONS PRODUCED BY ALTITUDE TRAINING

improved working capacity of muscles

increased muscle cell mitochondria

more efficient gaseous exchange in muscle cells

increased oxidative enzymes in mitochondria

Altitude training

- Hence altitude training is a predominantly **endurance-based exercise programme** used by elite endurance athletes from a range of sports.

- Most elite athletes have a minimum of 2 training blocks or visits per year, one long training block of between 4-6 weeks during the preparation training phase, and then a shorter block of between 2-3 weeks just prior to a major competition. During a second visit the body adapts more quickly.

- **Short-term symptoms** to altitude exposure include headaches and dizziness and increased breathing and heart rates. The key is to adjust gradually (**acclimatise**) to higher altitude.

- Hence during the first week of altitude training an elite athlete would normally work at between 60-70% of sea level intensity thus avoiding very hard lactate sessions.

- During the second week, the training would increase to full intensity (within days 10-14) and continues until returning to sea level. This would include 'tapering' or reducing the workload during the final couple of days just prior to a major competition. Paula Radcliffe (World record holder in the marathon) chose to compete within 2 days of returning to sea level.

- The process of altitude training will stimulate production of more **haemoglobin** and bigger increases in **myoglobin, mitochondria** and **oxidative enzymes** than at sea level in the way outlined above and in figure 8.30 page 117.

- Hence on return to sea level the sportsperson would have **increased $\dot{V}O_{2max}$** and tissue cell respiration, leading to enhanced aerobic performance.

- The optimum time to compete is within 2 to 14 days of return to sea-level. After this, the adaptations gradually return to sea-level norms over a period of weeks, depending on the time spent at altitude and the individual's basic physiological state.

Hypobaric (hypoxic) chambers or houses

This recent development uses dwelling places which use **low-oxygen environments** (hypobaric means low pressure) to simulate altitude training.

An athlete will live and sleep in a hypobaric house situated at sea level, and will train and exercise outside the chamber (at normal oxygen levels, and in his or her normal training environment). This has the effect of elevating EPO, red blood cell levels (hence haemoglobin), myoglobin, mitochondria and oxidative enzymes in a similar way to altitude training.

Hypobaric chambers are used by distance runners, triathletes and endurance cyclists.

A more recent development is the **hypoxic tent**. This is a less expensive system in which a tent is infused with low oxygen air (extra nitrogen infused) but at normal sea-level pressures. Hence a sportsperson can sleep in a tent and gain hypoxic adaptations while asleep (figure 8.31).

Intermittent Hypoxic Training (IHT) is achieved using aerobic and anaerobic interval training methods alternating between low oxygen air and normal air, using a mask attached to an altitude generator. Although substantially different than sleeping at altitude, the goal of IHT is the same: improving athletic performance or acclimatization to high altitude.

Thermoregulation

Thermoregulation is the ability to maintain body temperature within certain boundaries, even when the surrounding temperature is very different. The acceptable range is between 36.1 and 37.8°C.

The **thermoregulatory centre** is situated in the hypothalamus - in the brain. Changes in body temperature such as caused by exercise, are sensed by central and peripheral receptors, and body temperature is maintained by balancing heat input and heat loss. Figure 8.32 overleaf, and table 8.2 list the heat energy transfer methods from the human body.

Table 8.2 – **heat energy transfer methods**

heat input	heat output
metabolic heat	radiation
exercise	conduction
shivering	convection
solar radiation	evaporation

Thermoregulation

The proportions of different methods of heat energy transfer are different between at rest and during exercise, and are set out in table 8.3.

Table 8.3 – **proportions of the different methods of heat energy transfer from the body**

mechanism of heat loss	% of total at rest	% of total during exercise
conduction & convection	20	15
radiation	60	5
evaporation	20	80

- Activity of the sweat glands is controlled by **autonomic nerves** which in turn are controlled by the thermoregulatory centre (figure 8.33).
- Increased **skeletal muscle activity** increases the core temperature by increasing **metabolic heat** production.
- Increased **sweat gland activity** decreases the core temperature by increasing **evaporative heat loss** (as in table 8.3).
- **Smooth muscle** in the **skin arterioles** can cause these vessels to **vasodilate** to direct blood to the skin for heat transfer out of the body, or **vasoconstrict** to retain heat energy deep within the body.

- The **amount of heat generated** during tissue respiration depends mainly on the volume (therefore the **mass**) of the body.
- Because most of the heat is lost through the skin, the **surface area of the skin** determines the amount of heat lost.
- Hence the effectiveness of the mechanisms of body temperature control depend on the **surface area to mass ratio** of the body.
- Small people (children, gymnasts, distance runners, jockeys) therefore will lose temperature much more quickly than large people (weight lifters, sumo wrestlers, throwers, rugby players).

Exercising in hot conditions

- Under **hot conditions** the surrounding temperature can exceed both skin and core temperature. This makes evaporation the predominant method of heat loss compared with conduction, convection and radiation.
- **Skin cooling** occurs when sweat evaporates, so exercising in hot dry climates feels more comfortable than in cooler but more humid tropical conditions.
- This is because in **humid conditions** the presence of high water vapour pressure in the surrounding air suppresses evaporation even though large quantities of sweat bead on the skin.
- The practice of **removing sweat** with a towel before sweat evaporates will hinder evaporative cooling, since lack of moisture on the skin will mean that no evaporative cooling can take place.
- Hence a physically active person is vulnerable to the dangerous state of **dehydration** and **increased core temperature** (**hyperthermia**).

Adequate fluid intake before, during and after exercise is important. Fluid is needed to preserve plasma volume, maintain circulation and reduce the effects of the cardiovascular drift (see page 49).

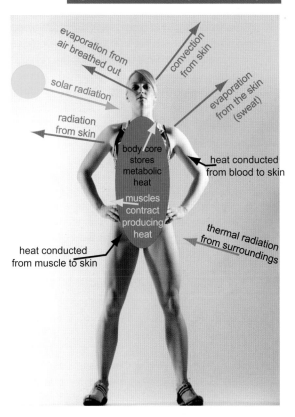

figure 8.32 – heat input and output

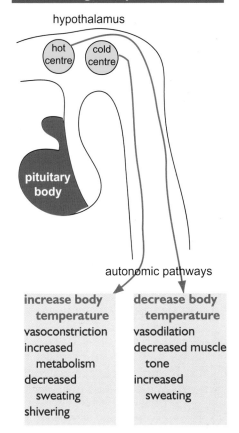

figure 8.33 – summary of main thermoregulatory mechanisms

Exercising in cold conditions

- Heat production by **shivering** (which is the very rapid alternate contraction and relaxation of the skeletal muscles) and physical activity, is the mechanism the body uses to offset heat flux to a cold environment.
- Withdrawal of blood from **peripheral body parts**, such as hands and feet, help to preserve core temperature, hence the skin will pale when exposed to a low temperature environment.
- **Increased water loss** occurs from the respiratory passages, and kidneys excrete more water as urine to reduce the total fluid volume (plasma volume) held centrally.
- Also if **thick clothing** is worn in these conditions, sweating can increase - which would again cause fluid loss and possible dehydration.
- Hence **fluid** will need to be **replaced** in cold conditions.

Wind chill

figure 8.34 – skiers require the maximum skin coverage against cold air

- **Wind** increases evaporative cooling of exposed body parts, and in cold conditions this is known as the **wind-chill factor** (temperature felt on exposed skin is lower than the air temperature).
- **Wet skin** exposed to the wind will cool even faster.
- Hence a sportsperson training in **cold windy conditions** should wear appropriate kit (figure 8.34) to reduce this effect and minimise the risk of **hypothermia**.
- Examples of this are a hat to reduce heat loss through the head, a Gore-tex training jacket to enable moisture to escape from the body while keeping out moisture from the environment, and suitable thermal gloves.

- Many of Britain's elite athletes have access to **indoor training** facilities and also go **warm-weather training** to escape the usual British cold, wet, winter weather conditions.

Training and competing in extreme climates requires time for an athlete to acclimatise or to get used to the prevailing conditions. In the case of heat acclimatisation, within 3 days there is an increase in plasma volume, thus supporting stroke volume and cardiac output, combined with the increased ability to sweat.

In the case of adaptation to cold conditions, the physiological effects are less pronounced than in hot conditions. Most of the effect is called **habituation**, in which people just get used to the conditions. A sportsperson will also have an increase in metabolic rate (producing more heat energy within the body), and the skin tends to become more **insulating** (after an extended period) which means that they will tend to develop thicker layers of subcutaneous fat. The effect of these cold-adaptations is to improve cold temperature tolerance.

2.2.13 Speeding up recovery

DOMS or Delayed Onset Muscle Soreness

Delayed onset muscle soreness is felt as tenderness and pain within a muscle belly, between 8 and 48 hours after intense training. It has two causes:
- **Excess lactic acid** delivered and retained in muscle following intense anaerobic exercise, primarily during eccentric muscle activity.
- **Micro-tears** and the resulting inflammation in muscle tissue occurring as part of the normal intense training process.

If intense exercise is repeated using muscles already affected by DOMS, there is a strong risk of muscle trauma.

DOMS can be reduced by having greater recovery between repetitions or sets or sessions, and by using therapies such as massage or ice. Soft-tissue treatment is an important part of the recovery process and **massage** is probably the most favoured method. Massage is used to speed recovery following heavy single workouts, competitions, or during high-intensity cycles. Ice therapies, such as **ice baths**, assist in the removal of lactic acid and **reduce inflammatio**n.

Training programmes should include a progressive build up of exercise loading, and moderate concentric exercise to protect against muscle soreness.

Cool-down

The aim of a cool-down (figure 8.35) is to gradually return the body to its former resting state. This is achieved by performing low intensity exercise such as jogging and stretching. Static stretches during cool-down can increase flexibility of joints.

figure 8.35 – cool-down

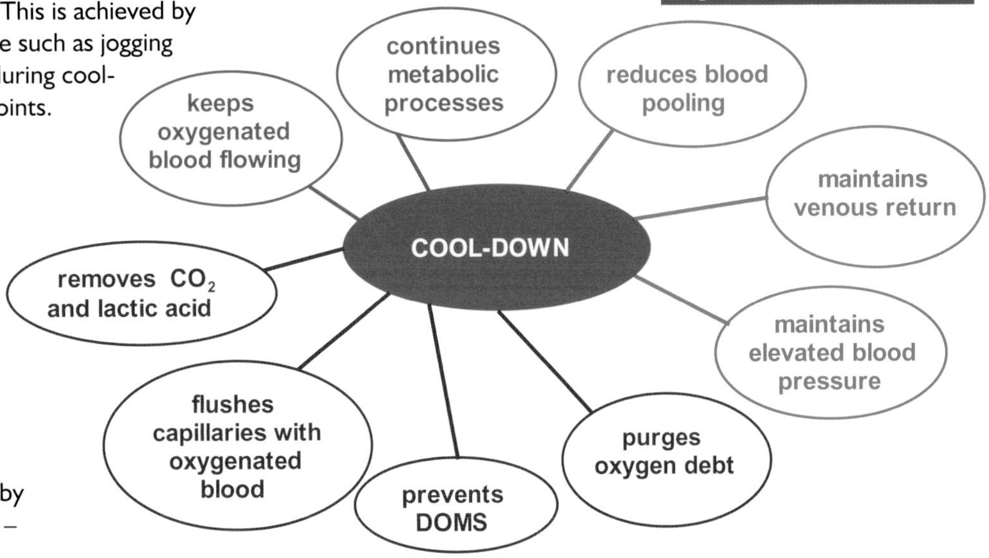

continues metabolic processes

keeps oxygenated blood flowing

reduces blood pooling

maintains venous return

COOL-DOWN

removes CO_2 and lactic acid

maintains elevated blood pressure

flushes capillaries with oxygenated blood

purges oxygen debt

prevents DOMS

Physiological value of cool-down

- Keeps muscle active and **capillaries open** for longer to enable **oxygenated blood** flowing to muscles to purge the **oxygen debt**.

- **Flushes** out **lactic acid** and helps oxidise lactic acid thereby **preventing** muscle soreness – **DOMS**.

- Active muscles will activate the skeletal muscle pump for **venous return** of blood to the heart thereby preventing **blood pooling** and dizziness (blood will remain in limbs if muscle action is stopped suddenly).

The outcome of a cool-down should be to allow heart rate to return to its pre-exercise level with reduced injury risk, and to help lower levels of blood adrenaline after a period of high arousal.

Cooling aids

Cold therapies (**cryotherapy**) are popular ergogenic aids for cooling core body temperatures. They reduce the effect of delayed onset of muscle soreness (DOMS) and are well established in the treatment of acute sports injuries.

The value of **cold therapy** lies in its ability to decrease cellular metabolism, reduce inflammation, swelling and pain, and promote vasoconstriction. Cold packs do this by absorbing heat from the injury. The more heat absorbed, the faster the pain relief and healing. There are a variety of cooling aids available ranging from ice jackets, wet ice packs, ice gels and chemical packs.

Ice or cooling jackets

Cooling jackets (packed with ice or chemical coolants) are used to attempt to reduce the core temperatures of sports participants in very hot conditions. For example, the Australian rowing eight in the Atlanta Olympic Games 1996 as shown in figure 8.36.

figure 8.36 – use of ice jackets in a competitive situation

Wet-ice packs

Water is a much better conductor of heat energy than air or plastic. By being wet, the wet-ice pack allows for greater heat energy transfer out of the body compared to gel or chemical packs. For example, tennis players use wet-ice packed towels during match intervals in long hot matches.

Ice baths

Ice baths (figure 8.37) use the fact that **chilling** the affected area can **reduce local inflammation**. Athletes use total immersion ice baths or cryogenic chambers to implement this therapy. The use of ice baths is very popular during the recovery phase of a training session as it assists in the removal of lactic acid (DOMS) and aids the healing process of damaged tissue.

Precautions should be taken because prolonged application (immersion) at very low temperatures could initiate frostbite!

Ice therapy and injury

The use of **cold therapy** in acute sports injuries as well as in rehabilitation of the injured athlete and injury prevention has become a generally accepted treatment method. Various cooling methods that are adjustable and compress the injured area are recommended.

Research has shown that the impact of injury is substantially reduced by the use of cold therapies. The sooner the cold therapy is used following injury, the more effective the therapy. The use of ice packs, ice towels, ice massage, frozen gel packs and ice baths are just a few examples of cold therapies that are used in acute sports injury treatments.

figure 8.37 – are ice baths fun?

Compression clothing

Research has shown that compression clothing (figure 8.38) will **increase venous return** and VO_{2max} during **high intensity exercise**, in both the trunk cavity and thigh and calves - hence the practice of distance runners wearing compression long socks.

Loughborough University and Canterbury (sport clothing) showed that a 2.7% increase in **peak power** could be achieved in short periods of high intensity cycle ergometer testing. This has the effect of improving the performance of rugby and other team players, and when worn after training, **recovery** is improved and **DOMS reduced**.

figure 8.38 – compression clothing

Exam style questions

1) Define the following principles of training: 3 marks

   a)   Progressive overload.

   b)   Specificity.

   c)   Reversibility.

2) What is meant by the FITT principles of training? Use examples to illustrate your answer.   8 marks

3) Explain why you would use the principles of training, shown in figure 8.1 on page 103, when developing a training programme to improve the fitness of 16+ physical education students.   8 marks

4) Explain how the fitness principles of progressive overload and specificity apply to flexibility.   2 marks

Exam style questions

5) a) Describe a method of determining your heart rate target zone.   3 marks

    b) Give one advantage and one disadvantage for the method you have selected.   2 marks

    c) Why is it important to monitor heart rate to make sure that it is in the desired heart rate zone?   2 marks

6) a) How can athletes make sure that they are exercising at an intensity that is within their heart rate training zone?   2 marks

    b) Identify four issues associated with using heart rate training zones.   4 marks

7) a) Explain how the Borg scale can be used to monitor exercise intensity.   2 marks

    b) Give one advantage and one disadvantage of using the Borg scale to measure exercise intensity.   2 marks

8) An alternative, effective method of calculating lower and upper threshold heart rate (HR) levels at a percentage of the difference between resting and maximum HR (termed heart rate reserve - HRR) is known as the Karvonen method. Using Karvonen's theory, calculate the training threshold of the lower training heart rate 50% to the upper training heart rate of 85% by completing the missing figures below.   4 marks

	heart rate - beats per minute
resting heart rate (bpm)	72
maximum heart rate (bpm)	
heart rate reserve (bpm)	
lower training heart rate (bpm)	
upper training heart rate (bpm)	

9) a) Stretching is a key element in any warm-up. Using an example, identify two other elements of a warm-up and explain how they help to prepare an athlete.   4 marks

    b) Describe three different methods of stretching and state a sport that would benefit most from each type.   6 marks

    c) Identify two physiological adaptations to skeletal tissue following a three-month flexibility training programme.   2 marks

10) Core stability and SAQ training methods are used by most sports performers. Briefly describe these two training methods and the advantages of using these training methods within a general training programme.   6 marks

11) The 2016 Olympic Games was held in Rio de Janeiro. Assess why an athlete might train at altitude for the 10,000 metres event prior to the Games.   8 marks

12) What does 'refinement in technique' mean to sports performers and coaches?   2 marks

13) How do the following technologies aid analysis and feedback for improvements in sporting performance?   12 marks

    a) Video and computer software analysis.
    b) Heart rate monitor.
    c) 3D scanning machine.
    d) Force plate technology.

14) Elite performers use the concept of the periodised year when planning their training programmes. Examine how technology, used to measure exercise intensity, can contribute to successful periodisation for these elite performers.

8 marks

15) Describe how an athlete is able to control his or her body temperature during a marathon race.   4 marks

16) What are the major avenues for loss of body heat energy?
Which of these four pathways is important for controlling body temperature at rest, and during exercise?   6 marks

17) Why is humidity an important factor when an athlete is performing in high temperatures? Why are wind and cloud cover important?   4 marks

18) What is meant by heat acclimatisation? Outline the main physiological adaptations which occur to allow an athlete to acclimatise to training and competition at high temperatures.   8 marks

19) Describe the conditions at altitude that could limit performance.   3 marks

20) Describe the major physiological responses and adaptations that accompany acclimatisation to altitude over a period of three weeks.   8 marks

21) What is meant by the concept 'living high and training low'? Identify two advantages of using this acclimatisation method.   6 marks

22) Following an intense training session, explain how the following ergogenic aids can assist with the recovery process: having an ice bath, having a massage, wearing full-body compression clothing, and ingesting a hypertonic sports drink.   8 marks

23) Comment on how the future of sport may be affected by the developments in technology. Illustrate your answer with examples.   12 marks

24) A Level. Periodisation is a training concept that explains the variation in training volume and intensity over a specific period of time. Outline the basic structure of a single periodised year and illustrate how a coach is able to use this structure when planning a training programme for an athletics group.   15 marks

25) A Level. Discuss the relationship between training loads, recovery, and regular field testing performances in young elite soccer players to develop training guidelines to enhance performance.   15 marks

Answers link: http://www.jroscoe.co.uk/downloads/as_a1_revise_pe_edexcel/EdexcelAS_A1_ch8_answers.pdf

SKILL ACQUISITION

CHAPTER 9 - 3.1 Coach and performer

3.1.1 Coaching styles

Coaching or teaching style determines the way in which information is transmitted to the learner.

Mosston's spectrum of teaching/coaching styles

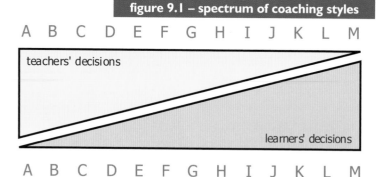

figure 9.1 – spectrum of coaching styles

In this method (see figure 9.1), the style is determined by the proportion of decisions the teacher or the learner makes. From figure 9.1, style A has all the decisions made by the teacher, and style M has all the decisions made by the learner. Style G has roughly half made by both teacher and learner. The more decisions made by the teacher, the more authoritarian the style (this means that the teacher tells the learner what to do – and the learner obeys this and follows exactly what the teacher says). The more decisions made by the learner, the more free-form the style and what is done is decided by the learner, and the teacher goes along with this completely.

figure 9.2 – coaching styles

There are four main styles (figure 9.2):
* **Command**.
* **Reciprocal**.
* **Discovery**.
* **Problem solving**.

Command style of coaching

This style involves mostly the teacher or coach making the decisions.
It is authoritarian with the teacher or coach telling the learner what to do (place A or B in Mosston's spectrum).
For example, in a hockey small game situation, the coach calls 'freeze' to preserve pitch position. The coach decides on all the drills and activities to be done in a training session.
This is **good** for:
* **Novices** (who need to be told what to do).
* **Quick responses** (discipline would be expected, and immediate action to the coach's commands expected).
* **Dangerous situations** (like rock climbing or canoeing).
* **Hostile groups** (a coach would expect attention to his or her instructions, without group members being involved with their own antagonisms).
* **Large groups** (where if too many different things were happening at once, there would be chaos).

The command style is **not good** for:
* **High level performers** (where it would be expected that the performer would know what to do, and make all adjustments to performance during the occasion by himself or herself).
* **Social interaction** (where the coach would expect members of a group to chat and get to know one another – this could not happen if the performers would have to listen to the coach and concentrate on obeying his or her instructions).
* **Creativity** (where the performer would be expected to initiate his or her own ideas about what to do).

Reciprocal style of coaching

This style involves learners becoming teachers of others for part of the teaching process (between D and J on the Mosston spectrum). The teacher or coach would set the task and monitor its progress, but the learners would for example work in pairs and teach one another. Or, in swimming, the coach teaches the skill of a tumble turn to some of the swimmers, who in turn then teach others.

This is **good** for:
- **Social interaction** (it would be important for the learner groups to communicate and interact with one another to complete the tasks).
- **Giving responsibility** (group members would need to take it upon themselves to complete the tasks).
- **Personal development** (the process would rely on group members to initiate the organisation of the tasks).
- **Feedback** (self-realisation of how good a performance is – or peer group information as to the quality of performance may have more impact).

The reciprocal style is **not good** for:
- **Discipline** (the style allows some freedom of movement and action within the learner group).
- **Correct information delivered** (the method allows for learners to interpret information as they feel is best, and sometimes inaccuracies in what is to be done can happen).
- **Beginners** (beginners need to be told what to do).
- Those who have **poor communication skills**.

Discovery style of coaching

This style involves decision making by the performer or learner. The teacher or coach would guide the learner to find the correct movement by giving clues or asking questions of the learner (between H and K on the Mosston spectrum). For example, the coach tells players in a hockey team to work out for themselves the strategies for a penalty corner. The players already know the rules for penalty corners, they just have to decide on the positions and movement of the players and who strikes the ball and so on.

This style is **good** for:
- **Creativity** (the learner can decode from his or her own feelings about a situation to perform certain tasks).
- **Motivation** (people who perform their own tasks are often highly motivated by their 'ownership' of the activity).
- The **high level performer** (who knows what to do after many years of practice, and who can make complex decisions based on experience).

The discovery style is **not good** for:
- **Efficiency** (the way in which a learner decides to perform a task may not always be the best or most efficient way).
- **Learning correct habits** (sometimes people may need to be told what is the correct way to do things).
- **Motivation** if things go wrong (sometimes people will get disheartened if their choice of activity proves to be incorrect).

Problem solving style of coaching

In this style, the teacher or coach would set a problem and the learner would decide (without prompting or help) how to solve the problem or perform the tasks (between L and M on the Mosston scale). There would be no limits set by the coach, and the aim would be to develop the cognitive abilities of the learner. There would be no correct solutions, only those decided by the learners.

The advantages and disadvantages of this style are similar to the discovery style, but should perhaps only be used when there are no correct outcomes to a task, where performers are experienced or expert, and there are no time limits to the process.

In a true teaching or coaching situation, a mixture of styles would be used according to the situation, the task, and the stage of learning of the performer.

Factors affecting use of coaching styles

- The **coach**, his or her philosophy, personality, experience, knowledge, capability at research, leadership style and ability.
- **Type of activity**, the demands on the learner, task complexity or organisation, risk or danger, practice style.
- The **learner**, his or her personality characteristics, skill, fitness, knowledge, age, interest, attitude, motivation.
- The **situation**, with environmental factors (weather, temperature, state of pitch), and resources, equipment, facilities.
- Time, and **danger** or risk.
- The final factor of **hand-eye coordination** such as badminton or tennis. But such a person may be able to run or swim effectively.

Where is the performer in relation to his or her stage or phase of learning?

Is he or she in the cognitive, associative or autonomous phase of learning?

If you are lucky enough to be in the autonomous phase, then your skill will be well-learnt and stable under stress. You will be able to make your own adjustments without guidance to most of the movements you make, but may occasionally need the advice or help of a coach during the performance situation. On the other hand, if you are in the cognitive phase, you will need extensive help from a coach or teacher, and will need plenty of practice of basic skill movements with extensive feedback from a coach about the success of the practice in order to avoid a learning plateau.

How well motivated is the performer?

If your motivation is intrinsic, then you will not need reminding to turn up to training or practice. On the other hand, if your motivation is extrinsic, you will need an incentive to complete a training regime, although success in this exam should be sufficient!

3.1.2 Development of tactics and strategies

To begin an analysis of the tactics and strategies within sport, we must first look generally how the different sports are categorised, since each sport will face different challenges depending on these features. Figure 9.3 shows approximately these categories.

Each sport will have its own range of skills, techniques and tactics, and such features will define the nature of the sport.

Technical demands

Technique amounts to the sequence of actions necessary to perform a physical skill accurately and efficiently.

This will depend on the physique and strength of the performer, the requirements of the sport or skill, and the mechanics of the desired movement.

Refinement of technique involves knowledge of the perfect technical model by a coach, knowledge of the mechanics of a skill, and being aware of methods by which technique can be changed.

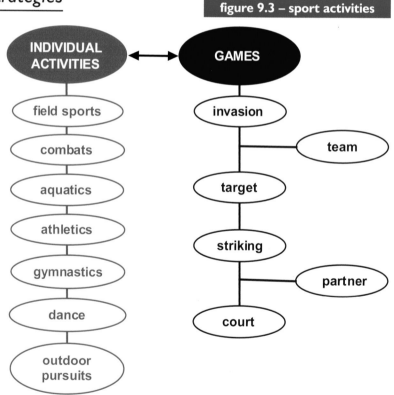

figure 9.3 – sport activities

The first step is to observe the performance by video analysis, and then compare this with the perfect technical model diplayed by an elite performer. Again, the precise way in which this is done will depend on the sports category as set out in figure 9.3. For example, a novice performer in tennis will need to master a number skills, involved in: the serve, a forehand, a backhand, a smash, a top spin lob, a backspin baseline shot, a dropshot and so on. Each of these elements will need to be analysed and perfected if the novice is to make substantial progress. Most of this skill learning will occur within the game situation, and probably will need to be mastered **before** tactics or strategy can be utilised.

Another example could be in basketball, where dribbling, passing, free throws, jump shots, lay-ups, rebounds, blocking, and stealing will need to be mastered.

Skill development

Skills will need to be developed according to the skill types itemised on page 133. The main feature of such skills will be that they should be mastered accurately by multiple practices (it is said that up to 10,000 successful practices will need to be made before accuracy and autonomous mastery of a skill will be achieved). Page 138 onwards below looks at the way practice can be organised and implemented.

It will be very important that skills are practiced correctly - and that novices should do so under the observation of a coach who can provide feedback about how well a skill is performed.

Tactics

A tactic involves a plan of action within a game or sport that aims to improve the chance of an individual or team winning or improving his or her performance taking into account his or her strengths and the opponents' weaknesses.

Basically, tactics are part of the skills used by a performer to win (as opposed to just playing a game for fun or fitness, for example). The idea of beating or outwitting an opponent is a crucial feature of tactics.

While technique is the way we apply skills in a selected sport, tactics are how we apply skills **successfuly** in competitive situations.

Factors that affect tactics are the playing conditions, the place of a game in the season, and the nature of the opposition (top of the league, or about to be relegated for example). A coach would analyse the opposition before the game and for example attempt to exploit the age and lack of speed of an ageing player when he or she is in a critical position on the field.

Tactics in sport are often concerned with whether a team is attacking or defending, and they are aften categorised in terms of defending strategies used to prevent opponents from scoring against you, or attacking strategies in which your team attempts to score against the opponent.

Strategies

A strategy involves a general approach to a competitive scenario that may not include specific techniques and tactics.

Coaches will find it difficult to coach strategies to the individuals in a team to be applied in a competitive situation. Hence a coach will attempt to simulate the competitive environment in which to practice strategies, but often it will be down to the experience of the players themselves to interpret the situation on the field, and how to apply the appropriate strategies.

The decisions made by performers, especially the captain of a team under pressure, will determine whether or not a strategy has been successful (the team will either have lost or have won).

Communication

A coach will need to communicate to performers in order to effectively adjust tactics to the situation on the field. This communication can be verbal (figure 9.4) or by sign language. Some premiership coaches or managers will bawl or shout from the sidelines, and although the players are probably the most sophisticated, autonomous and skilful on the planet, such a coach feels the need to get angry at variations from the tactical plan or strategy that is decided beforehand. The whole plan is to allow some responsibility by the players for interpreting the playing situation (as far as correct tactics are concerned), but the issues unseen by the players need to be transmitted to them.

figure 9.4 – a coach communicates

Hand signals (fingers behind the back for doubles tennis players or volleyball players for the server to serve a particular shot), or to the correct player who will be lifted in the line-out at rugby, will be the only way such tactics may be transmitted to the players.

Such coded communication will need to be accurate and clear if tactics are to be completed successfully.

Prior to 2014, it was forbidden for coaches to speak to athletes in the middle of an athletics field event competition. From 2016, It is possible not only to speak to them, but to show them film or video from the effort just completed so that technique or tactics could be altered.

3.1.3 Dissection of a skill to identify technical elements

Motor programmes

Motor and **executive programmes** are the **general movement patterns** stored in the long-term memory which enalble a perfomer to create and repeat a skill. For example, the general movement pattern associated with kicking a football, striking a forehand at tennis or squash, or performing a pole vault (figure 9.5).

This is a method of **dissection of a skill** or skills which will enable a coach to structure the skill learning process which will be needed to create or develop a skill.

A **motor programme** contains **all the information** required to make a movement and complete a skill, including which muscles to use, the order in which muscles are used, and the phasing and degree of contraction of muscles. They are formed through repetition of movements. For example, the repetition of a particular swimming dive will eventually cause the swimmer to perform the dive with little conscious effort (hence the requirement to perform a skill 10,000 times before it becomes fully learnt).

Such a **programme** enables a **skill** to be performed, and can be made up of a **large number of subroutines** which must be **adaptable** so that it can be altered when the environment or surroundings change.

figure 9.5 – a pole vaulter

the vaulter has a complex executive programme for this activity

Subroutines

figure 9.6 – a tennis serve

Subroutines are the segments of skills which go toward building a whole movement pattern or programme. They can be structured in **layers** (see figure 9.7 as an example for the pole vault and figure 9.8 for a tennis serve) where some subroutines or skills can be in turn dissected into further subroutines or skills which form smaller parts of a skill. Each subroutine is a **short fixed sequence** which, when fully learned, can be performed **automatically without conscious control**. When effectively broken down into subroutines, and learned thoroughly, a skill performed by a sportsperson can therefore contribute to his or her autonomous phase of learning (see page 138 below). It is the efficiency of the subroutine process which contributes most to the advancement of the skill into the autonomous phase.

figure 9.7 – subroutines for a pole vault

POLE VAULT

- initial preparation
  - correct body stance
  - grip on pole
  - pick up of pole
- run-up
  - running
  - carry of pole
  - placement of pole in box
- take-off and flight
  - flex pole
  - drive legs upwards
  - extend arms
  - push off pole
  - wrap legs and body over bar
  - land safely

figure 9.8– subroutines for a tennis serve

TENNIS SERVE

- initial preparation
  - correct body stance
  - grip on racquet
  - correct feet position
- throw up of ball
  - withdraw racquet
  - throw up ball
  - watch the ball
- strike of the ball
  - keep eyes on ball
  - wait for ball to fall
  - throw racquet head at the ball
  - move hips and legs
  - adjust racquet to strike in correct direction

Analysis of a skill

In order to determine whether or not a performer has technical faults it will be necessary to analyse current skill using video and a comparison programme as outlined in section 2.2.9 page 109. The purpose will be to find strengths and weaknesses of a skill and it will be up to the coach to decide how such a skill should be rebuilt, based on an analysis similar to those outlined in figures 9.7 and 9.8 on page 130.

Exam style questions

figure 9.1 – spectrum of coaching styles

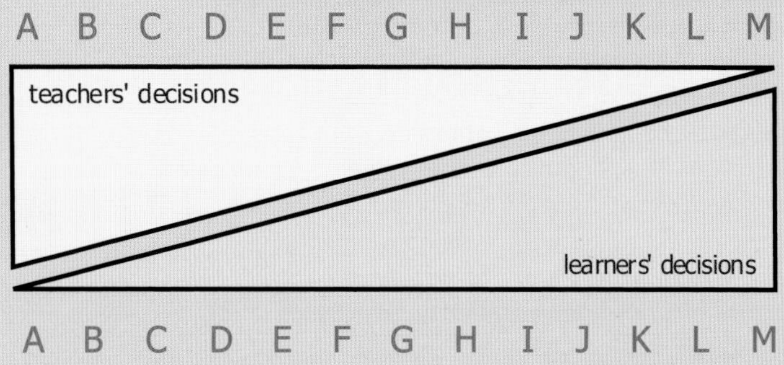

1) Figure 9.1 shows Mosston's spectrum of coaching styles in terms of decision making in the learning process.

   a) Identify the teaching style at A, and explain its consequences for teaching method.

   4 marks

   b) What are the advantages and disadvantages of this teaching style in teaching a sport or sport skill?

   4 marks

2) a) What is meant by the reciprocal teaching style and what are its drawbacks?

   5 marks

   b) What are the main advantages of the discovery method of teaching?

   3 marks

3) Identify three factors affecting the use of coaching styles.

   3 marks

4) How can the discovery style of coaching improve the performance of learners?

   4 marks

5) a) Distinguish between the terms tactics and strategies, using examples to illustrate your answer.

   4 marks

   b) Identify four factors that you may need to consider before choosing a tactic.

   4 marks

   c) Select an individual or team activity. Describe a tactic which you could use because of its strength against an opponent's weakness and describe why it is effective.

   4 marks

   d) Give three reasons for changing tactics during your selected individual or team actrivity.

   3 marks

6) A goal attack (netball player title) is down the other end of the court, in a noisy indoor league competition. Suggest how the coach can get messages across to this player effectively?

   2 marks

7) a) Using figure 9.9 dissect the throwing action into six different technical skill elements.

   6 marks

   b) Briefly explain how the analysis of skills will influence a coach in organising training for javelin throwing.

   4 marks

   figure 9.9– dissection of a javelin throw

Answers link: http://www.jroscoe.co.uk/downloads/as_a1_revise_pe_edexcel/EdexcelAS_A1_ch9_answers.pdf

CHAPTER 10 - Classification and transfer of skills

Characteristics and definitions of skill

The term **motor skill** is used to describe a **technique** within a game or sport (for example, passing, hitting, catching, controlling a ball), or in reference to **the sport itself** (diving, tennis, hammer throwing), or a **quality** possessed by a sportsperson. The characteristics of skill (see figure 10.1) are that it should be co-ordinated, controlled, with good technique, efficient, or pre-determined by practice or the observation of others performing the skill perfectly. As such the skill will be well-learned, efficient and consistent. The beauty or pleasing nature of a skill is its aesthetic quality (figure 10.2).

figure 10.1 – skill

Difference between motor and perceptual abilities

Characteristics of ability

Ability (see figure 10.3) is the foundation for skill learning. A successful sportsperson must be born with a number of relevant abilities. An ability is **genetically determined**, since we are born with our abilities, which means that it is **innate** and **enduring** – it is part of our constitution and will last all our lives. For example, some children can quickly pick up skills (such as catching a ball or riding a bike), whereas other children take much longer and are less successful at any given skill.

figure 10.2 – squash, a skilful activity?

Motor (psychomotor) ability

This is the ability to process information about how and when we move. For example, fast reaction time is an ability, a rugby player must react quickly to an oncoming player who changes direction. **Gross motor ability** is an ability in which the performer is able to move using simple muscle movements, for example, being able to run or ride a bike.

Perceptual ability

This is the ability to sense and interpret sensory inputs or information. For example, the awareness of a rugby player of the positions and actions of opponents.

Ability is an **enduring** trait. We largely hold on to our abilities throughout our lives, for example, riding a bike.

General ability

This does not really exist - we have specific abilities.

Specific abilities

This refers to the fact that skills require different abilities. For example, gymnastics involves balance, strength and flexibility.

Groups of abilities

A good sportsperson may have many different groups of abilities. For example, a good all round sportsman could have different specific abilities such as good hand-eye co-ordination and balance which could be transferred to lots of different sports activities.

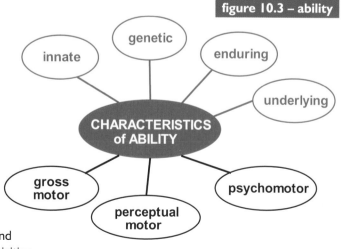
figure 10.3 – ability

Difference between skill and ability

Skill is acquired. Skills must be **learned**, which can require an extended process including the copying of expert models. On the other hand, **ability** is an **enduring** trait which can last throughout a person's life, and is genetic in basis. Abilities underpin and contribute to skills. For example, someone with good natural balance, shoulder and hip flexibility, and upper body and wrist strength, has all the abilities necessary to perform a handstand. But practice would be required to actually perform the skill of the handstand.

Types of skill

A **psychomotor skill** is a voluntary body movement with a pre-determined end result, for example, hitting a ball with a bat. **Fundamental psychomotor skills** are basic skills that are learned when young. They form the basis of more complex movements, for example, jumping.

A **perceptual skill** is about being able to interpret information quickly at a given time and to make an appropriate decision. For example, a goalkeeper in football assessing the movement of an opponent approaching.

A **cognitive skill** is about being able to make sense of a problem and to solve it. These skills affect perception.

3.2.1 Classification of skill

All skills are on a classification continuum. There are several types of continuum:

Muscular involvement

The muscular involvement continuum deals with **gross** and **fine skills**. **Gross skills** are those that use large muscle movements, for example, weight lifting. **Fine skills** are those that use small muscle movements, for example, darts. See further examples in figure 10.4.

figure 10.4 – muscular involvement continuum

GROSS							FINE
weight lifting	javelin throw	netball pass		cricket stroke	golf shot	ten pin bowling	darts/ snooker

Pacing

The pacing continuum deals with self-paced and externally-paced skills. **Self-paced skills** are those in which the performer has control over movement, for example, serving in volleyball. **Externally-paced skills** are those in which the environment has more control, for example, blocking in volleyball. See figure 10.5 for further examples.

figure 10.5 – pacing continuum

EXTERNALLY-PACED					SELF-PACED	
yachting	tennis receiving serve		soccer game	diving	tennis serve	weight lifting

Continuity

The continuity continuum deals with **discrete, serial** and **continuous skills**. Discrete skills are those that have a clear beginning and end, for example, taking a penalty kick at soccer. **Serial skills** are those that have a number of discrete elements linked together. For example, the triple jump in which the hop, step and jump are linked into one movement. **Continuous skills** are those that cannot be split up very easily into subroutines, for example, a hockey player dribbling a ball. See further examples in figure 10.6.

figure 10.6 – continuity continuum

DISCRETE			SERIAL		CONTINUOUS	
weight lifting	javelin throw		high jump		basketball dribble	running

Environmental influence

The environmental influence continuum deals with a range of skills labelled open to closed. **Open skills** are predominantly perceptual, with no clear beginning or end, are affected by environment, are externally-paced, in response to many actions of others. For example, receiving a pass at soccer or hockey. On the other hand, **closed skills** are predominantly habitual, with a clear beginning and end, and are not affected much by environment. For example, an athlete performing a shot-putt. See further examples in figure 10.7.

figure 10.7 – the environmental influence continuum

OPEN						CLOSED
soccer goal save	soccer pass	tennis stroke		tennis serve	soccer penalty	shot putt

The skill continuum

All skills have elements of **all** the classifications. For example, a golf swing may be predominantly a closed skill but it can be affected by strong weather conditions which would be an open skill characteristic. The swim start in figure 10.8 could be said to have gross and closed characteristics, but is it also self-paced and discrete?

Most skills have characteristics which make them near one end of a classification continuum. For example, a batsman in cricket as he plays a shot can be seen to be performing more of an open skill than a closed skill (he has to adapt to the speed and direction of the ball). But the cricket shot does have elements of closed characteristics too. The player has learned particular shots and almost automatically puts them into operation when the ball approaches at different speeds, with different spin, and in different directions.

3.2.2 The uses of transfer of skills

The term **transfer** (figure 10.9) describes the influence of one skill on the performance of another.

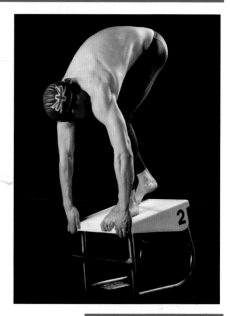

figure 10.8 – swim start, gross and closed skill?

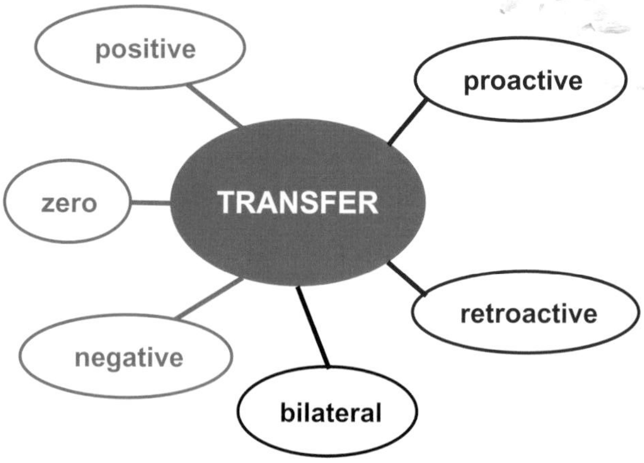

Positive transfer

This type of transfer occurs when **learning** in one task is enhanced by learning in **another task**. For example, learning a golf stroke may be enhanced by virtue of the fact that the player is a good cricketer.

Negative transfer

This occurs when the learning of a new task is **interfered** with by the knowledge of a similar activity. For example, the flexible use of the wrist needed for badminton may interfere with the firm wrist needed for tennis.

figure 10.9 – transfer

positive

proactive

zero   TRANSFER

retroactive

negative

bilateral

Proactive transfer

This type of transfer refers to the influence of one skill on a skill **yet to be learned**. For example, having learned the forehand drive in tennis, the action is then modified to the forehand drive with top spin.

Retroactive transfer

This type of transfer is where there is a negative influence of one skill on a skill that has **previously been learned**. For example, a hockey player learns the flicking skill which may have a negative effect on the previously learned push (the push pass may be lifted unnecessarily).

Zero transfer

This describes the situation where **no transfer at all** may occur even between skills which appear to be similar. For example, learning at squash may have zero transfer from weight training.

Bilateral transfer (limb to limb)

This is the transfer which takes place from **one limb to another**, sometimes called **lateralisation**. For example, a soccer player learns to kick a ball with the non-preferred foot, the actions are learnt through reference by the brain to the preferred foot.

Exam style questions

1) If you were watching a number of performers in sport, what characteristics would you expect the movements of a skilled performer to have? 　　4 marks

2) By using examples from sport, explain what is meant by fundamental psychomotor skills and why they are so important.
　　4 marks

3) a) Why is the shot put often regarded as a closed skill? 　　2 marks

   b) Using passing skills in a team game, explain what is meant by an open skill. 　　4 marks

   c) Give one example from sport of each of the following and state why you have chosen your example: continuous skills, serial skills, discrete skills. 　　3 marks

4) The diagram in figure 10.10 shows a profile for the racing start in swimming scaled across four different continua representing the skill characteristics of the movement.

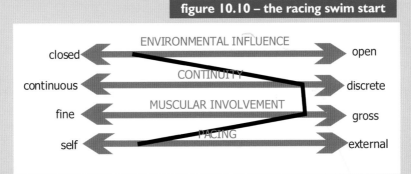

figure 10.10 – the racing swim start

   a) Referring to the profile, describe the swim racing start in terms of each of the four characteristics shown. 　　4 marks

   b) Using this same profile chart, sketch a profile which would describe the characteristics of a table tennis serve. 　3 marks

   c) Explain why you have chosen your particular characteristic for muscular involvement and environmental conditions.
　　4 marks

   d) Explain how your profile for the table tennis serve might assist a coach in planning practices for players learning this skill. 　　5 marks

5) Explain four different types of transfer of learning. 　　4 marks

6) a) Using a practical example, explain what is meant by the term 'transfer' in skill learning.
      How can transfer be detrimental to performance? Give a practical example. 　　5 marks

   b) How can a teacher or a coach ensure that as much positive transfer takes place as possible in a training session?
　　5 marks

Answers link: http://www.jroscoe.co.uk/downloads/as_a1_revise_pe_edexcel/EdexcelAS_A1_ch10_answers.pdf

CHAPTER 11 - LEARNING THEORIES and PRACTICES

3.3.1 Associationalist theories - the S-R bond

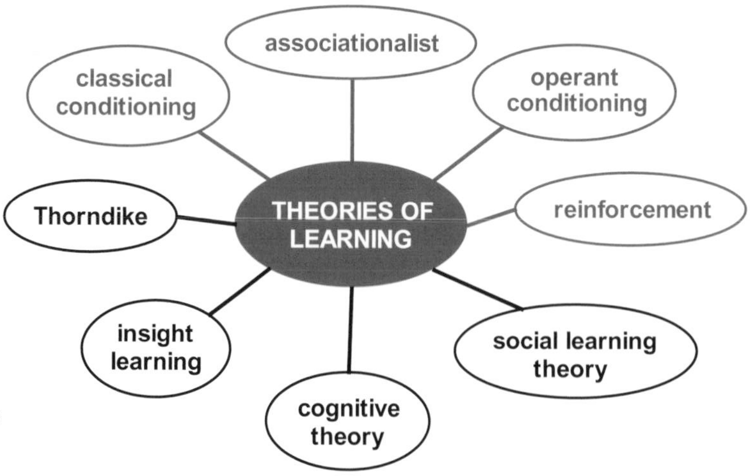

See figure 11.1 for a summary of the theories of learning.
Associationalist theories state that learning occurs as a result of the **association** or connection between a **stimulus** and a **response**, this stimulus-response connection is called the **S-R bond**.

figure 11.1 – theories of learning

Classical conditioning

The connection between stimulus and response is due to **conditioning**, which is a form of **training** which makes a certain behaviour into a **habit** (**habitualised** - unvarying). Such a habit is an ingrained and learned behaviour which becomes part of a person's **automatic** response to a stimulus.

A sports example of this would be the instant reaction of a soccer goalkeeper to a penalty taker's strike depending on the penalty taker's stance or body position.

Since **learning** involves a **change of behaviour**, learning takes place when a **connection** is made between stimulus and response.

An example of this could be the baton passing routine during a sprint relay. An incoming runner would shout 'hand', and the outgoing runner would present his or her hand to receive the baton. The shout is the stimulus, the reaching out of the hand the response. Eventually, the response is automatic (and learnt) and the baton will always be passed successfully.

Operant conditioning

Operant conditioning is concerned with **modifying behaviour** and hence **response** to a specific situation. This is the work of **Skinner** who used pigeons to whom he gave food if they pecked at and then hit a table tennis ball with their beaks.

Eventually, by developing the reinforcement (giving of food) when the desired response was achieved, the pigeons were able to knock a ball back and forth between them. This is based on **trial and error**, with the correct response **reinforced** (see page 137).

This can be used to learn from a **demonstration** that teaches how to perform the skill (shaping), and then **reinforced** after the performer has performed the skill successfully (through knowledge of results). For example, suppose a rugby player kicks when he or she should pass the ball. By rewarding (reinforcing using praise) every time the player passes, gradually the player learns to pass the ball (behaviour has been modified). The learner may not know **why** the response is correct only that it will be **rewarded**. To be effective, a reward will **closely follow** a correct response, and a coach will be concerned **to strengthen a correct S-R bond**, and weaken an incorrect S-R bond.

Cognitive theories

These theories are concerned with **understanding and insight**, and are the work of **Gestaltists** (German scientists who showed the importance of perceiving a problem in its **entirety**). **Intervening variables** are the factors which come between the stimulus occurring and a response being selected.

Social learning theory

Bandura's social learning theory describes learning by copying others (observational learning). In this theory, the performer is more likely to copy 'significant others', those who are seen as high status role models.

Reinforcement of movement behaviours

Reinforcement

Reinforcement (see figure 11.2) is concerned with ensuring the correct response is repeated.

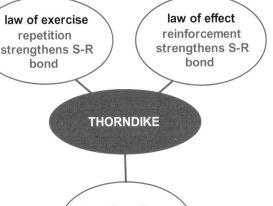

figure 11.2 – reinforcement

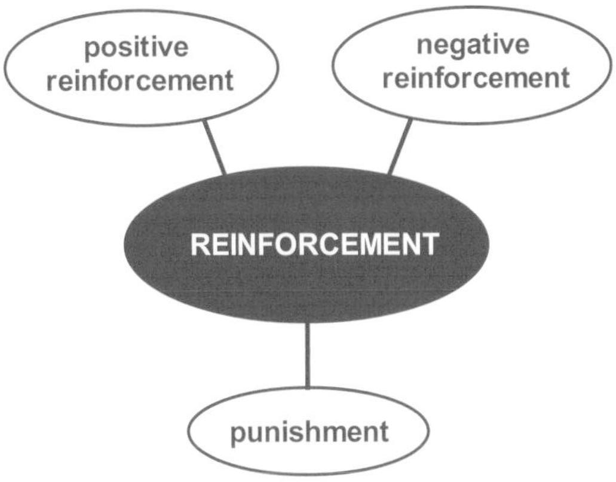

Positive reinforcement

Positive reinforcement uses rewards or praise to achieve the desired result. For example, a footballer might receive a bonus for scoring a goal, an amateur gymnast might be praised by the coach for a good performance.

Negative reinforcement

This means withdrawing rewards. For example, the same footballer may not receive a bonus when he fails to score a goal, the gymnast would not be praised if he or she performed inadequately.

Punishment

Punishment means inflicting retribution on a learner who performs incorrectly. This breaks a bond between the learner's learning process and an incorrect performance. For example, the footballer might be dropped from the team after he fails to score a goal, or a player is sent from the field if he or she fouls an opponent.

3.3.2 Thorndike's laws

Thorndike's laws (see figure 11.3) are concerned with **strengthening the S-R bond**, and hence the concept of reinforcement.

figure 11.3 – Thorndike's laws

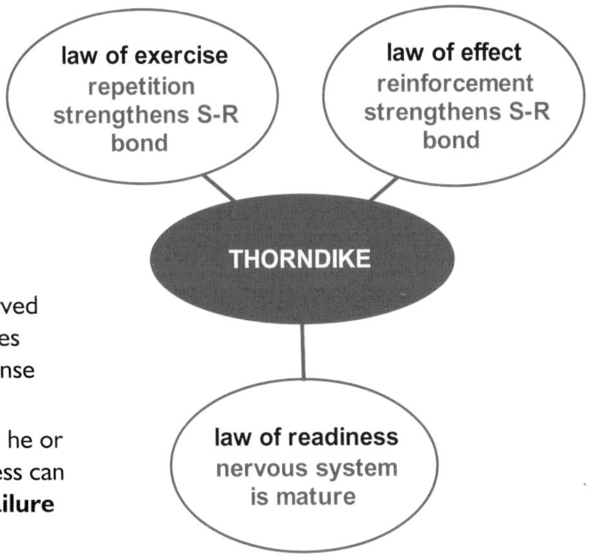

- **The law of exercise** explains that **repetition** strengthens the S-R bond.

  For example, the more a discus thrower practises throwing the more likely it is that this correct throwing technique will be repeated in the competitive situation. So **practice** is very important.

- **The law of effect** uses **reinforcement** (by praise, reward or observed success) which strengthens the S-R bond. Satisfying **reinforcers** (ones which make the learner feel good) increase the likelihood of a response being repeated.

  For example, if the thrower feels that the movement is correct then he or she is more likely to repeat the movement. A **trial and error** process can produce this effect, since **success** reinforces a response, whereas **failure** forces the performer to try new methods to achieve success.

- **The law of readiness** says that learning can only occur when the **nervous system** (and muscular system) is **sufficiently mature** to allow the appropriate S-R bond to happen.

  For example, the more a thrower is physically and mentally prepared to perform a throw then it is more likely to be performed well. People should learn **simple basic skills** (and become **basically fit**) **before** attempting to learn more complex skills. Also the performer needs to be **psychologically ready**.

3.3.3 Fitts and Posner's three stages of learning

The phases or stages of movement skill learning

The **phases of learning** (according to Fitts and Posner, see figure 11.4) are:

Cognitive

The **cognitive (early)** phase, in which the learner attempts to understand the skill, begins to look at techniques and memorise what is required, begins to practise and repeat the skill according to a simple model, and learns by trial and error. In this phase **guidance** would tend to be predominantly visual, with manual or mechanical guidance also being used, as basic body positions and movements are learnt. Here **feedback** involves reinforcement of success by the coach, with mistakes corrected by reference to the model. This phase applies to the novice player who can require a lot of support in order to achieve success.

Associative

The **associative (intermediate)** phase, in which the learner will understand the skill, and movement patterns will be more fluent and established (can be repeated at a reasonable level without much thought). In this phase **guidance** is more likely to be visual and verbal with some manual guidance to illustrate specific body positions or movements. The coach will give a lot of detail within this guidance. Here **feedback** involves the learner associating the 'feel' of the activity (via kinaesthesis) with the end results. This phase applies to the competent performer who still requires full support from a coach to correct mistakes.

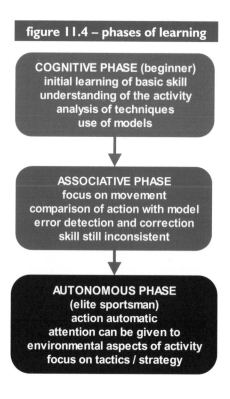

figure 11.4 – phases of learning

COGNITIVE PHASE (beginner)
initial learning of basic skill
understanding of the activity
analysis of techniques
use of models

ASSOCIATIVE PHASE
focus on movement
comparison of action with model
error detection and correction
skill still inconsistent

AUTONOMOUS PHASE
(elite sportsman)
action automatic
attention can be given to
environmental aspects of activity
focus on tactics / strategy

Autonomous

The **autonomous (final)** phase, in which movements are well integrated and automatic, with the learner able to perform without conscious effort. The performer can now give attention to the environment and wider cues about play (such as the position and movements of opponents). **Guidance** would not need to be extensive, but highly specific to situations which the performer would already have realised need attention. Verbal guidance would be the predominant method, with **feedback** being mostly via the learner being able to judge performances and make corrections by him or herself (often with the aid of video analysis of the performance). This phase applies to the player who can perform by him or herself, who can make decisions about tactics without prompting, and whose skill under pressure is stable.

The details of guidance are discussed in chapter 12 on page 142.

3.4.1, 3.4.2 The impact of practice on improving learning

This reflects the ways in which a skill **can be taught** to facilitate learning and maximise performance.

Factors affecting choice of method are: the **type** of skills to be taught, the **complexity** of the skill, the **classification** of the skill, the **environment**, the **ability** level of the **performer**, and the **motivational** level of the performer.

See figure 11.5 for the different methods of organisation of skill practice, and figure 11.6 on page 139 for the details of how the different methods are organised.

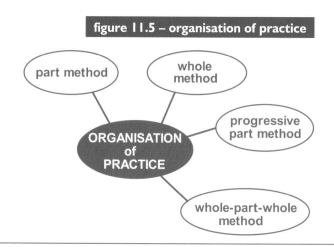

figure 11.5 – organisation of practice

part method

whole method

progressive part method

ORGANISATION of PRACTICE

whole-part-whole method

The whole method

In this method, the skill is **practised in total**. The method should be preferred **where the skill or task**:

- Is of low complexity or is a simple task.
- Has high organisation.
- Consists of interrelated subroutines.
- Has discrete skills of short duration (the movement is rapid or ballistic).

This method should be preferred **where the skill or task**:

- Cannot be broken down into parts.
- Or requires temporal or spatial coordination.

Examples of skills or activities where the whole method would be appropriate are:

- Somersault or tumble in gymnastics.
- Dart throw.
- Snooker or pool shot.
- Tennis serve.
- Soccer penalty kick.

The **performer**:

- Would be experienced.
- Has high levels of attention.
- Is in the later stages of learning.
- Is older and highly motivated.
- Uses distributed practice.

figure 11.6 – practice methods

WHOLE METHOD
whole practice only

PART METHOD
part A - part B - part C - part D practiced separately

PROGRESSIVE PART METHOD
part A - B - parts AB - part A - B - C - parts ABC - part A - B - C - D - whole ABCD

WHOLE - PART - WHOLE METHOD
whole (ABCD) practiced - then parts A - B - C - D practiced separately - then whole (ABCD)

The part method

In this method, the skill as a whole is **broken down into parts** for practice.
The part method should be preferred **where the skill or task**:

- Has high complexity.
- Is of low organisation.
- Has independent subroutines.
- Has slow or serial tasks, where the skill as a whole is of long duration.
- Or for dangerous skills.

Examples of skills or activities where the part method would be appropriate are:

- Triple jump in athletics.
- Full trampoline routine with ten different moves.
- Clean and jerk in weight-lifting.

The **performer**:

- Is a beginner.
- Has limited attention span.
- Is in the early stages of learning.
- Is having problems with a particular aspect of a skill.
- Has limited motivation.
- Uses massed practice.

The progressive part method

In this method, parts are practised separately, then combined into slightly bigger elements for practice, which in turn can be combined into the whole movement or bigger parts for further practice and so on. This method is suitable for:

- Complex tasks or skills.
- Chaining of complex skills learned independently.
- Skills which have limited attentional demands.
- Skills which require coordination of spatial / temporal components.
- Skills which have a good **transfer** to the whole movement.

The whole-part-whole method

This method is a **combination** of whole and part methods having the advantage of flexible application to almost any task and situation depending on the stage of learning of the performer and the task difficulty. A learner would first practise the whole movement and identify difficult components, which would then be practised separately. These difficult components might be different for different people. When sufficiently fluent, the parts can then be re-combined into the whole for further practice.

Practice Conditions - variable practice

Variable practice (see figure 11.7) is a method in which practice **conditions are varied** to encourage the formation of **the patterns in the brain which enable a sportsperson to perform skills with fluency and competence**. Practice activities would include a number of different activities which could be performed in different ways. Conditions should be as **realistic** as possible in **as many situations** as possible, as near to the **competitive** or match situation as possible. The method is relevant to **open skills**.

figure 11.7 – practice conditions

Distributed practice

Distributed practice is a method in which training sessions include **rest intervals** which could involve mental practice. Sessions would be short and spread over time with recovery periods between. Good for the **beginner** and most **skill learning**, gives **time to recover** physically and mentally and is good for potentially **dangerous** situations.

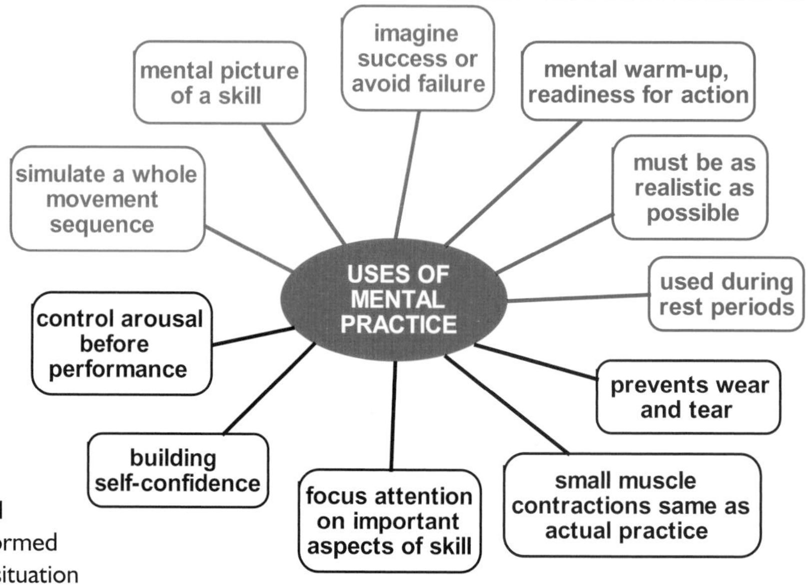

Massed practice

Massed practice is a method in which practice is done with **no rest intervals** with sessions **long in duration**. In this method, a single training session will last a relatively long time, and all the activities are performed one after the other. This method is good for 'grooving' of skills and to encourage an **habitual** response, is good for **discrete skills** of short duration, but can lead to **fatigue** and boredom and there may be elements of **negative transfer**.

figure 11.8 – mental practice

Overlearning

Overlearning involves a learned skill that is **habitual** because of many **repetitions. Such skills** are performed '**automatically**' in response to a game or sporting situation (stimulus). Hence **attention** can be directed **peripherally** to **other elements** of a game (for example, tactics or strategy).

Mental practice

Mental practice (figure 11.8) works by producing **small muscle contractions** in the same sequence as an actual practice, and since the gross movement of the skill does not actually happen, it **prevents** wear and tear.

Mental practice or rehearsal

- Creates a **mental picture** of a skill.
- Can be used to **simulate** a whole movement sequence or just part of it.
- Can be used to **imagine** and envisage success and avoid failure in a competitive situation.
- Can provide a mental warm-up in order to promote a state of **readiness** for action.
- Must be as **realistic** as possible to be effective.
- Can be used during **rest** and **recovery** periods **during** a performance or in between performances.
- Can be used to focus **attention** on important aspects of a skill.
- Builds **self-confidence** for an upcoming performance.
- **Controls arousal** and induce calmness before a performance.
- Can be used to enable the learner to **memorise** a skill or movement more effectively.

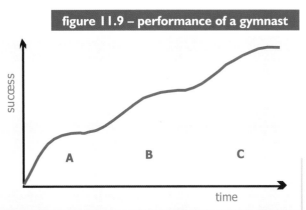

figure 11.9 – performance of a gymnast

Exam style questions

1) Figure 11.9 shows the improvement in performance of a gymnast over a period of time.

   a) Name the stages **A**, **B** and **C** shown on this chart and explain their significance to the gymnast. 6 marks

   b) Identify the characteristics of a performer in phase **C**. 4 marks

   c) How might the type of mental practice change in the last phase of learning? 4 marks

2) According to Fitts and Posner, learning passes through three stages. Use an example from one of your practical activities to describe the key characteristics of each of these stages. 5 marks

3) a) Explain how you would use operant conditioning to teach a sports skill of your choice. 5 marks

   b) Describe what is meant by reinforcement and give examples of different types. 4 marks

4) a) Using examples from sport explain what is meant by the S-R bond. 4 marks

   b) Explain how a coach in a sport could ensure that a correct response follows a particular stimulus. 5 marks

5) Stimulus-response bonding has been used to explain how a physical skill can be learned. What is a stimulus-response bond and how can a Physical Education teacher ensure that it is strengthened when teaching swimming or athletics? 6 marks

6) A coach reinforces good performances in training with praise. Why does this reinforcement work rather than punishing poor performance? Explain what is meant by reinforcement and punishment in this case. 5 marks

7) a) Explain the difference between massed and distributed practice. 2 marks

   b) Justify the choice of practice conditions for a training session of a sport of your choice. 6 marks

   c) Name two characteristics of the task, and two attributes of the learner which might lead you to decide which method (massed or distributed) of practice to use. 4 marks

8) Generally a skill should be taught as a whole as far as possible. Give reasons for this.
   Some skills need to be split up into parts to be taught effectively. What are the advantages and disadvantages of this type of skill presentation? 12 marks

9) A Level. Using Thorndike's laws, discuss how producing a satisfying effect in a particular situation becomes more likely to occur again in that situation, and responses that produce a discomforting effect become less likely to occur again in that situation. 15 marks

Answers link: http://www.jroscoe.co.uk/downloads/as_a1_revise_pe_edexcel/EdexcelAS_A1_ch11_answers.pdf

CHAPTER 12 - Guidance and feedback

3.5.1 Guidance methods

See figure 12.1 for a summary of methods of guidance.

Visual guidance

This method works mainly through **demonstration** (by **video** or poster, by human **live** model, or by demonstration of techniques by a **coach** or teacher). This demonstration should:

* **Be realistic**, **appropriate** and **not too complex**.
* Emphasise **relevant** aspects of a skill and be **repeated**.

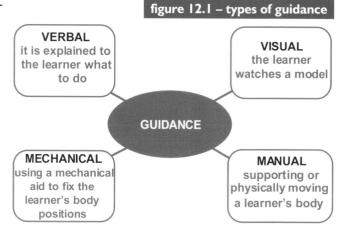

figure 12.1 – types of guidance

VERBAL
it is explained to the learner what to do

VISUAL
the learner watches a model

GUIDANCE

MECHANICAL
using a mechanical aid to fix the learner's body positions

MANUAL
supporting or physically moving a learner's body

Visual guidance is very important in the **cognitive** early stage of learning:
* The **learner** should be **attentive** and **retentive**, and should be **capable** of **matching** the demonstration (performer at the appropriate level of learning).
* The performer would learn by **watching** and **imitating** a **model** who should be of **high status** and technically correct.
* **The coach** should **reinforce** correct copying of skills.

Verbal guidance

This method is used often to **accompany visual** guidance and is used more with **competent** performers at a later stage (the autonomous stage) of learning. The amount of verbal guidance must be **controlled** and the **quality** of this guidance is important for effective coaching or teaching. Verbal guidance can be used for **conditioning** a response (giving reinforcement), which is useful for situations that require quick decisions. This type of guidance can create a mental image. Tactics can be explained, and technical information, key points and cues highlighted.

The **disadvantages** of the verbal method are that it can overload beginners with information, or the language used may be too complex for beginners. This could lead to learners **losing concentration**. Also, it is not as useful when used by itself, therefore should be combined with other forms of guidance to be effective.

Manual guidance

This method (figure 12.2) uses **physical support** (as in a coach supporting a gymnast during an asymmetric bar movement or performing somersaults), or **placing** limbs in correct positions (as for a novice thrower). This helps with **kinaesthetic** awareness, is useful for giving **confidence**, particularly for **beginners**, and is useful for **safety** reasons.

Mechanical guidance

This method uses a mechanical **aid**, for example:
* Stabilisers on a bike (see figure 12.3).
* Flotation devices for swimming.
* Belay ropes for climbers.
* Somersault rig for trampolinists.

This type of guidance gives **confidence** and ensures **safety**, gives some idea of **kinaesthetic** sense of movement, but must **not to be overdone** because this form of kinaesthesis is not the same as the real thing. The performer can become **over-reliant** on the mechanical device used.

figure 12.2 – manual guidance

figure 12.3 – mechanical guidance

3.5.2 Technologies to underpin guidance

This has been covered within Topic 2 on page 107 onwards above and so only the most relevant technologies that underpin guidance methods will be discussed here.

Verbal guidance technology

An MP3 player is an electronic device that can play digital audio files. Performers are able to listen to verbal guidance (from a peer or a coach) to reinforce technique or effort. The use of this technology is developing rapidly, due to an update facility of the audio file via a PC or Mac.

Visual guidance technology

Like other digital players, iPods and mobile phone apps can produce digital video displays, act as external data storage devices, and so can be used to transfer audio files, photos and videos that could provide visual guidance to both coach and performer at a later date (as opposed to in real time).

3.6.1, 3.6.2 Feedback

Feedback is a term which describes the way in which information is received by a performer about a performance either just completed, or sometimes during the performance itself.

Intrinsic feedback

This form of feedback takes place when the feeling of a movement tells a performer whether it was successful or not (see figure 12.4). Part of this is **kinaesthetic** and is provided by the **proprioception** within joints and muscles which tells a person of the muscle tension and joint angles during a movement. This is an **ability** which is usually a part of the person from birth, and is genetic and enduring. A person who has more effective kinaesthetic feedback about movements made by his or her body is more likely to be a successful sports performer.

Extrinsic feedback

Extrinsic feedback is from an external source to the performer that can affect performance, and either **motivate** or demotivate the performer depending on the quality of the feedback.

This has two forms in which the the first is **knowledge of performance**:
• Where information is obtained about a performance. For example, its **quality**, **rhythm** or **aesthetics** from a coach, video, or from the press or TV.

The second form is **knowledge of results** in which a performer has:
• Information about the **outcome** of a performance.
• Success or failure, or the distance, height or time performed.
• Information can be from a number of sources, the coach, video, or press and TV.

Feedback dependency

Feedback dependency occurs when some performers can become **dependent** on feedback:
• For example, from a coach or significant other about the quality of performance or technical competence.
• If this feedback is withdrawn or cannot be given then performance **can deteriorate**.
• This might occur in a field event athlete in a major games who cannot function without feedback from a coach about his or her technique, and who therefore will fail.

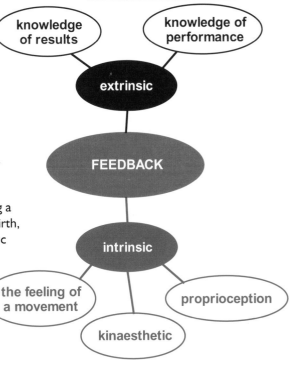

figure 12.4 – type of feedback

Terminal feedback

This occurs **after** a performance has finished which is important because it **strengthens the schema** in learning.

Concurrent feedback

Concurrent feedback occurs **during** a performance and has the aim of improving skills or techniques **while a performer is in action**.

Positive feedback

Positive feedback is feedback which gives information aimed at a **constructive** development of performance. It uses positive reinforcement, **praise** and **encouragement** about good performances, and the knowledge from poor performances which gives insight about **errors and their possible correction**. For example, a coach who praises a performer and encourages him or her to repeat the skills being praised will be giving positive feedback.

Negative feedback

This type of feedback is information which could **depress performance** and would consist of negative reinforcement or negative criticism about **poor** performances. For example, in this case, a coach who repeatedly feeds back information about faults, and gives little help about how to correct them would be giving negative feedback.

Feedback used in sport

Figure 12.5 summarises the types of feedback used in sport.

In the case of a squash player (figure 12.6), in open play the skill is an **open** one (movements are altered according to the position and direction and action of the other player, the stroke played, and the subsequent direction and speed of the ball). Feedback to the player occurs during the movement, and he alters his position, stance, movement pattern and stroke outcome in response. Part of this feedback is **kinaesthetic**, in that his position, speed and posture are sensed by the orientation of his limbs and tension in his musculature, and changes are then made according to the sensations and feelings from this – in response to the game situation.

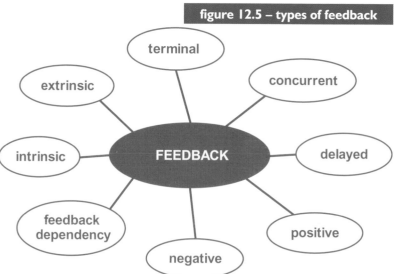

figure 12.5 – types of feedback

figure 12.6 – squash requires feedback

3.6.3 Use of technology in feedback

This has been covered within Topic 2 on page 107 above and so only the most relevant technologies that underpin feedback methods will be discussed here.

Video analysis

With the huge advantage of **playback**, **slow motion**, **split screens** and **freeze frame** features, this technology helps the coach and performer to analyse performance as part of **terminal** feedback. Incredible detail can be observed in a way that cannot be achieved by observing in real time. In addition there are numerous software applications that give both coach and performer the ability to extract data, draw and notate, and even calculate angles, such as the assessment of hip angles during a complex dive. Software such as Quintic and Dartfish (refer to page 109) offer all these applications, in addition to providing tools for biomechanical motion analysis that can compare individual and elite performances and be stored and used at any time.

However, video analysis is **expensive** and **time consuming**,

Within a global sports event, such as the Olympic Games, elite performers often have the benefit of **replays** on big screens to assess their performance during events such as a high jump competition or a 10,000 metre race.

Notational analysis systems

Otherwise known as tally chart feedback, this is achieved by using a statistical or graphical format that highlights categories of strengths and weaknesses for future consideration as part of a training programme. It provides in-depth analysis by merely **counting** (quantitative) the different observations, such as the number of unforced errors and total points won in a tennis match. This type of match analysis provides significant athlete or coach feedback in terms of technical, tactical, mental and physical aspects of the game. Hence this is crucial for the improvement for elite athletes such as professional tennis players. For example, which stroke - forehand or backhand - makes more unforced errors? Too many times, players are convinced that their forehand is a better shot, and a match analysis like this can show that their aggressive margin on the forehand shot is negative! Meaning, they make more mistakes with it than points. With this type of feedback, the coach is able to change the player's tactics.

figure 12.7 – a GPS outlay on google earth of a soccer training match

Global positioning systems

GPS analysis is used in a wide variety of sports from cycling to athletics and has been discussed already on page 108. GPS is used to provide feedback.

Also, heart rate monitors, such as the Garmin range (see page 108), provides concurrent and terminal feedback that can be used to optimise performance. For example, runners can check pace or rhythm **during** a performance. They would also be able to access their distance and speeds post performance (terminal feedback).

Other examples of GPS systems are GPsports and Hawkeye which analyse players' movements. In figure 12.7, the movement of a soccer player during a 2 hour training match, from which his average speed, total distance travelled and positional locations in relation to opposition players can be computed.

3.6.4 Open and closed loop control

Open loop control

Open loop control (see figure 12.8) applies to executive programmes whose subroutines are:
- **Simple** and **well-learned**.
- **Automatic** (no conscious thought is necessary).
- Particularly relevant to the **autonomous phase** of learning.
- They are then completed **rapidly** without time for feedback.
- Apply to **closed and self-paced** skills.
- Examples are the tennis serve and a discus throw.

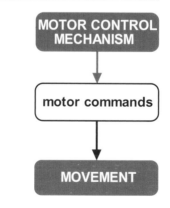

figure 12.8 – open loop control

Closed loop control

Closed loop control (see figure 12.9) applies to:
- **Ongoing movements** in which only **part** of the information necessary to complete a movement is sent to effector organs (neuromuscular system).
- The remaining information is sent following **feedback** via **kinaesthesis**.
- Information about balance and body position can be used to allow the performer to change balance and body position **during** a movement.
- Examples are riding a bike and performing a gymnastic move or a complex dive.

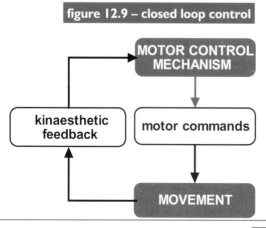

figure 12.9 – closed loop control

Exam style questions

1) a) Why is visual guidance particularly suitable for learning a new skill?   2 marks

    b) Why can verbal guidance be of limited use on its own?   2 marks

    c) What are the benefits of verbal guidance?   3 marks

    d) When are manual or mechanical guidance best used?   4 marks

2) Discuss briefly how technology can benefit guidance methods   6 marks

3) a) Other than visual guidance, what other main methods of guidance are there? Give a practical example for each.
                                                                                                    6 marks
    b) How would you optimise the use of visual guidance in teaching motor skills? What are the drawbacks of this method?
                                                                                                    4 marks

4) a) Identify two different mechanical items which might assist movement skill learning.   2 marks

    b) Give reasons for the use of these mechanical items to help a learner come to grips with a motor skill.   4 marks

5) a) Define the term feedback, and briefly describe three functions of feedback.   4 marks

    b) How would you make feedback effective when teaching a motor skill?   4 marks

6) Distinguish between intrinsic and extrinsic feedback.   2 marks

7) Using figure 12.6 on page 144, what feedback might a coach give to the player (in the black kit) who has just played a forehand drive and is attempting to read his opponent's next shot.   3 marks

8) Explain how feedback differs through the associative and autonomous stages of learning as a performer makes progress.
                                                                                                    4 marks

9) a) How is closed loop theory used to make a movement more skilful?   3 marks

    b) Explain the contribution of the use of subroutines to open loop control and the autonomous phase of learning.
                                                                                                    6 marks

10) Explain how feedback in a sports skill learning situation helps the sportsperson improve performance.   4 marks

11) Discuss the idea that improvement in skill performance is dependent upon the nature and frequency of feedback provided by the coach.   12 marks

12) A Level. Feedback is used by coaches to develop sports skills. Discuss how different types of feedback benefit from the use of technology.   15 marks

Answers link: http://www.jroscoe.co.uk/downloads/as_a1_revise_pe_edexcel/EdexcelAS_A1_ch12_answers.pdf

SPORT PSYCHOLOGY

CHAPTER 13 – Personality, attitudes, arousal and anxiety

4.1.1 Personality theories

Personality

Personality is the term which describes the **unique** characteristics of an individual which makes him or her act as they do. Knowledge about personality is important to ensure **optimum** sporting performance.

Figure 13.1 outlines the main ideas various theorists have used to explain and describe personality and its features.

figure 13.1 – features of personality

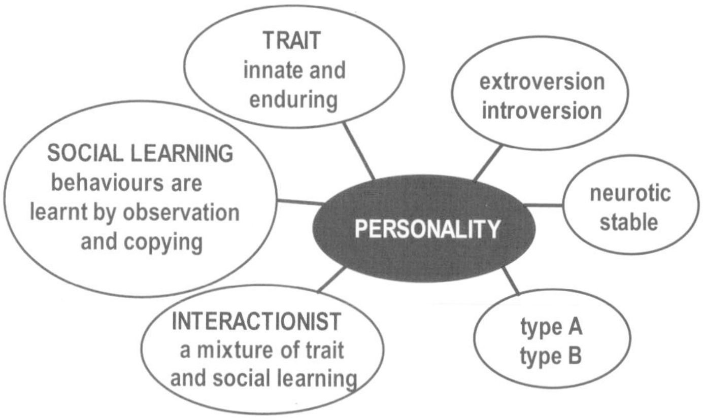

- TRAIT innate and enduring
- extroversion introversion
- SOCIAL LEARNING behaviours are learnt by observation and copying
- **PERSONALITY**
- neurotic stable
- INTERACTIONIST a mixture of trait and social learning
- type A type B

Trait theories

Trait theories use the idea that a person has always had a feature of his or her personality, and always will have. Such features will be **general** (covering all situations), **underlying** (inside of and part of the person), **enduring** (long lasting), and include **predispositions** (inclinations or motives formed earlier). Such predispositions will tell you how a person will behave when faced with certain situations. For example, the prospect of failure such as losing an important sporting match or competition.

Most trait theories use labels for features of behaviour, and you should remember that such labels (attached to a person) would be intended to last for ever. Some labels for aspects of personality are:
- **Extroversion** (including liveliness, sociability, impulsiveness, activity, excitability).
- **Introversion** (including isolation, independence, shyness, quiet).
- **Stability** (including unchanging behaviour patterns).
- **Neuroticism** (including the fact that behaviour may change unpredictably).

Eysenck identified a **two dimensional** view of personality as four primary types:
- A **stable extrovert** would be talkative, outgoing, easy going, carefree, and showing leader qualities.
- A **neurotic extrovert** would be restless, aggressive, excitable, and changeable.
- A **neurotic introvert** would be anxious, sober, rigid, or pessimistic.
- A **stable introvert** would be careful, thoughtful, controlled, reliable, and even-tempered.

At a later date Eysenck added a third scale of **psychoticism** as a measure of how tough-minded a person is, assessed in a test called Eysenck's personality questionnaire.

Which set of characteristics would enable you to predict who would become the next British Olympic champions (figure 13.2)?

Cattell is another trait theorist who identified a much larger number of personality traits which he measured in a questionnaire called Cattell's 16PF.

Social learning theories

Social learning theory explains behaviour in terms of the reaction to specific situations. The main point of social learning theory is that we learn to deal with situations by **observing others** or by observing the results of our own behaviour on others and by **modelling** our own behaviour on what we have seen. Athletes learn **behaviour** by watching others. This is in addition to the idea of being able to learn skills by watching then copying others (this is the social learning theory of skill development).

figure 13.2 – which features of Chris Hoy's personality have led to him becoming a multiple Olympic champion?

Bandura says that behaviour is determined by the situation. In other words there is social comparison, and a person will behave the same way as the peer group. Social approval or disapproval determines our responses since such behaviour is reinforced or penalised by **the peer group**.

Vicarious conditioning is the learning of emotional responses through observational learning. For example, learning to become angry after a valid referee decision has gone against him or her by watching other players do the same.

Interactionist theories

Interactionist theories (figure 13.3) are those which assert that a combination of trait and a person's situation or environment builds up a person's personality, and that traits determine behaviour but can be modified by situations. **Lewin** was the theorist who stated that behaviour is a function of both the person (personality P) and the environment (E), and put this in the mathematical form:

$$B = f(P,E)$$

Example of the interactionist theory approach

A young field event athlete shows promise, but worries about competing in important competitions and underperforms in these situations. Her coach works with her on anxiety management strategies and her next competition sees a personal best.

The innate (**trait**) factors of the athlete's personality cannot be changed by a coach, so the coach must therefore get her to view her **anxiety** (which could be a trait which emerges whenever undue stress is placed on her) in terms of the specific situation of the next competition. The anxiety could be channelled into positive images of her technical model, rejecting poor efforts as due to external factors (for example, the weather or the wind), and building on positive images of successful technical elements achieved. The athlete can then build success by focusing on factors other than her own anxiety.

This enables her to adjust her behaviour according to internal factors such as rhythm and fluency, and this strategy should enable the athlete to remove the stress from the situation and hence reduce anxiety - even if she competes poorly.

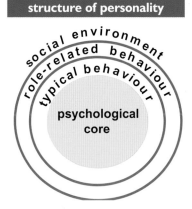

figure 13.3 – the interactionist model of personality

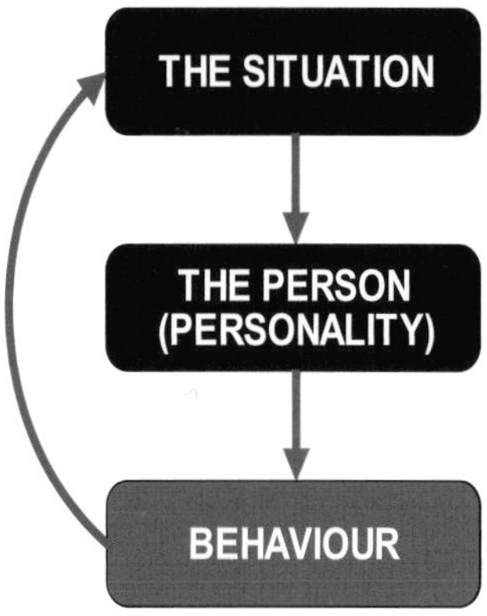

THE SITUATION

THE PERSON (PERSONALITY)

BEHAVIOUR

Types A and B personalities

Table 13.1 – **differences between personality types A and B**

type A characterised by:	type B characterised by:
impatience	relaxed and patient
works at a rapid pace	allows time for tasks to be completed
higher levels of stress	low personal stress
strong desire to succeed	less competitive
easily aroused and shows anxiety in stressful situations	calm and unflappable in most situations
lacking in tolerance	tolerance of others' mistakes
has a need to be in control	delegates easily
makes decisions quickly without much preparation or thought	prepared to wait and assess all options when decisions need to be made

Hollander's structure of personality

Figure 13.4 outlines the structure of personality as proposed by Hollander.

figure 13.4 – Hollander's structure of personality

In this model:
*   The **psychological core** (the inner core of beliefs) describes the beliefs and values that remain more or less permanent. For example, a sportsman's belief that fair play underlies his attitude on the field of play.
*   **Typical behaviour** describes the way in which an individual responds in certain situations, for example, to stop fighting at the bell during a boxing bout.
*   **Role-related behaviour** describes the fact that in other situations we may behave differently, for example, striking our opponents after the bell when annoyed or frustrated. This is the most changeable aspect of personality.
*   **Social environment** describes how the behaviour and expectations of others affect our role. For example, a player argues with the referee because others have done so and he or she has got away with it before.

social environment
role-related behaviour
typical behaviour
psychological core

Martens structure of personality

Martens produced a theory of personality which was again a mixture of traits (enduring fixed elements) and factors depending on behaviour and external influences.

External and dynamic factors are related to behaviour (role related) which depend on elements outside the core of the person involved. This would involve issues such as the person's position on the field of play, or his or her standing in the ranking list for the activity, for example.

The internal and consistent elements depend on the core traits of the individual such as his or her response to a game when under pressure, whether or not the person remains calm and will continue to strive to achieve a goal (winning) or will capitulate, hang his or her head and give up when faced with stress.

The typical responses will depend on the bahavioural element and the core features of the person's personality.

figure 13.5 – Martens' model of personality

EXTERNAL   **ROLE RELATED BEHAVIOUR** example : **good captain**   DYNAMIC

TYPICAL RESPONSES example : **'win at all costs'** - **instrumental aggression**

INTERNAL   **PSYCHOLOGICAL CORE :** attitudes, values, beliefs, motives example : **achievement motivation**   CONSISTENT

4.1.2 Attitudes

Attitudes are combinations of **beliefs** and **feelings** which lead us to think and behave **positively** or **negatively**.

Attitudes are combinations of beliefs and feelings about objects, people and situations (called attitude objects) which predispose us to behave in a certain way towards them. They are learned or organised through experience, and are evaluative (lead us to think and behave positively or negatively) about an attitude object. Sporting attitude objects would include lady bodybuilders as in figure 13.8 on page 151. Attitudes tend to be deep seated and enduring, but can change or be changed.

Components of attitude, Wood's triadic model

This model is outlined in figure 13.6, which lists the **cognitive**, **affective**, and **behavioural** components of attitude.

Influences on formation of attitudes

The major influences on the formation of attitudes are outlined in figure 13.7.

Additionally, **conditioning** (such as the use of rewards such as praise) will tend to strengthen attitudes, and **social learning** will have the same effect, in which people will learn by observing and imitating significant others.

Familiarity with an attitude object can change an attitude towards that object.

Prejudice

Prejudice is a prejudgement of a person, group, or situation, usually based on **inadequate** information, or inaccurate or biased information. This prejudice tends to reinforce **stereotypes**. For example, women are often excluded from male dominated sports clubs or events (historically golf, rugby and snooker clubs have been guilty of this).

figure 13.6 – Wood's triadic model of components of attitude

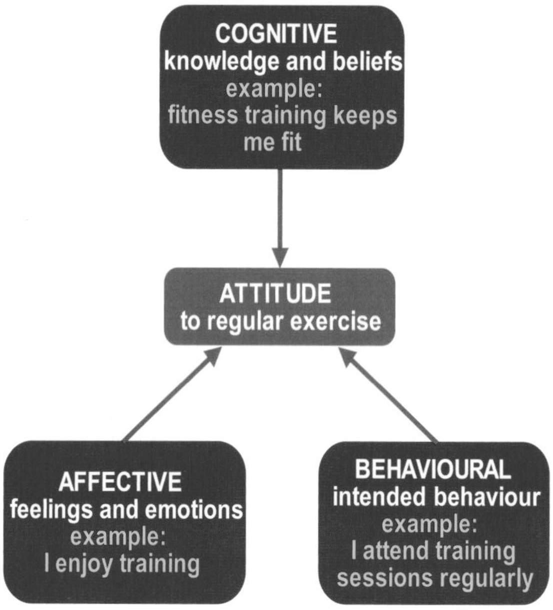

COGNITIVE knowledge and beliefs example: fitness training keeps me fit

ATTITUDE to regular exercise

AFFECTIVE feelings and emotions example: I enjoy training

BEHAVIOURAL intended behaviour example: I attend training sessions regularly

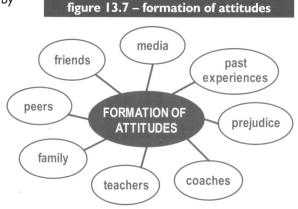

figure 13.7 – formation of attitudes

friends, media, peers, past experiences, family, **FORMATION OF ATTITUDES**, prejudice, teachers, coaches

Sport stereotypes

In the general population, people form attitudes which are negative stereotypes about certain groups participating in sport.

For example:
- Women in strength, endurance and contact sports, see figure 13.8.
- Participation of the disabled in physical activity.
- Older age groups' interest and ability at sport.
- Participation of particular ethnic groups in specific sports or positions within teams, for example:
    - The black quarterback in American football.
    - The white sprinter.
    - The black skier or swimmer.

figure 13.8 – participation in some sports has a negative stereotype with some members of the public

Changing attitudes

Sometimes, a coach or sport leader will want to change an attitude of a sports player or performer, particularly if this person displays aggression or negative feelings towards a colleague. There are two generally accepted ways of tackling this.

Attitude change by persuasive communication

In order for this method to be effective, the subject (the person whose attitude is hopefully to be changed) must pay attention, and must understand, accept and retain the message being given. The coach must be expert and be trustworthy, and the message must be clear, be unambiguous, be balanced between emotion and logic, and be balanced between pros and cons.

Attitude change by cognitive dissonance (theory due to Festinger)

Cognitive dissonance occurs when two completely different and contradictory facts affect the behaviour of a sportsperson. The most clear example of this is when a successful sports performer knows that to maintain his or her success, he or she must maximise the use of his or her lungs, and knows therefore that smoking is bad, yet continues to smoke because he or she likes the sensations produced.

In order to change the attitude of such a person (to smoking), he or she must be consistent between cognitive, affective, and behavioural components, and must realise that there is a conflict between the two behaviours (fitness and smoking). At this point, cognitive dissonance will occur and force the performer to change an attitude to smoking (or perhaps to participation in top level sport!).

4.1.3 Arousal and its effects on performance

Arousal is a state of **mental** and **physical preparedness** for action. This is the level of inner drives which forces the sportsperson to strive to achieve. It needs to be under control and at the right level depending on the task and is closely related to **anxiety**. The symptoms of arousal are:
- A faster **heart rate**.
- Faster **breathing rate**.
- **Sweating**.
- Ability to focus (**concentrate**).
- Response to danger (**fight or flight** adrenaline response).

The **reticular activating system** (RAS) is a system within the brain which causes arousal. Extroverts have lower levels of intrinsic arousal than introverts, hence extroverts seek situations of high arousal whereas introverts seek low arousal situations.

Theories linking arousal and performance

Hull's drive theory

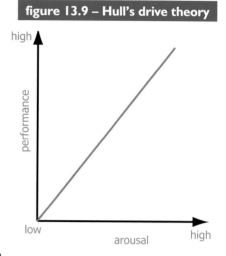

figure 13.9 – Hull's drive theory

This theory (see figure 13.9) describes the **simple** situation where the **higher** the **arousal** level, the **higher** the achievement or **performance** level.

This theory applies to gross skills like weight lifting and sprinting. The theory also states that the more arousal, the more likely that a **well-learned** skill (a **dominant response**) will be reproduced. This means that older more deep-seated skills will tend to be produced when a person is very aroused rather than newer less well-learnt skills practised more recently. The implication of this is that a highly aroused performer will need to focus very hard and direct his or her attention very strongly towards a **desired response**, particularly if this response includes recently learned elements. Otherwise the state of arousal will cause the person to regress to an older, less desirable but dominant response. This theory explains why in some sporting activities, a sportsperson who **tries too hard** (and who therefore is in a state of high arousal) fails to reproduce his or her best performance.

Inverted U theory

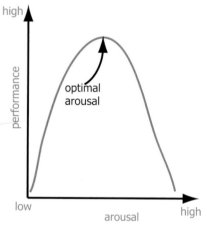

figure 13.10 – inverted U theory

In **inverted U theory** (figure 13.10) there is an **optimum arousal** level. As arousal increases, performance increases up to a certain point, if aroused more than this, the performance will **go down**.
Optimum arousal depends on:

- **Type of activity**, for example, **gross** skills (like weight lifting) require **high arousal**, whereas **fine** skills (like snooker) require **low arousal**.
- The **skill level of the performer**, the more skilful the performer the **higher** the optimum arousal level could be.
- The **personality of the performer**, in which the more **extrovert** the performer, the **higher** the arousal likely to have to be attained by the performer to produce **optimum** performance.

Zone of optimum functioning

Hanin worked out that the optimum level of arousal is not always at mid-point of the inverted U, and that best performance will vary between sportspeople. For example, some athletes will peak at low arousal, and other athletes will peak at medium or high arousal.

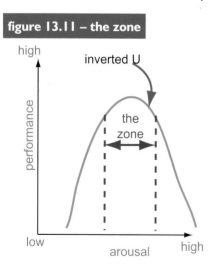

figure 13.11 – the zone

Also, an athlete's best performance will be in a **zone** (not just a point of optimum performance - figures 13.11 and 13.12), and different athletes will have **different zones of arousal** for optimum performances. This will depend on **personality**, **skill** or **task** and degree of **habit**.

Habit is defined as the strength and **permanence** of a correctly learned skill.

figure 13.12 – Usain Bolt in the zone?

Effects of arousal on technique

- The **point of optimum arousal** is of crucial importance to the learning and stability of a sportsperson's technique.
- Technique is the sequence of actions which enables a performer to successfully perform the skill of his or her event.
- Trying too hard (overarousal) can cause a performer to change his or her technique in an uncontrolled way - with a resultant loss of performance.
- This can be made worse by the anxiety which would accompany a major event - such as a major at tennis or an open at golf.

Anxiety affects arousal, and these theories can also apply to how anxiety affects performance.

4.1.4 Anxiety linked to arousal

Anxiety can be explained as an emotional state similar to fear, associated with:
- **Somatic (physiological)** arousal or anxiety - connected with raised heart rate, raised breathing rate, sweating and so on.
- **Cognitive (psychological)** arousal - worry and negative feelings about the situation, feelings of nervousness, feelings of **apprehension**.

Anxiety is closely linked to arousal, since an anxious person is more likely to become aroused than a calm person. Hence the various theories linking arousal with performance (drive, inverted U, catastrophe) can also apply to link anxiety with performance.

It can have **behavioural** consequences - in which a person will experience:
- Tension.
- Agitation.
- Restlessness.

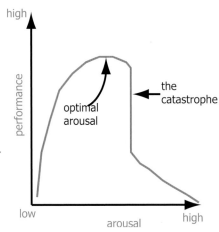
figure 13.13 – catastrophe theory

Trait anxiety - A-trait (Speilberger)

Trait anxiety is an inbuilt (**trait**) **part of the personality** which gives a person:
- A tendency to be **fearful** of unfamiliar situations.
- A tendency to perceive competitive situations as **threatening**.
- A tendency to respond to competitive situations with **apprehension** and **tension**.

State anxiety - A-state

State anxiety is an emotional response to a **particular situation**, characterised by feelings of nervousness and apprehension which is often **temporary** - as you might expect if the anxiety is related to a certain situation which of course will change as daily activities change.

Choking and over-arousal

High arousal can cause a performer to have negative thoughts. **Negative thoughts of failure** or lack of success can creep in if a performer is **over-aroused**. These thoughts can affect the performer's confidence and create an almost complete inability to perform skills properly. This is **choking** and is an aspect of inverted U theory.

Examples are:
- The snooker player who misses an easy shot when in the final frame of an important match.
- The golfer who misses the fairway from the tee when in the lead in a competition.
- This particularly applies to sports which use a fine skill.
- Choking can be controlled by **cognitive management techniques** (see page 155).

Catastrophe theory

Catastrophe theory (see figure 13.13) is a variation of inverted U theory in which performance **increases** as arousal **increases**, but if **arousal** gets **too high** a **complete** loss of performance occurs (the catastrophe). The performance line on the graph plummets rapidly towards disaster. This almost always happens when the performer tries too hard!

For example, the golfer who tries too hard and completely misses the fairway from his drive at the 18th hole when in a winning position, or the gymnast who completely messes up her previously well-executed routine in a national final.

STUDENT NOTE

There are three methods of measuring anxiety, namely by **observation**, by **questionnaire** and using **physiological** measures. The observation and questionnaire methods are not included in your current syllabus.

figure 13.14 – stress and stressors

Stress

Stress and **anxiety** are closely linked, with stress being a major cause of health issues in our society. Figure 13.14 outlines the main factors associated with stress and stressors.

Stress is a response of the body to any demands made on it. The symptoms of stress (figure 13.14) are **physiological**, **psychological** or **behavioural** (see table 13.2 on page 155 for details).

Stressors

Stressors are the cause of stress and are:

*   **Social** including the disapproval of parents or peers, the rejection by peers or parents, or isolation from normal social interactions.
*   **Chemical** or **biochemical** in which harm is inflicted by ingestion of nasty substances.
*   **Bacterial**, which would be an illness caused by micro-organisms.
*   **Physical** in which a person would suffer injury, pain or exhaustion.
*   **Climatic** in which extremes of weather are experienced, such as hot weather for endurance activities, or rain and cold on bare skin.
*   **Psychological**, in which there is a mismatch between the perception of the demands of a task and the ability of a person to cope with these demands.

Physiological measurements of stress

Physiological measuring equipment are heart rate monitoring devices and skin conductivity devices (these devices measure sweating). The **disadvantages** are that the use of, and results produced by such devices, are affected by the exercise intensity being undertaken (as opposed to the anxiety or stress of the performer). Also, since the performer has to be 'wired up' (figure 13.15) to make the measurements, there may be difficulties associated with the equipment being used in certain games or situations (in contact sports for example).

Physiological measures have the following major **advantages**.
*   They can be made during, before or after the event, and are directly related to performance.
*   Also they can be systematically and scientifically recorded (either by charting, or by numerical data).
*   This would enable a person to quantify accurately the measures being made.
*   Most of these measures can be used to assess **stress** or **anxiety**.

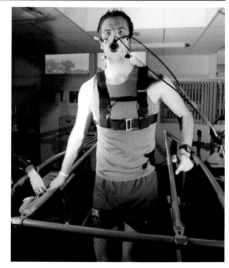

figure 13.15 – measuring anxiety?

Questions

1) What is meant by the term stress?

2) Explain two psychological symptoms of stress.

3) Identify three main stressors in the context of sport.

Symptoms of stress

Table 13.2 – **symptoms of stress**

physiological symptoms	psychological symptoms	behavioural symptoms
increased heart rate	worry	rapid talking
increased blood pressure	feeling overwhelmed	nail biting
increased sweating	inability to make decisions	pacing
increased breathing rate	inability to concentrate	scowling
decreased flow of blood to the skin	inability to direct attention appropriately	yawning
increased oxygen uptake	narrowing of attention	trembling
dry mouth	feeling out of control	raised voice pitch
		frequent urination

Control of stress and anxiety

Stress and anxiety management techniques become important for sports performers when performances fall, or failure is experienced.

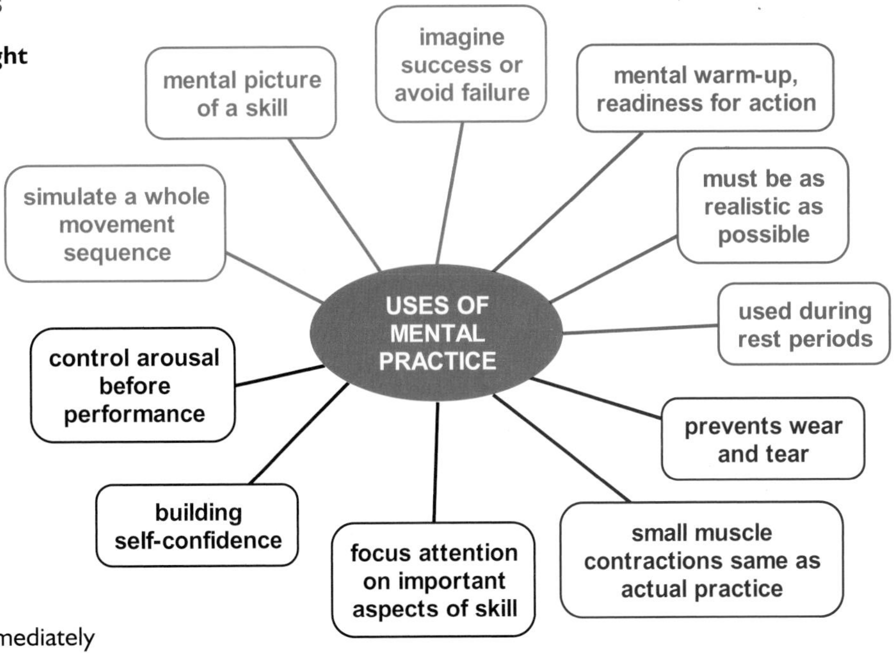

Cognitive relaxation techniques

These techniques use the power of **thought** to redirect attention away from failure or perceived failure. A performer will take **control** of emotions and thought processes, will **eliminate negative feelings**, and will develop **self-confidence**.

figure 13.16 – mental practice or rehearsal

- **Imagery relaxation**, in which a performer will think of a place with associations of warmth and relaxation, then imagine the activity or technique. This process involves practice in non-stressful situations, and will be used prior to competition.

- **Thought stopping**, in which when negative thoughts or worry (about failure) begin, a performer should immediately think 'stop', and substitute a **positive thought**.

- **Mental rehearsal** or practice (**visualisation**), in which the mental or cognitive rehearsal of a skill without actual physical movement is undertaken by a performer. The performer will consciously imagine a performance or rerun a past experience, and will continue with a preview of hoped-for success. This process helps concentration, and helps the performer to focus on strengths and weaknesses. This technique is used by most top level sportsmen, and is often prompted by video or talk from a coach. The point of this in stress or anxiety control is that it brings an activity away from the actual performance, and therefore away from any anxieties associated with the performance itself. Figure 13.16 outlines the main features of this process.

- **Pre-game routines** are a set of drills or practices which simulate the competitive situation. The performer will physically perform certain pre-practised routines in the aim of initiating a rhythmic, automatic and relaxed response in which he or she will enter the zone of optimal arousal for the tasks ahead.

Concentration

Concentration is a state of mind in which attention is directed towards a specific aim or activity. Concentration and **attentional focus** (**control of attention** towards a task) are essential components of a sportsperson's armoury of mental techniques to assist performance (figure 13.17).

Attentional narrowing (concentration) occurs when some parts of a performance become automatic. The information relevant to those parts then does not require attention, which gives the performer spare attentional capacity. This **spare capacity** will allow the performer to attend to **new elements** of a skill such as tactics or anticipating the moves of an opponent.

figure 13.17 – concentration is important

The **coach** will need to help the performer to make best use of spare attentional capacity, and direct the attention of the performer to enable him or her to concentrate. This would reduce the chance of **attentional switching** to irrelevant information or distractions.

Use of cognitive techniques to assist concentration

Cognitive techniques such as **imagery** and **mental rehearsal** or relaxation can be used to direct the sportsperson's mind towards a specific task as above. These techniques can be used to **manage the stress** of the situation, or to manage anxiety in a productive way.

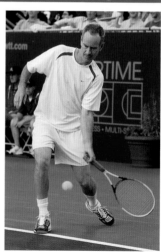

figure 13.18 – John McEnroe used centring

Cognitive relaxation techniques

*   **Self-talk** is a procedure where a person will talk through the process of a competitive situation, talking positively and building self-confidence.

Somatic relaxation techniques

Somatic relaxation techniques control the physiological symptoms of stress and anxiety.

*   **Progressive muscle relaxation**, sometimes called **self-directed muscle relaxation training**, enables a performer to focus on each of the major muscle groups in turn, then to allow breathing to become slow and easy. The athlete will visualise the tension flowing out of a muscle group until it is completely relaxed. Eventually a sportsperson will be able to combine muscle groups, and achieve total relaxation quickly.

*   **Centring** involves the control of physiological symptoms of stress by focusing on control of the diaphragm and deep breathing. The famous John McEnroe (famous for throwing tantrums on court 'you can't be serious', then going on to win Wimbledon titles, figure 13.18), used centring to bring himself down from a major row with a court official to playing the perfect serve or shot - within 10 seconds!

*   **Biofeedback** is the process of monitoring skin temperature (cold if stressed, warm if unstressed), and the galvanic skin response in which the electrical conductivity of skin increases when moist (tense muscle causes sweating). A further measurement is made by electromyography, in which electrodes are taped to specific muscles which can detect electrical activity and hence tension in muscle. The point is that these measures are perceived by the sportsperson during a performance, and he or she can then alter his or her behaviour to reduce the symptoms of stress or anxiety.

Exam style questions

1) a)   What do we mean by the term personality? Why is it important for sports psychologists to know about personality?

3 marks

    b)   Eysenck identified two dimensions of personality as in figure 13.19 on page 157. Describe the trait approach to personality. What do the traits extroversion and stability mean?

4 marks

Exam style questions

figure 13.19 – dimensions of personality

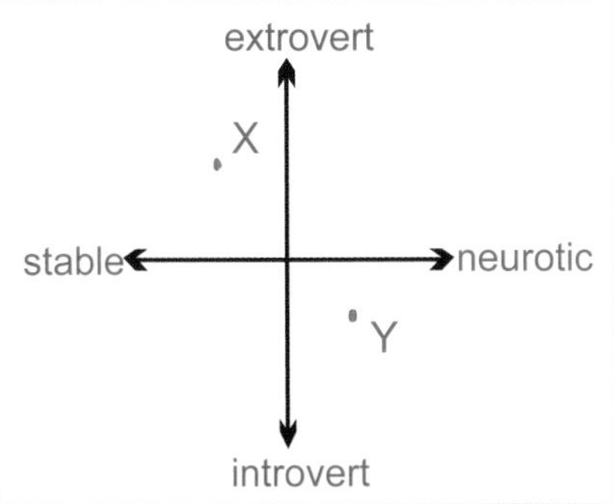

2) a)   From figure 13.19 describe the characteristics of players **X** and **Y**.   4 marks

   b)   By using an example from sport, outline the social learning approach to personality.   3 marks

   c)   What do we mean by the interactionist approach?   2 marks

3) Hollander (1971) viewed personality as a structure with layers of influence. Using examples from sport, explain Hollander's structure of personality.   8 marks

4) List six ways in which a coach might use personality theory to help an athlete during training or competition.   6 marks

5) Discuss theories that are used to explain personality, and apply them to sporting situations.   12 marks

6) a)   What do we mean by the term attitude?   1 mark

   b)   We often refer to someone as having a positive attitude in sport. Using Wood's triadic model describe the characteristics of a positive attitude.   3 marks

   c)   What factors influence our attitudes?   4 marks

7) a)   If you wished to change a young person's negative attitude to sport into a positive one, what strategies would you employ? Use psychological theory to back up your answer.   4 marks

   b)   What do we mean by the term prejudice and how does it manifest itself in sport?   4 marks

8) The catastrophe theory is used to explain a golfer's disastrous failure to win a match having been 3 strokes in the lead coming up to the last green. Explain this situation and why this theory might be useful in preventing a repetition.   4 marks

9) A number of PE students are attending trials at their chosen sport. Describe the Inverted U theory and explain how it might affect a student's performance at the trials.   5 marks

10) a)   What is the difference between state and trait anxiety?   2 marks

    b)   What coping strategies should the anxious performer draw upon?   5 marks

11) a)   Discuss the possible relationships between anxiety and performance in sporting activities.   7 marks

    b)   High levels of arousal have often been linked with stress. Sketch a graph showing the relationship between the performance of a complex skill and level of arousal.   2 marks

    c)   Add a second curve to your graph showing how performance of a simple skill might be affected by arousal.   2 marks

12) With reference to sporting performance, explain how cognitive and somatic anxiety differ.   5 marks

13) A Level. Discuss the role of techniques in the control of stress and anxiety for sports performers.   15 marks

14) A Level. Discuss Hull's drive theory and the inverted U hypothesis as explanations of the anxiety-performance relationship.   15 marks

15) Under-arousal can lead to poor performance. Discuss methods an athlete could use to increase his or her level of arousal to optimal levels.   12 marks

Answers link: http://www.jroscoe.co.uk/downloads/as_a1_revise_pe_edexcel/EdexcelAS_A1_ch13_answers.pdf

CHAPTER 14 - Aggression, motivation and social facilitation

4.1.5 Aggression v. assertion

- **Aggression** (figure 14.1) involves arousal and anger and intention to harm outside the rules.

- **Assertion** has no intent to harm and uses legitimate force within the rules, displays unusual effort, and may carry unusual energy. This is sometimes called **channelled aggression** (figure 14.2).

- **Hostile aggression** has the intent to harm. The goal is to harm with arousal and anger involved.

- **Instrumental aggression** has the intent to harm with the goal to win. This is used as a tactic and is commonly named '**dirty play**'. There is no anger involved and is illegal in all sports except boxing and other martial arts sports.

figure 14.1 – aggression - the details

- intention to harm another participant, player, spectator or umpire
- verbal aggression if intended to embarrass or hurt
- outside the rules of the sport
- **AGGRESSION**
- not including accidentally injuring or harming
- not including eyeballing or intentionally damaging equipment

Theories of aggression

- **Instinct theory** (due to Lorentz, figure 14.3) suggests that aggression is innate and instinctive - caused by a 'survival of the species' response to situations as they arise. In this theory, sport releases built-up aggression, and the aggressive response is cathartic - it gets the aggression out of the system, and purges the person of aggressive intent.

- **Frustration aggression theory** (due to Dollard) states that aggression is caused by frustration as the sportsperson is being blocked in the achievement of a goal. This causes a drive towards the source of frustration.

- **Social learning theory** (due to Bandura) suggests that aggression is learned by observation of others' behaviour. Then imitation of this aggressive behaviour is reinforced by social acceptance of the behaviour.

- **Aggressive cue hypothesis** (due to Berkowitz) states that frustration causes anger and arousal which creates a readiness for aggression. The aggression itself can be initiated by an incident during the performance or game (the cue), so that the aggression is a learned response. For example, a player sees a colleague fouled then decides to join in.

figure 14.2 – aggression or assertion?

figure 14.3 – theories of aggression

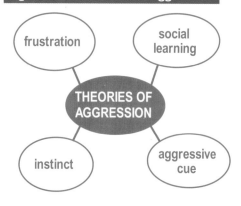

- frustration
- social learning
- **THEORIES OF AGGRESSION**
- instinct
- aggressive cue

Deindividuation

The theory of deindividuation concerns the fact that people sometimes behave differently when by themselves, as compared with behaviour in a football crowd. The contrast between the behaviour of people with worthwhile jobs, in the workplace as compared with the terraces, has often been observed.

Responsibility for aggression

Responsibility for aggression lies within the factors listed in figure 14.4. Influential others can exert a moderating influence on the performer, but the performer must accept that aggression is the wrong thing to do, and modify behaviour accordingly. **Reinforcement** of good behaviour will be important to ensure behavioural change.

Causes of aggression

- **Physiological arousal** in which anger towards another person causes an increase in arousal. This is because the sportsperson is highly motivated.

- **Underdeveloped moral reasoning** in which players with low levels of moral reasoning are more likely to be aggressive.

- **Bracketed morality** in which there is a double standard of condoning aggressive behaviour in sport, but not in life in general. This way of dealing with aggressive behaviour may retard a player's moral development.

Other causes of aggression

- High environmental temperature.
- Home or away - reaction to a hostile crowd.
- Embarrassment.
- Losing - excessive pressure to win.
- Physical pain.
- Unfair officiating.
- Playing below capability.
- Large score difference - frustration at poor performance.
- Low league standing - low self-esteem.
- Later stage of play (near the end of a game) - fatigue and niggles.
- Reputation of opposition (get your retaliation in first).
- Copying the behaviour of others.

Strategies to reduce aggressive behaviour

Governing Bodies

Governing Bodies are responsible for **player codes of conduct** which should involve coaches, players and officials. They will:
- Use strong officials where appropriate.
- Alter rules of games and implement punishment (remove league points, use sin bins and so on).
- Reward non-aggressive acts (for example, the FIFA fair play award).
- Encourage suitable use of language.
- Attempt to reduce media sensationalism in connection with aggression on or off the field of play.

A coach education programme is essential to reduce and control aggressive behaviour among players.

Coaches and players

- Coaches and players (figure 14.5) should promote ethical and sporting behaviour.
- They should control aggressive behaviour using stress management strategies and **relaxation techniques** among players.
- Coaches should initiate **self-control** strategies, and attempt to reduce levels of arousal in players.

- Both coaches and players should maintain a **healthy will-to-win** without winning being everything, and set **performance goals** rather than outcome goals.

- Coaches should **remove players** from the field if it is determined that he or she is at risk of aggression.
- Their tactic would be to enable **channelling of aggression** towards a performance goal, and to use **peer pressure** to 'avoid letting the side down'.

figure 14.4 – responsibility for aggression

figure 14.5 – controlling aggression?

4.1.6 Motivation

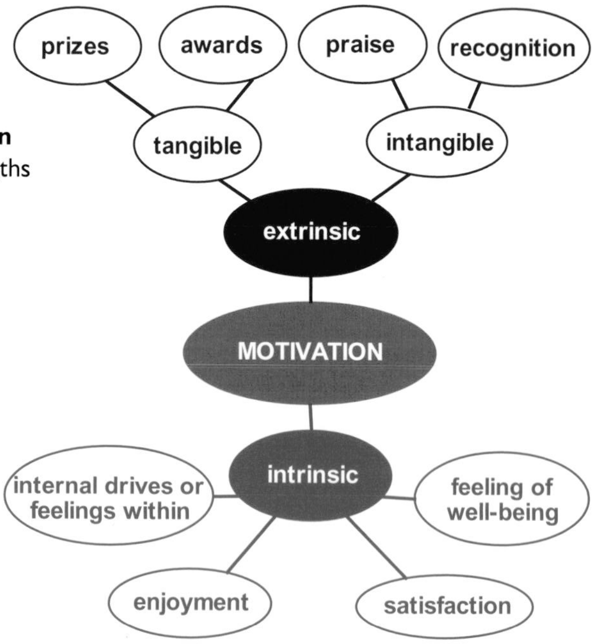

A **motive** is seen as a cause of behaviour which **energises**, **directs** and **sustains** the behaviour. It can be explained as a **drive** to **strive** to meet the needs of the situation in which a person finds him or herself. The strength of such a drive (or motive) depends on the **person** and the **situation**. Different people will have different types and strengths of motives (drives) to meet the needs of the situation. In a sporting context, the term **motivation** implies the driving and striving to **succeed**, to **win**, to **improve performance**, and to **pursue goals** (having set them in the first place).

Intrinsic motivation

Intrinsic motivation (figure 14.6) is the term which describes the **internal** drives or feelings that make us do things.

These feelings come from **within** the performer and involve **enjoyment** of the performance, **satisfaction** of performing, **pride** and the feeling of **well-being** from a job well done.

Extrinsic motivation

Extrinsic motivation (figure 14.6) describes the feelings coming from rewards **externally** derived (from outside the performer).

These rewards could be **tangible** such as prizes, money, or awards. For example, a gymnastics badge, or wanting to win at basketball because a trophy may be won, or an Olympic medal. Or rewards could be **intangible**, such as approval, praise or recognition from others. For example, attaining a World record initiates praise by the media, initiates national recognition, and reinforces the glory of the situation. Raising social status is a further intangible reward which would reinforce extrinsic motivation.

Arousal

Arousal is a term which describes the level of **inner drives** and which forces the sportsperson to **strive to achieve**. It needs to be **under control** and at the **right level** depending on the task. This striving is linked with the concept of motivation.

Drive reduction theory

This theory (see figure 14.7) explains why it is sometimes necessary to **vary or renew** the need to learn to stimulate motivation.

The theory says that the **need to learn** to solve a problem, to learn a skill, or to achieve mastery inspires **motivation**, the **drive** to succeed at the task. This leads to the performer **achieving** the desired outcome (action) which in turn leads to a **reduction in drive** (motivation) to achieve the **same outcome** (since it has already been achieved). This is known as **inhibition**.

The theory explains why people give up sport when it becomes routine, and why changes in for example training venue, training partner, coach or manager, can renew motivation to succeed and continue with a high level of commitment of time and effort.

Motivational strategies

These ideas should aim at avoiding or **reducing drive reduction** (reduce **inhibition** of motivation) by changing the **importance** of a task (raise its **status**), or **matching** the task to the performer's needs ('you need to do this to be able to progress towards the Olympic Gold').

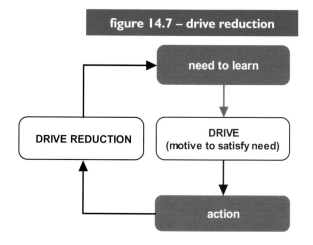

figure 14.6 – motivation

figure 14.7 – drive reduction

Developing and enhancing motivation

Motivation is a combination of personal characteristics and situational aspects.

Motivation is **highest** when:
* The performer is keen to **participate**.
* The performer is keen to **learn**.
* The performer is keen to **perform**.
* The performer is keen to **perform effectively**.
* The motivational **climate** is right.
* The training programme is **interesting** and **varied**.

Enhancing motivation

Motivation is **reduced** by:
* **Routine**.
* **Competition between motives**.

People:
* Have **multiple** motives.
* **Share** motives.
* Have **unique** motivational profiles.
* Need **variation** in **training** and competition.
* Need **variation** in **intensity** and competitiveness.
* Need **structured coaching** and teaching environments.

Motives change over time, and teachers and coaches are important motivators.

Achievement motivation theory (Atkinson and McLelland)

Achievement motivation is the drive to achieve success for its own sake, and is related to competitiveness, persistence, and striving for perfection.

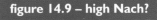

figure 14.8 – personality aspects of achievement motivation

high Nach (Ts)

A

low Naf (Taf)   high Naf (Taf)

B

low Nach (Ts)

Achievement motivation is influenced by:
* **Personality** factors, which are:
  * The need to achieve (Nach).
  * The need to avoid failure (Naf).
* **Situational** factors, which are:
  * Probability of success.
  * Incentive value of success.

Personality components of achievement motivation

* **The need to achieve (Nach) or tendency to approach success (Ts)** personality type likes a challenge, likes feedback, is not afraid of failure and has high task persistence.
* **The need to avoid failure (Naf) or tendency to avoid failure (Taf)** personality type avoids challenges, does not take risks, often gives up, and does not want feedback.

figure 14.9 – high Nach?

The chart in figure 14.8 shows Nach against Naf. Most people participating in sport will occupy a small region of the chart, for example regions **A** and **B** as shown on the chart.

A = someone with a high need to achieve who will probably have a low need to avoid failure. Such a person will choose difficult or demanding tasks which are more risky, for example, the hard route up a rock face (figure 14.9).

B = someone with a high need to avoid failure who will probably have a low need to achieve, and who will choose tasks which are less risky and more easily achieved. For example, this person will take the easy route up the rock face.

Situational factors affecting achievement motivation

The chart in figure 14.10 shows probability of success against incentive value of success, and again most people will occupy a small region (examples here are marked **C** and **D**).

C = region of the chart where a task's **probability of success** is **low** (for example, competing against the World champion), and therefore the sportsperson has to strive very hard to win. The **incentive** to **achieve success** is **very high**, and the sportsperson will be highly chuffed if he or she wins.

D = region of the chart where **probability of success** is **high** (for example, competing in local club match), and the sportsperson therefore doesn't need to try as hard to win. Hence the **incentive to achieve** is **low**, because the person expects to win easily, and of course this is not so pleasing to the performer.

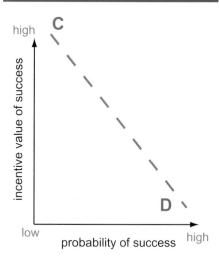

figure 14.10 – situational factors in achievement motivation

What should the coach do?

The prime need for a coach is to improve need and motive to achieve (Nach) in a sportsperson. This is the positive way to deal with motivational issues, and there are strategies he or she could use to **promote Nach**:
- Increase **positive reinforcement** hence increasing pride and satisfaction.
- Ensure that goals are **achievable**.
- Ensure that at least some situations **guarantee success**.
- And subsequently gradually **increase task difficulty** in line with progress.
- Ensure that tasks are **challenging**.
- Ensure that the **probability of success is good**.
- Ensure that the **incentive value of the success is high** (is the race worth winning?).

The coach should also **reduce tendency and motive to avoid failure** (Naf), and this can be done by:
- **Reducing punishment** hence lowering the chance of performer worrying about failure.
- **Focusing negative feedback** on effort rather than ability.
- This avoids the performer tending to believe that causes of failure are internal (due to lack of ability for example).
- And reduces the risk of learned helplessness.
- **Avoiding** situations where defeat or **failure is inevitable** (such as performing against a much superior opponent).
- If this is not possible **alter the criteria for success** (you will have succeeded if you only lose by 2 goals).

Summary of how goal setting can enhance motivation

- A performer will set goals as part of the motivation process, and will therefore be inclined to **pursue these goals.**
- Ensure that goals are **achievable**.

4.1.7 Social facilitation and inhibition

Social facilitation concerns how people other than the performer can influence his or her attitudes and behaviour.

The effect that the presence of spectators has on the way sportspeople play or perform can be positive (called **facilitation**), or negative (called **inhibition**). For example, a crowd (figure 14.11) encourages a team playing well (positive or facilitation), or the crowd jeers at a team not playing well (negative or inhibition).

figure 14.11 – effects of audience?

Facilitation

Facilitation of a performance by an audience tends to lead to the fact that high arousal leads to improved performance by a highly skilled or extrovert performer. Gross or simple skills tend to be improved by audience effects. See the link between arousal and performance in drive theory (see page 152 figure 13.9).

Inhibition

Where the presence of an audience **inhibits performance**, high arousal tends to lead to reduced performance by novices whose skills are not well-learned. This also applies to introvert performers. Fine and complex skills requiring great concentration will also tend to have performance levels reduced by negative audience effects.

Different types of audience

Passive others (social facilitation) are audience and co-actors, and **interactive others** are competitors.

figure 14.12 – ball-boys as co-actors

Co-actors

Co-actors are a passive form of audience involved in the same activity and at the same time as the performer, but not competing directly. For example:
* Officials, umpires or referees.
* Members of a player's own team.
* Ball-boys (figure 14.12) or helpers during a performance.

Factors affecting performance

* **Size of audience** - larger crowds create more arousal.

* **Proximity of audience** - the closer the audience the greater the arousal.

* **Intentions of the audience** - can be positive or negative. If spectators are negative about a player (shouting or jeering) this may suppress arousal or increase arousal depending on the personality of the performer.

figure 14.13 – fine skills or gross skills

* **Skill level** or **difficulty** of the task - performance improves for a well-learned skill and decreases if the skill is not well-learned.
* **Personality** of the performer - extroverts perform better when aroused, but introverts can be over-aroused.
* **Type of task** (figure 14.13) - fine skills need lower levels of arousal whereas gross skills could be improved by increased arousal.

Zajonc's model

Zajonc's theory says that the mere **presence of others** creates **arousal**, which then affects performance negatively if a skill is poorly-learnt (early in the learning curve - figure 14.14).

In this case, arousal causes an incorrect response because the incorrect response is dominant.

On the other hand, if a skill is **well-learnt** (later in the learning curve), then **arousal** causes a **correct response** because the correct response is dominant.

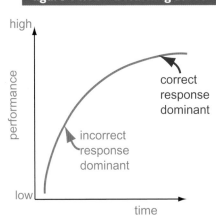

figure 14.14 – a learning curve

Evaluation apprehension

This theory (due to Cottrell - figure 14.15) explains that an **audience is perceived as evaluating** (assessing the value or worth of) performance. This **causes anxiety** - which in turn causes arousal.

STUDENT NOTE

Look at inverted U theory (figure 13.9 page 152) for the connection between arousal and performance.

The distraction effect

Baron's distraction-conflict theory says that **distraction** is an aspect of concentration (or **lack of concentration**). Attentional focus is very important for the effective sportsperson and if this is disrupted then he or she is distracted from his or her task. Audience and evaluation apprehension can act as a distraction. The sportsperson needs therefore to practise in distracting circumstances, and practise switching attentional focus when faced with potentially distracting circumstances.

figure 14.16 – World Cup 1966 - Wembley, 97,000 spectators, homefield advantage?

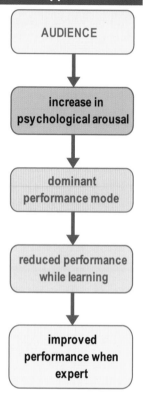

figure 14.15 – the process of evaluation apprehension

AUDIENCE

↓

increase in psychological arousal

↓

dominant performance mode

↓

reduced performance while learning

↓

improved performance when expert

Homefield advantage

Home or away effect on performance concerns the fact that more teams win at home than away.

A crowd may be judged as supportive or hostile (facilitation or inhibition), and high levels of anxiety caused by hostility may reduce performance.

The environment of their own stadium or playing situation is familiar to home teams, therefore home players are more comfortable. This limits anxiety and enables a worry-free and hopefully successful performance (figure 14.16).

Strategies for coping with social inhibition

Strategies include:
*   Stress management (see page 156).
*   Mental rehearsal (see page 155).
*   Selective attention (away from evaluators).
*   Lowering the importance of the situation.
*   Training with an audience present (see page 163).

Exam style questions

1) a)   What do we mean by the term aggression in sports psychology? Give an example from a sport or game which would illustrate your answer.   2 marks

   b)   Using examples from sport, briefly describe the differences between aggression and assertion?   2 marks

   c)   Some team players display unwanted aggression. What are the possible causes of such aggression?   4 marks

2) Explain in more detail what is meant by social learning when applied to aggression.
   How can aggressive tendencies be eliminated in a sports situation?   12 marks

3) a)   The aggressive cue hypothesis (Berkowitz 1969), is a theory which explains why aggression may be experienced by sports performers. Using an example from sport, describe the aggressive cue hypothesis.   4 marks

   b)   Using examples from sport, explain the frustration aggression hypothesis.   4 marks

4) A Level. Discuss how theories of aggression can be applied to sport.   15 marks

Exam style questions

5) Using examples from sporting situations, explain what is meant by instrumental and hostile aggression, and assertive behaviour. **9 marks**

6) a) What do you understand by the term motivation? **2 marks**

 b) Explain the difference between intrinsic and extrinsic motivation, giving sporting examples to illustrate you answer. **4 marks**

 c) How could a coach use the different types of motivation with a group of beginners? **2 marks**

7) a) Describe the characteristics of the positive motive: 'the need to achieve'. **4 marks**

 b) Describe an example from sport of someone who has a high motive to avoid failure. **3 marks**

 c) Identify factors which could affect the use of motives to achieve and to avoid failure in sporting situations. **3 marks**

8) How would you promote the need to achieve motive, rather than the need to avoid failure motive? **8 marks**

9) Using figure 14.7 on page 160, explain drive reduction theory. **4 marks**

10) Situational factors affect achievement motivation.
 a) Sketch a graph showing the relationship between incentive value of success and probability of success. **3 marks**

 b) How can this relationship affect sporting performance? **2 marks**

11) A Level. Explain Atkinson and McCelland's theory of achievement motivation and describe the personal and situational factors that interact to determine achievement behaviour. How can a coach use this theory to motivate his or her athletes? **15 marks**

12) a) What is meant by social facilitation and what is its main effect? **3 marks**

 b) What effects can be experienced by an individual if there is an audience present? **5 marks**

13) a) Using figure 14.15 on page 164 and examples from sport, explain what is meant by evaluation apprehension. **5 marks**

 b) Briefly outline the causes of evaluation apprehension. **2 marks**

 c) As a coach of an individual who is affected adversely by the presence of an audience, how would you help him or her to overcome negative influences? **4 marks**

14) Two groups of male sportspeople (of the same age) undertook an arms-length weight hold endurance test. Success at this exercise was measured by the length of time the weight was held. The table below shows the average times for group 1 (who did the exercise alone) and group 2 (who did the exercise in the presence of an audience).

	group 1 no audience	group 2 with audience
average time held in seconds	46.5	50.5

 a) What effect (if any) did the audience have on the performance of the exercise? **1 mark**

 b) How would you account for this effect (or lack of effect)? **4 marks**

 c) The audience in this exercise (for group 2) was not known to the participants. Explain any effect you think there would be if the audience was known to the group. **6 marks**

Answers link: http://www.jroscoe.co.uk/downloads/as_a1_revise_pe_edexcel/EdexcelAS_A1_ch14_answers.pdf

CHAPTER 15 – *Groups and goal setting*

4.2.1 Dynamics of groups and teams

A **group** consists of two or more people **interacting** with one another so that each person influences and is influenced by the others. A group will have a **collective identity** and a sense of **shared purpose**, and is a **social aggregate** involving **mutual awareness** and **potential interaction** with structured patterns of **communication**. For example, a crowd at a soccer match, a soccer team or parents watching their children swim.

Successful groups:
*   Have a strong collective identity in which members have an opportunity to **socialise** and who **share goals**, **ambitions** and **ownership** of ideas.
*   Will have members who are able to **communicate effectively** (on the same wavelength).
*   Will have strong **cohesion** (see below).
*   Have members who **value relationships** within the group.

Group cohesion

Cohesion points at the way in which group members **gel** together, or feel **collective affection** for one another, or feel a strong **sense of sharing** whatever it is that the group does. It is the extent to which members of a group exhibit a desire to **achieve common goals** and **group identity**. The two themes of cooperation and coordination are strong elements of this idea.

*   Sometimes this can mean selection of less skilled but more co-operative players for a team.
*   Unfortunately, friendship groups can have negative effects.

figure 15.1 – cohesion is important for some teams

Cohesion has both **task** and **social** elements:
*   **Task cohesion** is about people who are willing to work together (see figure 15.1) whether or not they get on personally, hence the group would have the potential to be successful. Task cohesion is more required for success than social cohesion.
*   **Social cohesion** covers the notion that teams with high social cohesion but low task cohesion are less successful.

On other words, a team will like socialising together and enjoying each other's company, but the greatest success will be achieved when the task the team faces (winning in the cup final for example) is large and dominant.

Carron's model

This model (figure 15.2) outlines **four** factors that affect the development of cohesion:

*   **Environmental factors** which bind members to a team, for example, contracts, location, age, eligibility. To make cohesion stronger, you should avoid a star system and provide opportunities for socialising.

*   **Personal factors** which feature characteristics that members believe are important, and include motives for taking part. To optimise on cohesion, a coach should give opportunities for motives to be realised, and develop ownership feelings and social groupings within the team.

*   **Leadership factors** which are about the behaviour of leaders and coaches. Coaches should use all leadership behaviours to influence different individuals.

*   **Team factors** relating to the group, including team identity, targets, member ability and role, creation of team short-term and long-term goals, and the rewarding of individual and team efforts. These factors reflect all the characteristics of the group, norms and stability factors.

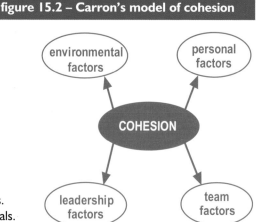

figure 15.2 – Carron's model of cohesion

This model also differentiates between **group outcomes**, which include the stability and performance of the team, and **individual outcomes,** including member satisfaction and individual performance.

Steiner's model of a group or team

Steiner produced a model to show the relationship between the performance of a team and the individuals.

Actual productivity = potential productivity – losses due to faulty processes

Actual productivity is a team's level of achievement on a specific task. For example, a rugby team reaching the semi-final of a cup competition.

Potential productivity is the best possible level of achievement of a cohesive team for this rugby team to win the cup competition.

Losses due to 'faulty' processes are coordination and motivational problems the team faces, which reduce the level of cohesion and as a result lower the level of achievement.

'Faulty' processes falls into two categories:
- **Coordination problems** (for players) occur if there should be a high level of interaction between players, but one (or more) player is being selfish or aggressive, or if a defence is not working together, and hence overall team performance suffers.
- **Motivational problems** in which groups tend to make individuals perform below their own best potential.

The Ringlemann effect

- **Motivational problems** occur because people seem to work less hard in a group than they do on their own. For example, in rowing, times of winning double sculls are often only slightly faster than single sculls.
- The **Ringlemann Effect** refers to this fact of average individual performance decreasing with increasing group size.

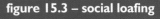
figure 15.3 – social loafing

Social loafing

- Hence individuals appear to **reduce their effort** when in a group (figure 15.3), and can **hide their lack of effort** amongst the effort of other group members. The term **social loafing** ascribes the reason for this as being due to motivational losses.
- **Motivational losses** occur because individuals may not share the same motives. This leads to loss of group cohesion, for example, some players may play a game for social reasons, others in order to win.
- It can be eliminated if the contribution of an individual **can be identified** as with **player statistics** (American football, rugby league, cricket, basketball).
- The **need** for interaction between players varies between sports.
- **Cooperation** between players can be significant in eliminating social loafing.

Coaching strategies used to develop group cohesion

- Put together a group with **high potential productivity** whilst trying to minimise losses due to faulty processes.
- **Minimising losses** could be achieved by organising practices so that all team members are certain of their role, over learning set plays in order to get the timing right and manipulating the use of rewards to optimise motivation levels.
- Coaches should not just pick the best players for a team, but those who are most likely **to get on with each other**.
- **Measure** both group and individual performances within the group. If people know they are being monitored, they will conform.
- Use **Peer Pressure**. If most of the group aren't of similar disposition, then this should help as he or she will probably be ostracized.
- Give **Feedback**. It is possible that the loafer is unaware of his or her behaviour. The coach should provide positive feedback, focusing on observations, the impact, and what actions will be taken to remedy the situation.

4.3.1 Goal setting and SMARTER goals

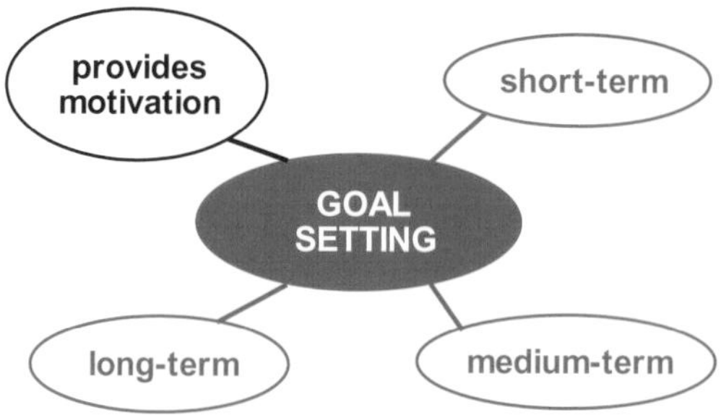

Many research studies have validated the link between goal setting and performance.

The main function of goal setting (figure 15.4) is to increase **motivation**. The feeling of satisfaction gained from achieving a goal brings about this motivation. Goal setting can also be used as a means of **managing anxiety** or stress.

figure 15.4 – goal setting

Goals can be **short**-term, **medium**-term or **long**-term. Short-term goals can be used as targets for single training sessions, or what can be expected after a period of training. Long-term goals may or may not be achieved, but are placed in the background of a performer's mind and can underpin everything he or she does. Kelly Holmes had the ambition (goal) of getting an Olympic gold, and she **eventually** did this – twice! This goal motivated Kelly to keep going through injury and disappointment, to keep her training through bad weather and good times.

S.M.A.R.T.E.R. goals

SPECIFIC
> directly related to a sporting situation.

MEASURABLE
> progress can be assessed.

ACHIEVABLE
> by the performer, coach and manager.

REALISTIC
> challenging but within the capability of the performer.

TIME-BOUND
> a date is set for completion.

EVALUATED
> assessed by the coach and performer.

RECORDED
> written down.

For example, the **smarter** goal of running a 400 metres in 48 seconds. This would be achieved after 5 racing attempts, agreed by both performer and coach, assessed at an 80% s uccess rate, providing an exciting challenge, with a record of training and racing times.

Goal setting

Goals (figure 15.5) should be:
- **Easily** attained initially and therefore **realistic**.
- **Incremental**, a little bit at a time.
- **Challenging** but **achievable**.
- **Progressively** more difficult.
- **Training goals** should be planned around **overall goals**.

Goals are either:
- **Outcome oriented**:
- Towards the end result of the sporting activity. For example to win a race.

- **Performance oriented**:
- Judged against other performances, and related to improvement and enhancing the performer's current standard. For example to beat his or her best time.

- **Process oriented**:
- To obtain an improvement in techniques.

figure 15.5 – goals should be?

Effective goal setting

figure 15.6 – effective goals

Goals (figure 15.6) should be:

- Stated **positively**.
- **Specific** to the situation and the performer.
- **Time phased**, to be achieved in one week or two months for example.
- **Challenging and aspirational**.
- **Achievable and realistic**.
- **Measurable**, so that you can actually say exactly whether or not a goal has been achieved.
- **Negotiated** between sportsperson and coach.
- **Progressive**, from short-term to long-term.
- **Performance oriented** rather than outcome oriented.
- **Written** down.
- **Reviewed** regularly (with downward adjustment if necessary - in the case of injury).
- **Achievement oriented** rather than failure oriented.

Failure to achieve goals should be followed by the resetting of goals to maintain the performer's **self-esteem**.

Goal setting and performance

- Give the performer an aim or **focus**.
- Increase **motivation** when the goal is accomplished.
- Increase **confidence** levels.
- Control **arousal** or anxiety levels.
- Focus **efforts in training** on game or competitive situations.

Exam style questions

1) a) What is meant by cohesion in the context of teams? 4 marks

   b) Explain what is meant by social loafing by using examples from sport. 3 marks

   c) What advice would you give a coach of a team to ensure maximum productivity? 5 marks

2) Elite performers sometimes train on their own and sometimes as part of a group. How would you distinguish between a group and a collection of individuals? 3 marks

3) a) Explain the Ringlemann effect, and its related term, social loafing. 4 marks

   b) How can social loafing be reduced? 3 marks

4) Describe Carron's conceptual model of cohesion. 4 marks

5) a) Explain Steiner's model of group performance:
        Actual productivity = potential productivity – losses due to faulty processes 6 marks

   b) What factors stop a team performing to its true potential? 6 marks

Exam style questions

6) A Level. Discuss and apply to sporting situations, theories that affect formation and development of group cohesion. What strategies could a coach use to develop group cohesion? **15 marks**

7) According to Carron (1982) the following factors influence group cohesion. For each factor give an example to explain how this happens.
   a) Environmental factors.

   b) Leadership factors.

   c) Personal factors.

   d) Team factors. **8 marks**

8) a) Identify five characteristics of goals which a performer might set to achieve an aim. **5 marks**

   b) Explain how outcome goals and performance goals can affect motivation, anxiety and stress. **4 marks**

9) a) Show what is meant by short-term goals and long-term goals by using examples from sport. **4 marks**

   b) What are the main positive effects of setting goals in sport? **2 marks**

   c) As a coach how would you ensure that your goal setting was as effective as possible? **6 marks**

   d) How does performance profiling assist in goal setting? **3 marks**

10) Explain the meaning of the acronym S.M.A.R.T.E.R. in relation to goal setting. **7 marks**

11) Explain the many important factors that have to be taken into account when setting goals. What effect does goal setting have on performance? **12 marks**

Answers link: http://www.jroscoe.co.uk/downloads/as_a1_revise_pe_edexcel/EdexcelAS_A1_ch15_answers.pdf

SPORT AND SOCIETY

TOPIC 5 - SPORT AND SOCIETY

CHAPTER 16 – Emergence and development of modern day sport

It is important to understand the structure and function of popular recreation as it existed in pre-industrial Britain. Some of these recreations continued in rural society well after industrialisation, and others have been revived today as ethnic festival occasions.

The emergence of rational recreation was very much triggered by pupils and staff at upper middle class schools as they converted **mob** schoolboy sports into a controlled format. This controlled **athleticism** was seen to be a vehicle for desirable values and a way of life for respectable society.

Sport in pre-industrial England

The rise of **aristocratic and popular sports in England** reflected the influence of the Roman conquest on the existing Ancient British Celts and subsequent waves of invaders including the Anglo-Saxons and Vikings. By the time of the Norman Conquest, many folk activities existed, but the Norman aristocracy imposed their own activities, which divided sporting pastimes into **aristocratic pursuits** and **folk games**. Aristocrats indulged in such pastimes as 'par force' hunting, which combined most of the attributes of the killing of 'game', while the **folk games** emerged as religious festivals. These festivals were imposed on older pagan customs and became **holy day** celebrations and **wakes**. At this time, **violent annual mob games** existed in many towns and blood sports remained part of a cruel public ritual.

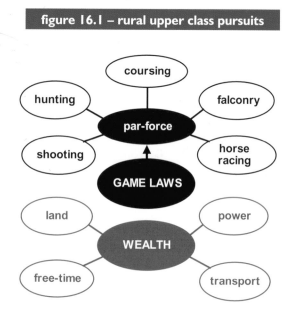

figure 16.1 – rural upper class pursuits

Many such activities continued until the end of the 19th century. In feudal times, **popular** sports were only possible with the sanction of the **clergy** and often the involvement of the landowners.

Rural upper class pursuits

The rural upper class (figures 16.1, 16.2 and 16.3) instigated game laws as and when they liked without interference from the public. Gradually, aristocratic constraints were relaxed to include an emerging county gentry.

figure 16.2 – hunting as a sport?

figure 16.3 – falconry as an upper class pursuit

Popular recreations

The culture of the English lower classes before the late 19th century was linked with social conditions and formed the characteristics of their recreation and pastimes (figure 16.4) – in so far as there were any!

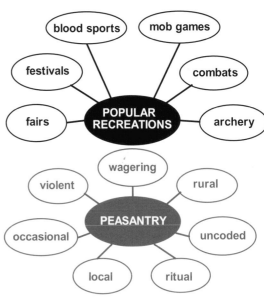

figure 16.4 – popular recreations

- They were **occasional** because there was limited free time.
- They were **local** because there was limited transport.
- They were **uncoded** (figure 16.5) because the peasantry was often illiterate.
- They were **ritualised** because of the influence of older pagan and existing church influences.
- Any recreations of a sporting nature were often in the context of village fêtes or **fairs** held on holydays.
- The activities were often **violent and cruel** (figure 16.6), because life was hard and harsh at that time.
- **Wagering** was a primary feature of life at this time, and wagers would be made on the outcome of any contest.

Many of these activities have survived both at an aristocratic and popular level, but many have been either curtailed or reformed. Nor is there the clean separation between the two groups (upper and lower classes) within our present democracy.

Among the **upper class sports**, coursing is pretty-well banned in this country, hunting is now legally restricted and shooting is strictly controlled.
- Popular recreations like **baiting** have long since been made illegal.
- **Festivals** are more respectable.

figure 16.5 – mob football as a lower class pursuit

figure 16.6 – bull baiting, brutal but exciting

figure 16.7 – archery as preparation for war?

Archery (figure 16.7) has changed from military combat practice to a codified target sport.
- And **mob football** has only survived in rural areas which escaped the impact of reform.

The **socio-cultural influences** which brought about the evolution of the various pastimes of the middle ages are summarised in figure 16.8 (page 174)

The changes which led to modern versions of existing sports will be explained later with the focus on the mid 19th century development of **public school athleticism** and **rational sport**.

Questions

1) What were the characteristics of popular recreation?

2) How did the activities, illustrated in figures 16.2 (page 172) and 16.5, reflect pre-industrial society in the United Kingdom?

5.1.2 Emergence of rational sport as a product of the industrial revolution

Changes in society

The development of **physical education** and **sport** reflected changes in British society (figure 16.8). Hence we place **social and cultural** changes in the context of elitist **institutions** like the **English public schools**.

The major changes which occurred in society influenced participation in sport today. We will now discuss how society changed during the period over which the industrial revolution occurred, as it influenced **development and change** in English institutions.

The early 19th century marked the beginnings of **three social revolutions** in England:

- The **agrarian revolution** (figure 16.9) which involved the gradual movement of workers from the countryside to the larger towns, caused by:
  - The emergence of a **gentry** class.
  - The **enclosure** of much of the countryside.
  - The growth of the **Methodist** movement.
  - The gradual increased significance of **respectability** in early Victorian society.
  - The **poor wages** of the rural working class.
  - The gradual **mechanisation** of tenant farms.

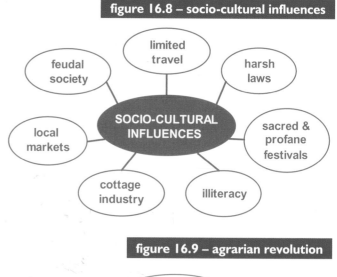

figure 16.8 – socio-cultural influences

figure 16.9 – agrarian revolution

- The **industrial revolution**, in which this mechanisation meant that people started to migrate into towns and villages and away from the land. Work became available in the factories for this surplus labour, hence the industrialsation of the economy. This gave increased power to the middle classes, better wages for some of the industrial working class and greater prosperity for the country at large.

- The **urban revolution**, which marked a massive rise in the population, as industrial and commercially well-placed towns grew in size and national significance.

Popular and rational recreation

These two strands of development towards modern sport had the characteristics identified in figures 16.10 and 16.11.

Popular and rational recreation are not totally different. They both involve **physical activity**, they are both **competitive** and they are both **enjoyable** and **fulfilling**. They both have features of **ritual** and **festival** and both have elements to be seen in modern sport.

figure 16.10 – characteristics of popular recreation

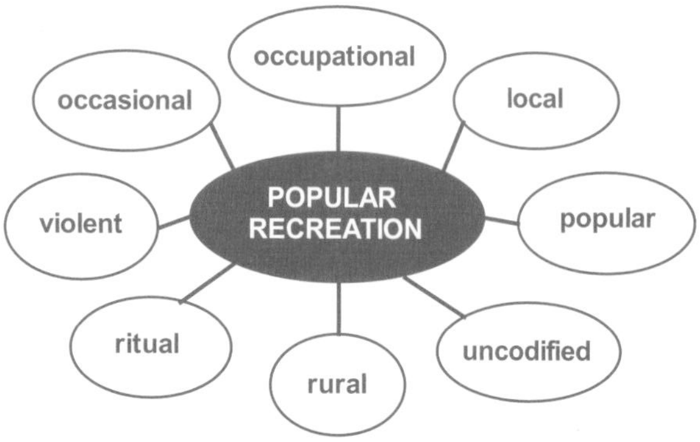

figure 16.11 – characteristics of rational recreation

Table 16.1 – the cultural factors which influenced the conversion of popular sports into rational sports

popular	rational
agrarian	industrial and urban
feudal	emergent middle class
limited travel	railways
illiterate	elementary education
cottage industry	factories
payment in kind	wages
limited free-time	regular free-time and the Saturday half day
markets	shopping centres
harsh laws	law and policing
church festivals	muscular Christianity - athleticism
fields and rivers	parks and baths

The effects of industrialisation on the development of rational recreation

Industrialisation had the effect of improving three major **developmental** factors in society, these were:

figure 16.12 – 1859 - excursion to Brighton for 3s 6d

- **Communication**, the sporting press (rather than just current affairs) was established, receiving results quickly kept spectators interested in their favourite sport, and newspapers were transported by rail.

- **Transport**, better transport meant fixtures could be played in different towns thus leagues and competitions became more developed. Factory owners would arrange excursions to the coast (figure 16.12), hence workers' morale was maintained. Rail travel was vastly improved with the arrival of steam power, so spectators and racehorses could be transported to different events. Also, as cycling grew more popular, road improvements were demanded.

- **Technology**, clothing was made by machines in the mills, and sport specific clothing and footwear became available. More sophisticated timing devices (stop watches) and other sport equipment (balls, racquets, athletic equipment) made sport more fair and more competitive. Printing presses were used to produce the popular press as literacy amongst the working class improved. The electric telegraph meant results of games could be distributed faster, to more places.

The effects of urbanisation and industrialisation and education on sport

- There was less open land-space for pre-industrial games to take place.
- Transport from towns to the country was poor which deterred country-based people from travelling in order to participate.
- Long working hours in factories decreased leisure time.
- Low wages meant that there was little disposable income available for participation in sport.
- Women and children were used as cheap labour.
- Workers were too tired for leisure activities.
- The 12 hour working day meant that it was dark before and after work in the winter months. The **1847 factories act** reduced the working day to 10 hours, hence slightly more time for leisure activities, encouraging the growth of factory teams.
- In the 1800s, learning became available even to the poorest people, hence more people became aspirational towards how to use their futures, and wider opportunities in the management and operation of factories became available.
- Hence the middle class gradually increased in size, and had more time for recreational activities - but not for the poorest people living in the slums and working long hours in the factories.

The development of professional sport

Popular recreation is normally centred on the **lower classes**, with **aristocratic** or **gentry** sports co-existing alongside peasant sports. Normally, **patronage** by the gentry not only determined whether the popular activities and **festivals** flourished in a community, but it was also why they were allowed to continue well after levels of industrialisation and urbanisation had increased.

The key factors were:

* The significance of **wagering and possible corruption**.
* The **limited free time** available to the urban lower class and agricultural labourers.
* The **minimal pay** for workers who were on the bread-line.
* The **lack of transport** except for the wealthiest classes.

As a result, the **occasional festival** and fair offered the chance to **earn money prizes** through sporting competition to young people with talent and bravery. If they were good enough, they could increase their income by travelling to different fairs and wakes to compete in combat sports like single stick play and wrestling or running events. In addition to prize money, there was always **wagering** where you could risk money on backing yourself to win or lose!

Amateurism and professionalism in the 19th century

* The distinction between amateurs and professionals in so far as sport is concerned was mainly on a **class basis**.
* In cricket, the **'gentlemen'** were the amateurs who played for the fun, the **'players'** were professionals - usually employed by the gentlemen.
* 'Players' started as the employed groundsmen who prepared the pitches, but also played for the teams.
* This was deemed the correct way of paying professional players in what was essentially an amateur sport.

* In **rugby**, it was expected that players would not be paid and were therefore amateur.
* This changed in 1895 when the Rugby League was formed, but Rugby Union remained amateur until 1995.
* **Soccer** became a professional sport in 1885, because players were mostly working class.
* **Athletics**, **swimming** and **rowing** remained strictly amateur until the 1980s.
* **Tennis** had both amateur and professional factions until the 1950s, when the Lawn Tennis Association (LTA) and Wimbledon began to pay winning players, and the sport was unified.

Female sport in the 19th century

* Historically, sport was a male pastime. Sport had evolved from violent activities undertaken by males in connection with the need to prepare for war (fencing, jousting, stave fighting, archery, wrestling and fist fighting), and since hunting and horse riding were gentry pastimes, women tended not to be involved until later.

* The **middle classes** did not expect their wives to work, but increasingly they were allowed to play as long as the activities were private and genteel. As a result croquet, lawn tennis and golf were acceptable.
* **Working class women** did not generally have the time, money or provision for sport until the end of the 19th century.

Victorian attitudes to women led to females being excluded from rational sport on the grounds that:

* It was too manly.
* It could endanger childbirth.
* **Victorian fashion**, among upper and middle classes (restrictive clothing), prevented freedom of movement and so discouraged women from vigorous activity.
* It was not expected that Victorian women should display their bodies.
* Or be competitive and sweat!

Questions

1) What is meant by the term social control?

2) Describe and explain the effect that the industrial revolution had on sport after 1800.

3) Define the terms 'Gentleman Amateurs' and 'Playing Professionals'.

4) Discuss the sporting opportunities available to females in the 19th century.

5.1.3 The impact of nineteenth century public schools

figure 16.13 – public schools

Nineteenth century public schools and athleticism

The **characteristics** of the 19th century public schools included the facts that they were for the **sons of the gentry** and they were **boarding, fee paying,** and **non-local** establishments (figure 16.13).

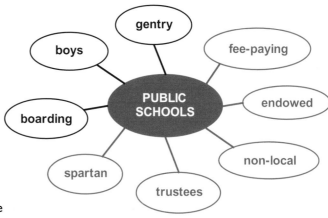

- The non-local feature of these schools was very important in that the developments that occurred in the schools became spread across the nation.

- There were also scholars from poorer families and by the 1870s the number of schools had increased to accommodate an emergent middle class.

The **Clarendon Commission** was a Royal Commission established in 1861 to investigate the state of nine leading public schools in England in the wake of complaints about the finances, buildings and management of Eton College. It sat until 1864 when its **Report** was published with general recommendations on questions of curriculum and governance, and highlighted topics such as fagging and bullying, thus providing a detailed picture of public school life (later called the Barbarian Schools by Matthew Arnold). As a consequence of its publication, the **Public Schools' Act** was passed in 1868 which enabled the British Parliament to reform and regulate the first seven of the nine leading boarding English boys' schools, namely Eton, Harrow, Charterhouse, Westminster, Winchester, Rugby, Shrewsbury (known collectively as EHCWWRS) and day schools - St Pauls and Merchant Taylors. Following reforms, these seven boarding schools were the centre of later **expansion of boarding schools** as middle class copies appeared throughout the country.

- There was a delay before similar selective high schools emerged for **upper and middle class girls**.

- By the end of the nineteenth century, there was public or grammar school access for wealthy and bright boys and girls. The schools had an active policy of **athleticism (goodness, manliness, restraint** and **discipline)**. Other reforms also occurred such as a broader curriculum, reduced flogging, and control of school sport by the Sixth Form.

- The characteristics of these schools are identified in the model (in figure 16.13), where each component had a positive effect on the growth of athleticism.

Athleticism

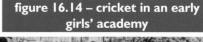

Athleticism was originally defined as '**a muscular Christian view of manliness reflecting physical endeavour and moral integrity**'. By the end of the 19th century, athleticism had become so popular that some authorities felt that it was undermining other educational values. Hence a second critical definition was given as '**the exultation and disproportionate regard for games, which often resulted in the denigration of academic work and in anti-intellectualism**'.

The growth of this movement is best broken up into **three stages**.

Stage one – schoolboys' recreations

- There is a link between developments in the schools and changes in society. At the beginning of the 19th century, communications were limited to carts, stage coaches and wagons. Only the **very wealthy** had the **time, money** and **transport** to travel any distance.

- As a result they were the only people with the tradition of sending their sons to boarding schools. It is important to mention that at this time the daughters of the very wealthy either had governesses or went to **academies** near to home (figure 16.14).

- **Recreations** within this first stage followed local folk customs and practices.

- With game laws in place, hunting and shooting were controlled by the upper classes, and traditional festivals were held in the towns and villages on occasional **holy days** and chartered fair days.

- The upper class played a courtly role and the lower classes made the most of a festival day, which of course was a day off from the grind of work.

Stage one

The **boys** therefore took local **folk activities to school**, so that there were regular fights, mob games (figure 16.15), cricket (of course), swimming in the river or open pools, and boating. Very few schools had hounds, so the young boys became the **hares** and the seniors chased them labelled as **hounds**. This was the basis of the '**boy culture**' within which these schools flourished.

figure 16.15 – mob games

Stage two – Arnold and Christian gentlemen

By 1830, a **new breed of headmasters** were **reforming** their schools and starting to link Christianity with the Ancient Greek model of **Mind, Body and Spirit**. They chose to link the energy identifiable in the games and sports with education. The Headmaster would have led the revised programmes, with prefects and junior members of staff establishing basic rules. House matches allowed healthy, social competition.

Social control (figure 16.16) was an important objective of this process. It was an attempt to reduce the bullying and lawlessness in the schools and the effect of the boy culture outlined above. Dr Thomas Arnold is known to have led this reform, but much of his reputation comes from the book Tom Brown's Schooldays, rather than research evidence. In the eyes of Arnold and others, the **desire to produce Christian gentlemen** was central and the moral code of **fair play** was introduced at this level.

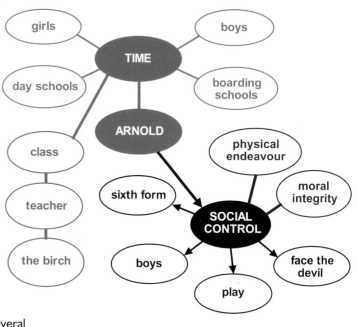

figure 16.16 – Arnold and social control

Stage three – Corinthian athleticism and the emergence of rational recreation

With more regular play of games and sports, **written rules** were established. But because this was an internal programme, each school devised its own version of rules depending on the facilities available. Only the game of **cricket** had a set of **universal rules** across several different schools throughout the country at this time. **Football** and **fives** rules were different in each school. **Swimming** was popular wherever there were lakes, ponds or rivers available, as in the Duck Puddle bathing pool at Harrow (figure 16.17).

At Eton, **boating** was encouraged instead of swimming in the Thames, but Shrewsbury and Eton established safety rules that only those boys who could swim, could row.

As the schools and society changed to meet the energy and reforming zeal of Victorian England, so the lesser gentry and **industrial middle class** presumed the right to public boarding school education. They were not allowed into the Clarendon Schools and so they built new ones. These new schools had extensive sports facilities, were built in attractive spa towns and other wealthy areas, and were linked by the new **railway** system.

figure 16.17 – the Harrow School Duck Puddle

Middle class developments

- The middle classes were not only wealthy and industrious, they wanted the status previously reserved for the gentry and they felt that the **public schools** would at least give that to their sons.
- Meanwhile, with some upper class women gaining access to Oxbridge, these women opened boarding schools for their daughters.
- This was eventually taken up by the middle class with a **girls' high school** opening in every major town.

Sport in public schools

Sport in public schools was now **widespread**, as teachers moved schools to obtain headships and took the notion of sport as part of a school with them. But certain idiosyncrasies remained, such as soccer and rugby having separate codes and fives having several versions. **Regular play** and **written codes** evolved as senior boys continued with sport at the **universities** and, as **old boys**, they continued to encourage athleticism in their old school and in amateur sport.

figure 16.18 – lacrosse as a girls' game

- For example, a group of **university graduates** discussed the rules of football. They accepted the divide between the two codes of association and rugby, and established the **governing bodies** of the Football Association (FA) in 1863, and the Rugby Football Union (RFU) in 1870.

- The notion of the **gentleman amateur** continued, while several games had acknowledged the place of the **professional** performer.

- In **cricket** and **association football**, the professional player and club were controlled by middle class administrators, who accepted the code of **physical endeavour and moral integrity** as the basis of all modern games and sports. Hence the nineteenth century public schools had a major part to play in the development of most modern day sports and games.

Some cultural changes, such as working class free time, elementary education and the emancipation of the lower class female, took more time. But the cultural changes were under way, and perhaps sport led the way.

Girls' schools started with callisthenics and girls also played organised games based on similar principles to the boys. Established men's games were generally avoided. The girls played **hockey** and **lacrosse** (figure 16.18) in the winter and **lawn tennis** in the summer, but cricket was often limited to junior girls.

Spreading the message

With the lead coming from university graduates, there was a focus on the things men had learnt at school and university. These men were experienced **all-round** sportsmen, often getting 'blues' in several sports at university. They formed **elite clubs** (for example, Leander for rowing and the Corinthians for cricket and soccer), setting a high standard of sportsmanship. This process was the basis of early **amateur governing bodies** and the birth of **rational recreation**. See figure 16.19 for an outline of the factors affecting the birth of rational recreation via the public schools.

The next step - the governing bodies

In turn, young men drawn from the middle classes went back to their factories, commercial businesses and schools. There, they set up clubs for children, friends and salaried workers. This expansion led to benevolent businessmen forming **social and sports clubs** for their **workforce**. With this impact **physical education** was carried into grammar schools and later into primary and secondary comprehensive schools.

All this development reflected the improved wage structure for working men and the **provision** of town sports facilities. Specialist teacher training colleges were set up where physical educationists were trained.

The code set by the governing bodies held true to the amateur ethic until the last 30 years, when they reluctantly allowed amateur rules on financial aid to be revoked. Today, **professionalism** has taken over the status of most sports.

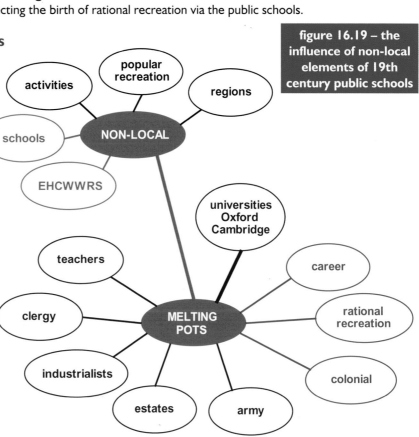

figure 16.19 – the influence of non-local elements of 19th century public schools

Fair play, sportsmanship, gamesmanship and cheating

Nevertheless, governing bodies continue to also represent grass roots development which has remained amateur. However, with media coverage showing regular examples of **gamesmanship and cheating**, it is increasingly difficult to maintain the importance of **sportsmanship** in sport. In spite of this trend in society, the teaching of **fair play** is still a basic principle underlying the role of sport in society.

Activity development and the Oxbridge melting pot

We can use examples of different activities to **explain** how development occurred. The main popular example is of **mob football** which tended to differ in each school:

* Eton played a field game and a wall game.

* Rugby School played a handling game.

* Harrow and Charterhouse played a so-called dribbling game.

* Local conditions (the availability of large grassy areas or pitches, and whether or not the areas were bounded by fences or walls) at each school largely determined these differences.

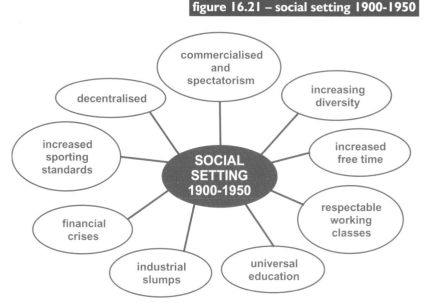

figure 16.20 – inter-school cricket by 1851

When the boys left school for **Oxford or Cambridge** Universities, they had already established an acceptable combination of the rules in public schools to produce a **set of rules** which allowed them to play at their university college. From there it was necessary to produce unified rules and a stringent organisation for competitions **between** university colleges, and finally a set of rules for **inter-varsity** games and contests, with the reward of **blues** for representation.

'**Melting pot**' is a concept that is used to describe how a combination of different things produces a new outcome. And so the mixing of all the factors via the public schools (shown in figure 16.19 on page 179) formed the basis of the early amateur governing bodies and the birth of rational recreation. A large number of these boys returned to teach in the public schools after graduation, and spread the new rules to the next generation of schoolboys. Hence inter-school matches (figure 16.20) and competitions were held according to the new unified rules, and the word was spread.

Professionalisation and the development of factory teams

Amateurism and professionalism

The twentieth century brought a further reduction in the elitism of **amateurism**. In the early part of the century, though the **barrier** between amateurs and professionals remained strong, several sports like athletics and swimming opened their doors to amateurs from **all classes**. Women had their own governing bodies and they also broadened the definition of amateurism.

figure 16.21 – social setting 1900-1950

commercialised and spectatorism

decentralised

increasing diversity

increased sporting standards

SOCIAL SETTING 1900-1950

increased free time

financial crises

respectable working classes

industrial slumps

universal education

Amateurism changed in meaning as defined by governing body regulations:

* Firstly, to a **no financial gain** regulation.

* Then to the justification for **legitimate expenses** where this later included **lost time**.

* And eventually, **funding** and **sponsorship** were allowed to help in the achievement of excellence.

* The owners and managers of the embrionic factories of the early 1900s the new middle classes spread their knowledge of sports to their workforce, hence the formation of factory teams like Arsenal, the members of which were paid as part of the workforce.

Meanwhile, **professional** performers were getting higher wages and prize money, such that the idea of professionals being lower class all but disappeared as middle class competitors were attracted by the rewards and kudos.

The social setting

figure 16.22 – £8.00 per week 1948

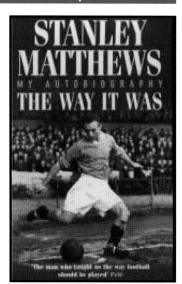

The social setting within which cultural and sporting developments occurred in the first half of the century are summarised in figure 16.21 (page 180).

- **Governing bodies** for all sports became established as independent bodies who regulated their sports.

- Apart from setting out the rules for a sport, the **regulations** had to take into account the changes such as professionalism which were being demanded by the sportspeople they represented.

- **Regulations** had to account for player violence, changes in clothing and equipment, and changes in the ways in which sport as a whole was becoming financed by **commercial** sponsorship and TV rights.

- **Professional soccer players** playing in the then English first division in 1948 were restricted to £8.00 per week as a cap on wages (figure 16.22).

- In 1957, John Charles (figure 16.23) became the first British soccer player to transfer into the Italian Football League for a transfer fee of £65,000. By the end of the 20th century, player wages reached £50,000 per week, with transfer fees in excess of £25 million.

- The expansion of professional sports was financed by the **spectators** who paid to watch games.

- This was possible because the **working conditions** of working men began to include Saturday afternoons off.

- Most **spectators** at professional soccer games were **men** who were able to spend some money at the turnstiles to support their local team.

figure 16.23 – John Charles, £65,000 in 1957

Development of the sporting press

The gradual emergence of the **sports journalist** can be traced against a background of an expanding newspaper industry. The 1850s saw the gradual lowering and then abandonment of punitive newspaper taxes.

A steady improvement in **living standards**, increasing **educational opportunities** and a growth in **disposable incomes**, combined with urban expansion, led to the emergence of a reading public of commercial proportions.

Advances in **rail transport** together with **technological innovations in printing** and the telegraph system eased the way for a rapid expansion in newspaper production and a classless readership.

The establishment and development of clubs, NGBs, a **sporting calendar** for spectator and player, and a dramatic increase in the range of sports available and in the number of people who played and watched them, led to the introduction of the **sports column** and then the sports page. This also partly led to the growth and development of rationalised sport due to the newspapers contributing to free publicity and sports coverage.

5.1.4 The emergence of corporations dealing with sport

Corporations (bodies set up to perform a function – business, government – the local council – or sport) began to be set up to act for the top soccer clubs. Most corporations were arrived at by historical accident (at least in Britain), but in the USA, football, basketball, baseball, ice hockey have been incorporated from the beginning.
For example, the Lancashire and Yorkshire railway company - Newton Heath football club was founded in 1878 and based at Belle-Vue stadium Manchester. The Heathens' became a professional football team in 1885 and adopted its present name in 1902, namely Manchester United FC. The club came from modest beginnings as a working mens' social club - in 1886 the team won its first trophy, the Manchester Senior Cup. Initially, this corporation was geographically based, since all the players came from an area near Manchester, (see website: http://www.manchester2002-uk.com/sports/footballers5.html).

Corporations

Nowadays, most professional sports are organised and run by corporations. Often, these corporations are sponsored by commercial structures which are notionally nothing to do with sport - such as Red Bull who sponsor the New York Red Bulls soccer team, the Barclays' Premier League of soccer in the UK, and the Sky Bet football league.

- Some teams are **named** as the corporation name itself, for example the Ferrari formula one car racing team.
- Some athletes are more **accountable** to the sponsor than the team in some cases.
- Some athletes are getting **paid** as much by their sponsors as by their professional sporting contracts in some cases, for example Andy Murray and his sponsorship by the Under Armour kit provider.
- TV corporations **dictate** which day and time a sporting event takes place, for example Sky Monday or Friday night football.
- TV corporations dictate when the commercial breaks take place.
- Athletes' kits are plastered with different **sponsors' names**, for example Tour de France cyclists.
- Corporations pay vast sums for naming rights for stadia.

Exam style questions

1) What do you understand by the terms codified, regulated, and respectable in relation to rational recreation? 6 marks

2) What influence did 'non-local' admission to the public schools and universities have on the development of rational sport? 6 marks

3) Public schools, such as Rugby and Eton, played an important part in the development of rational games in society from mid 19th century onwards. Explain the role played by 'old boys' of such public schools in the development of rational recreation. 4 marks

4) Church organisations promoted sport amongst their local communities in the late 19th century. Explain their reasons for doing this and how they achieved it. 4 marks

5) What was the purpose of the Clarendon Commission and how did the Clarendon Report and government legislation in the Public Schools Act of 1868 change public school life? 5 marks

6) Why were Oxford and Cambridge Universities able to make such an impressive contribution to elite sport in the late 19th century? 6 marks

7) Participation in sports and games was a key feature of 19th century public schools.
Describe three factors which lead to increased participation in physical activity by young people in public schools in Stage three of development (the 'cult' of athleticism). How do these factors continue to impact upon participation and performance in physical activity in schools today? 9 marks

8) How were games used by Thomas Arnold (figure 16.16 page 178) as a means of social control in Rugby School? 4 marks

9) What is meant by the term 'melting pot' in connection with 19th century public school athleticism? 6 marks

10) a) Discuss the development of Saturday Half-Day and the emergence of working class sport. 4 marks.

    b) Account for the delay in the opportunities for the working class to be able to play games such as lawn tennis 4 marks

11) Modern sports are partly a result of changes that occurred in the 19th century.
How did English public schools influence the technical development of games? 3 marks

12) A Level. Explain the emergence of physical endeavour and moral integrity in 19th century public school athleticism and discuss the issues which threaten it in today's sport. 15 marks

13) Many NGBs of sport were set up in England between the late 1800s and early 1900s. Why was it necessary to form these governing bodies and why did some of them prevent professional athletes from competing in their sport? 6 marks

14) What was impact of the sporting press on sports' partipication and spectatorship in the 19th century? 4 marks

15) Using sporting examples, explain the view that many teams and athletes are now influenced by corporations. 6 marks

Answers link: http://www.jroscoe.co.uk/downloads/as_a1_revise_pe_edexcel/EdexcelAS_A1_ch16_answers.pdf

CHAPTER 17 - Equality, diversity and migration

5.1.5 Equality and diversity of disability and gender

The **participation** in physical activity and achievement of sporting excellence by people may be affected by class status, personal financial circumstances, inability to travel, or not having the time to participate. This takes us into the major groups where discrimination may occur:

- Women.
- People belonging to some racial minority groups.
- Older people.
- People with lower than average disposable income.
- People with disability.

Social exclusion is the exclusion from the prevailing social system and its rights and privileges, typically those belonging to the minority groups listed above.

Disability

The term **disability** implies loss of ability in certain activities due to **impairment**. Impairment covers various categories including:

- Mental, visual, and hearing impairments.
- Cerebral Palsy.
- Les autres.
- Quadriplegic and paraplegic conditions.
- Amputees.

figure 17.1 – disabled athletes are becoming higher profile

There has always been a conflict of attitude between ability and disability in the context of sport, since most conditions have little or no effect on the capability of a person to **participate** in (figure 17.1) and enjoy sporting activities. **Opportunity** is often limited by the **attitudes** of the able-bodied, and also by the low **self-esteem** of some who suffer from impairments. The main issue being tackled is **access**, where public sport facilities are now required to have ramps and wide doorways to allow wheelchair access. **The Paralympic Games** and numerous marathons have highlighted disabled people's potential success at World level.

English Federation of Disability Sport and other English disability sports organisations

The following organisations influence disability sport in the UK: Disability Sport England, UK Deaf Sport, British Blind Sport, and the British Paralympic Association.

The **English Federation of Disability Sport (EFDS)** (figure 17.2) has a mission: '**To be the united voice of disability sport seeking to promote inclusion and achieve equality of sporting opportunities for disabled people.**'
www.efds.co.uk

figure 17.2 – EFDS logo

The EFDS was launched in 1998, and is the umbrella organisation for disability sport in England. It has 9 regional federations, and includes:

- British Amputees and Les Autres Sports Association.
- British Blind Sport.
- WheelPower – British Wheelchair Sport.
- Mencap Sport.
- UK Deaf Sport.

The ParaSport Movement

The ParaSport movement is a non-profitmaking charitable foundation supporting development of organisaions such as Paralympic sports throughout the World. It serves as a long-term source of financial assistance in physical rehabilitation, social adaptation for athletes and people with **physical**, **sensory** and **intellectual** impairments, and promotes equal opportunities for all members of the modern community.

The ParaSport movement began as recently as the 1940s, evolving from the efforts to rehabilitate soldiers wounded during the second World War with spinal injuries. People with such injuries up to that point had mostly been left to die or looked after in hospitals. One of these hospitals, Stoke Mandeville hospital for spinal injuries, developed games for wheelchair users, leading to the 1948 International Wheelchair Games held at Stoke Mandeville in coincidence with the 1948 Olympic Games held in London.

ParaSport works in close partnership with the national Paralympic organisations.

The Stoke Mandeville Games were therefore precursor to the Paralympic Games which first officially took place in Rome in 1960. The sixties also saw the introduction of ParaSport for people with intellectual disabilities through the **Special Olympics movement**.

The modern Paralympic Games are held in the period immediately after the Olympic Games at the same venues as the Olympic Games. The Paralympic games are designed to emphasize the participants' athletic achievements and not their disability. The games have grown from 400 athletes in Rome in 1960 to over 3,900 athletes from 146 countries in Beijing in 2008, and the Paralympic Summer and Winter Games are recognized on the World stage with media coverage and medal counts as at the Olympic Games. The Paralympics is no longer held solely for British war veterans or just for athletes in wheelchairs, but for elite athletes with a wide variety of disabilities from all over the World.

Gender

Traditionally, **women** have participated less in sport than men. This was because **Victorian attitudes** to women led to females being excluded from rational sport on the grounds that it was too manly and could endanger childbirth. **Fashions** among the upper and middle classes in terms of restrictive clothing prevented freedom of movement and also discouraged women from vigorous activity. This was extended to include any activity which brought women's femininity into question, such as competition, sweating and display of bodies.

Some upper class women, with abundant **free time and status**, excluded themselves from this **stereotype** and developed select sports on their own private land or in private schools. On the other hand, lower class women were obliged to work to supplement their husbands' wages, as well as bring up their families. This meant that lower class women had very **limited free time** and no place in working men's sports. Modern feminist movements have advanced the rights of women in sport, but this trend is still resisted by some men and women. Only a minority of games involve women on equal terms (for example equestrianism).

Figure 17.3 outlines the factors which limit modern female participation in sport via the elements of **opportunity**, **provision** and **esteem**. That an outstanding athlete like Paula Radcliffe (figure 17.4) should succeed in having her profile enhanced, and that anything to do with her health and well-being should be of interest to the UK's media, is a comment on how far gender equality has moved in this country. But there is still a long way to go. Combat sports, such as boxing and wrestling, are still generally deemed undesirable for women but are becoming more popular. Ladies' rugby is becoming increasingly widespread, even though in many cases women have only associate membership in male clubs. Equally, removal of discrimination of women in athletics has now led to full participation in triple jump, hammer throwing, steeplechase, and pole vault.

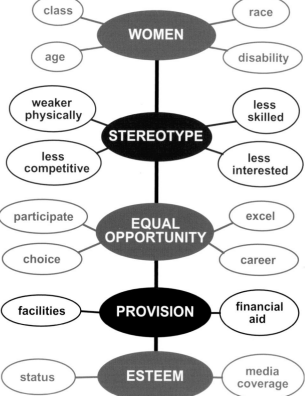

figure 17.3 – the gender axis

class — WOMEN — race
age — WOMEN — disability

weaker physically — STEREOTYPE — less skilled
less competitive — STEREOTYPE — less interested

participate — EQUAL OPPORTUNITY — excel
choice — EQUAL OPPORTUNITY — career

facilities — PROVISION — financial aid

status — ESTEEM — media coverage

figure 17.4 – Paula Radcliffe, superstar

Gender

These athletic events and ladies boxing, wrestling and rugby are now in the Olympic Games, with Nicola Adams (figure 17.5) as a feature of an expanding Boxercise movement.

figure 17.5 - Nicola Adams, Olympic winner

Ladies' soccer (figure 17.6) is increasing its participation - led by the USA in which soccer is the major female sport. Perhaps this is because soccer is not met by the same gender prejudices as female soccer in Europe. Hence school, collegiate and national level female soccer teams have all seen a massive increase in number of players in recent years. Also, England's women got the bronze medal in the 2015 women's World cup for soccer, hence there has been a big increase in participtaion and media coverage of women's soccer in the UK.

Work of specialist agencies for women's sport

These agencies aim to promote sport to target groups, and to educate people about these target groups, in order to break down barriers to participation and progression in sport.

figure 17.6 - women's soccer increasing

Women's Sports Foundation

Set up in 1984, the Women's Sports Foundation (**WSF** – figure 17.7) is now the UK's leading organisation for improving and promoting sporting opportunities for females. The foundation is funded primarily by Sport England, but receives grants and sponsorship from several other companies, including SAQ international.

The WSF challenges government targets and policies and provides advice and information using up-to-date research. It influences national strategies in order to ensure sports programmes are equitable, and aims to promote sport and motivate women into participating through best practice.

Currently, eight out of ten women do too little physical activity to benefit their health and just three per cent play organised team sports. This is the background against which the WSF is operating.

figure 17.7 – the WSF banner

Projects led by the WSF include:

* The National Action Plan for Women's and Girls' Sport and Physical Activity (1999-2001).
* Women into High Performance Coaching Project (2000).
* Women Get Set Go (in partnership with the British Sports Trust).

www.wsf.org.uk/

Questions

1) Define the term disability.

2) Describe what is meant by the ParaSport Movement.

3) Suggest reasons why rugby football is still only played by a small proportion of women.

4) Using the information in figure 17.3 on page 184, identify the three main elements which limit female participation in sport.

5.1.6 Migration patterns of sporting labour

Athletes are on the move (figure 17.8).

In some sports this involves **sport labour movement** from one country to another within or between continents. In other sports athletes assume an almost **nomadic migratory lifestyle**, constantly on the move from one sport festival to another.

Migration patterns of sporting labour have developed globally since the 1990's, particularly since the introduction of the club's licence to contract players and with the professionalism and organisation in male professional team sports.

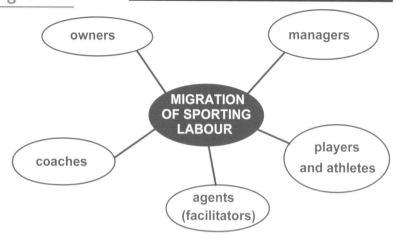

figure 17.8 - migration of sporting labour

Historical reasons for migration

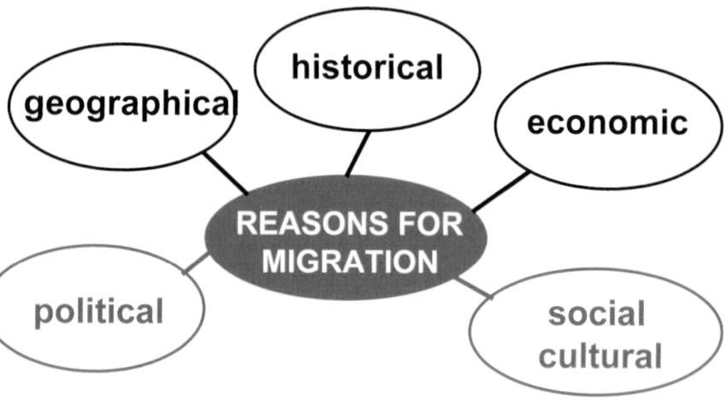

Up to around the 1960s, migration used to be local within the boundaries of a country (and hence **geographical** in nature - figure 17.9). But with the increased role of the media, such as TV contracts, sponsorship and overseas investors, professional football clubs have increased their wealth and status, resulting in increased labour mobility – for example, within the EU there is greater European integration and so easier to move location and work.

Recent indication is that elite female football players are becoming part of the network of global migration.

figure 17.9 - reasons for migration

Economic reasons for migration

Huge transfer fees are paid for elite global male football players to the extent that many of the UK 's premier league clubs such as Manchester United and Arsenal, are predominantly made up of overseas players. More than half of the English Premier League clubs (the corporations) are owned by foreign businessmen, and are perceived as non-profit making, but highly valued as 'global investors' of multi-national enterprises.

Facility investment is also partly responsible for player and coach migration – for example, NBA which has built state-of-the art basketball arenas in China and is attracting global talent.

The entire revenue of the US Big Four sports of football, baseball, basketball and ice hockey represents only a small percentage of the US economy, but is perceived as a very important part of **cultural** lifestyle.

As figure 17.10 on page 187 shows, global sport stars, such as Usain Bolt and Andy Murray, obtain sponsorship, advertise products, and are exposed to extensive media hype, which enhances their financial worth to a sponsor.

Geographical reasons for migration

Many of the transfers within the football, rugby and other sports are close to home and so the cultural and social transitions for both players and family are not too drastic.

During the 2014-15 season Canada attracted 31 international players to its NBA league - do they want to live in Canada?

Political reasons for migration

World leaders are also passionate about sport, for example Barack Obama's love for basketball adds further global appeal and attractiveness, national identity and acceptance of African Americans within global markets. Changing political systems and the associated redrawing of political boundaries has also contributed to an increase in sport labour migration, for example, the exodus of Russian hockey players to the NHL was a prime example of this movement.

Social and cultural reasons for migration

New global migration and mobility patterns have altered **cultural composition** to create cosmopolitan communities and intercultural acceptance within communities, teams and clubs. Many of these transfers are close to home and so the cultural and social transitions for both players and family are not too drastic.

Note the 2016 PFA awards for the player of the year (premiership) was Riyad Mahrez of Leicester City Football Club, who is a Frenchman of Algerian background. The significance of this is that the vote was made by all the professional footballers in the Premiership, hence his acceptance into the community of players.

Other facts about sporting migration

During the 2014-15 season Canada attracted 31 international players to its NBA league.

Elite performers are supported by elite coaches, agents and national governing bodies (NGBs) across the globe.

Global coaches attract elite sports stars (figure 17.10) with the athlete travelling to the coach for training blocks. For example, Rana Reider (US track and field coach – currently based in Holland) oversees a diverse group of sprinters, jumpers and hurdlers such as Tiffany Porter, Shara Proctor, Martyn Rooney, Christian Taylor (2012 Gold medallist triple jumper), and Dafne Schippers (2015 World championship gold medallist 200m).

figure 17.10 - migration - who does it involve?

agents · governing bodies · clubs · sponsors · WHO DOES IT INVOLVE? · elite performers · managers · scouts · coaches · media · owners

Many of the UK's NGBs employ non-UK coaches and managers (figure 17.10). For example Charles van Commenee (Dutch) was head coach of UK athletics until 2012.

Managers are on the move – which is very evident within professional football where managers are sacked and replaced within days, **scouts** travel extensively to find and steer talent into their organisations. And there is the role of **agents** and **governing bodies** assist in the transfer of players on the global market - where agents facilitate migration by serving as intermediaries.

Talent pipelines

The demands of global rugby are having an impact.

Since the 1990s several Fijians and Kiwi rugby players have received lucrative contracts to play in professional club rugby in Japan where rugby is a minor team sport. Players and coaches are attracted by secure contracts offering multi-year secure deals, new cars and free or subsidised apartments and full-time sporting careers that are sponsored by large corporations who dominate Japanese rugby, which are far better financial and long-term contracts than NZ offer. For example, Shane Williams (Wales star rugby winger figure 17.11) had a three year contract with a Japanese club after ending his international career.

This sometimes creates a **player drain** which depletes the country of its talent pool, but some of these elite sports performers become full-time residents and represent their adopted country at International global events.

figure 17.11 - Shane Williams, rugby superstar

Media involvement

Sports events have become global spectacles and are far and away the most watched television programmes in the World. For example, 30 billion viewers watched the 2006 Soccer World cup and 4.7 billion viewers watched the 2008 Beijing Olympics. Superbowl reaches around 160 million viewers across the globe every year.

This global following attracts publicity and sponsorship and networks that encourage global migration.

Sporting icons such as David Beckham, Ronaldino, and Michael Jordan are now recognised and admired the World over as stereotypes, with their skilful performances and ability to enhance the reputation (shop window effect) and desirability for other sports performers to migrate to their sporting locations and clubs (see figure 17.10 on page 187).

Exam style questions

1) What does the term 'social exclusion' mean and what measures can be taken to address this issue.   3 marks

2) Identify three problems faced by the disabled in the sporting context and outline ways in which these problems have been addressed.   6 marks

3) What is the significance of the emergence of 'Disability sport?'   3 marks

4) What are the advantages and disadvantages to a performer with a disability taking part in an integrated sports programme?   6 marks

5) Disability Sport England has a responsibility to promote participation in sport for people with all forms of disability. Physical disability is one major category, state two other categories of disability.   2 marks

6) a) Trace the development of the ParaSport movement since the end of World War 11.   4 marks

   b) How does the ParaSport movement enable disabled people to access the sport of their choice throughout their lives and progress to the level they choose?   3 marks

7) Discuss the terms opportunity, provision and esteem in the context of female discrimination in sport   5 marks

8) How might women experience discrimination in recreational and sporting activities?   3 marks

9) Sport England has a role to play in identifying and targeting minority sub-cultures who for various reasons do not fully participate in Active Sport.

   a) What are the main reasons why young women do not have as high a profile as their male counterparts in sport in the England?   4 marks

   b) Suggest reasons why women over 50 years of age participate in sport less than other minority sub-groups.   4 marks

   c) Outline ways in which some of these problems have been addressed.   4 marks

10) Explain the social and cultural factors that have led to an increase in the opportunities for women to participate in activities such as football.   4 marks

11) Explain the roles and impact of scouts, managers and media on the migration patterns of sporting labour.   6 marks

12) All contemporary professional sports leagues include a wide diversity of nationalities and ethnicities within their playing and coaching staff. Discuss the historical and contemporary reasons why this is the case. What is the impact of the migration of sporting labour on domestic and national teams?   12 marks

Answers link: http://www.jroscoe.co.uk/downloads/as_a1_revise_pe_edexcel/EdexcelAS_A1_ch17_answers.pdf

CHAPTER 18 - 5.2.1 Globalisation of sport

Globalisation refers to the spreading of the knowledge and customs of sport across the World.

This happened by various means depending on the sport, but in the case of sports originating in England or the UK, as mentioned earlier, the Oxbridge melting pot (see page 180) of ex-public school boys (between 1840 and 1900) got jobs and careers across the World in the former British Empire, and spread their games and pastimes accordingly. Hence cricket and rugby developed in Australia, India, Pakistan, New Zealand, South Africa from this formative history.

These countries (and others) eventually organised competition between themselves, until such '**test matches**' became regular fixtures. Up until 1950, travel to such events was by boat (taking 4 to 6 weeks to travel to Australia from the UK for example).

Globalisation therefore describes the importance of sport in most societies across the World:
- The **infrastructure** (sports stadia, indoor and outdoor facilities).
- The involvement of people in sports activities.
- The **commercialism** and money involved.
- The **media** (print and electronic), and so on.
- **Industry** (clothing, footwear and equipment).

Modern sport is bound up in a global network of interdependent chains that are marked by global flows and uneven power relations. People across the globe regularly view satellite broadcasts of English Premier League and European Champions League matches, where the best players drawn from Europe, South America and Africa perform.

Players use **equipment** – boots, balls, uniforms etc - that are designed in the West, are financed by multi-national corporations such as Adidas and Nike, and are hand-stitched, in the case of soccer balls, in Asia using child labour. This equipment is then sold, at significant profit, to a mass market in our towns and cities.

'**Glocalisation**' (global + localisation) is a term used to explain the integration of local practices and global considerations thus reflecting and reinforcing both local, national and international values. Many global corporations have developed and still retain local practices such as club chants 'The Matt Busby Way' for Manchester United Football Club.

Global media sport complex

The global media sport complex (figure 18.1) has five dimensions:
- The international **movement of people** such as tourists, migrants, and guest workers and superstars of the various sports (see page 186).
- The **technology** dimension is created by the flow between countries of the machinery and equipment produced by corporations.
- The **economic** dimension centres on the rapid flow of money on the international trade in personnel, prize money and endorsements around the World.

figure 18.1 – global media sport complex

- The **media** dimension entails the flow of images and information between countries that is produced by newspapers, magazines, radio, film, TV, video, satellite, cable and the internet (social media).
- The **ideological** dimension is the flow of values centrally associated with state or counter-state ideologies and movements.

The West is dominant in terms of the design, production and marketing of sports equipment, innovations emerge within the West, sport federations tend to be controlled by Western officials and global sport tournaments are usually located within the West.

White, male groups control and regulate access to global sport, and the same groups control how indigenous peoples both resist these processes and recycle their own cultural products (if at all).
For example, the Haka, or chant made by the All-Black (New Zealand Rugby Team) made just before a match is an element of Maori culture in New Zealand, and has been reincorporated within the Global Rugby Union World cup.

5.2.2 Colonial diffusion

The globalisation of individual sports

Britain invented most modern sports, including association football (soccer), rugby both Union and League, lawn tennis, badminton, table tennis, curling, cricket and squash. The British mania for codifying the rules of sports in the 19th century gave them a special influence, and they spread not only to the **British Empire**, but to everywhere Britons took themselves.

The historical migration of different sports through the British Empire was as follows:

- Cricket: India, Australia, South Africa, Caribbean Islands, New Zealand, Pakistan, Ceylon (Sri Lanka).
- Soccer: Minority sport in India, South America and USA: modified rules in Australia.
- Rugby: Australia, New Zealand, South Africa, Polynesia (especially Fiji, Samoa, and Tonga).
- Snooker started in India: UK, Australia, New Zealand, Hong Kong, Canada.
- Polo started in India, UK, Australia, USA, Argentina.
- Croquet: Australia, New Zealand.

'When people go in large numbers to other countries, and establish colonies there', writes cricket historian Rowland Bowen, 'so far from abandoning their social habits and customs, they do their best to maintain them and; not only that, to maintain them in the state they knew when the first substantial number of them arrived in their new homeland'. This, he explains, is why cricket can be found in various forms all around the World, and most especially in countries which once fell under the banner of the British Empire.

Case study - the story of cricket

Cricket was a sport spread by schools, although here it was often the missionary schools that did the work. Cricket was a noble game, a manly game, and cricket embodied the British virtues of strength, persistence, courage, healthy rivalries, camaraderie, and sportsmanship. It was a respectable game, a **Gentleman's game.**

By the late 1600s, English settlers had begun to play cricket in New England, and the game was first played in Calcutta and Bombay by the early 1700s. India, Sri Lanka, Pakistan and Bangladesh, and the British West Indian islands, Kenya, Rhodesia (now Zimbabwe), Ceylon then followed suit. Virtually every British outpost soon developed its own cricket establishment, and all took the sport up with enthusiasm. In Australia and New Zealand, cricket was introduced early in the 19th century, and made its first appearance in Cape Town, South Africa with the first British occupation of the Western Cape in the late 18th Century. The map of Africa (figure 18.2) shows in red the states and regions which formed part of the British Empire in the 19th century, and in which sport on the British pattern could flourish.

figure 18.2 – the Africa map and the Empire

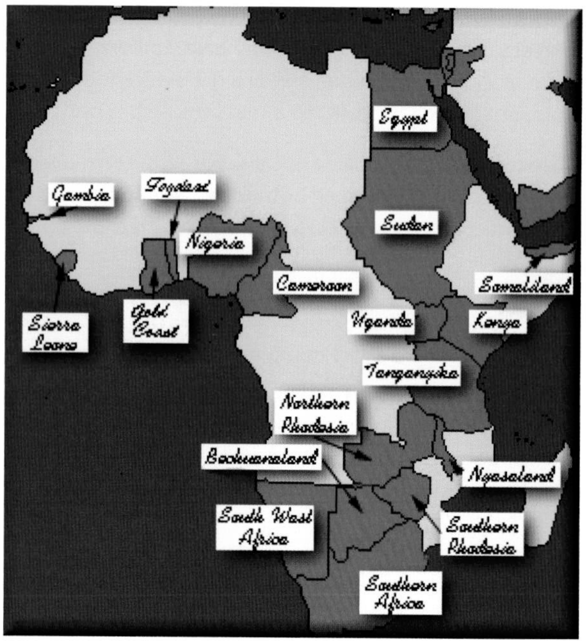

5.2.3 Development of NGBs and IGBs

UK governing bodies were originally based on the principle of amateurism and even today many governing bodies remain decentralised, supported by voluntary processes of organising and administering sport. This is a result of the historical background whereby most NGBs and sports clubs were formed by keen volunteers over 100 years ago.

The game of football (cited below) is used as an example of a case study, and briefly highlights some of the historical developments that have taken football from the pre and post creation of the Football Association to modern day settings. Note each NGB developed specifically from different timescales, geographical locations, social backgrounds and technologies in its planned approach to the provision of facilities and opportunities to participate in sport. Below are some of the issues that NGBs have encountered on this journey.

National Governing Bodies (NGBs)

Today an NGB's role is to structure the sport and oversee and organise its existing and future direction.

Each NGB is required to produce a **whole sport plan** (refer to page 208), which should include everything relating to its particular sport, through the full range of abilities from participation at the basic level, to elite level. The plan must state how that sport will achieve Sport England's '**start, stay and succeed**' objectives. Today almost £500 million has been allocated to 46 NGBs who have submitted whole sport plans that will create opportunities for more people to play community sport.

Centralised model – the way forward?

All NGBs started off as decentralised models with grass roots clubs and local associations being self governing. Many governing bodies have moved away from the decentralised model and focused on a centralised approach where all product marketing, development and promotions are controlled through one central location.

In the case of cycling the location is the National Cycling Centre in Manchester. Supported by Lottery funding, UK cycling became the World number one team from 2007 onwards. Many other governing bodies have copied this model which benefits from consistency and cost saving efficiencies. The success of GB cycling ensures a home and global fan base that is enriched and breeds success for the next generation of international athletes.

Governing bodies – amateur or professional?

The code set by governing bodies held true to the amateur ethic until the last 30 years, when they reluctantly allowed amateur rules on financial aid to be revoked. Today true professionalism has taken over the status of most sports.

Sports such as table tennis receive their funding from membership, sponsorship and lottery funding. Although table tennis is an Olympic sport, it is low in the pecking order when compared with large organisations such as British Cycling and the LTA (Lawn Tennis Association). Generally, governing bodies with small budgets and few media opportunities and sponsors are less likely to support professional elite players and thus retain many of the features of amateur sports associations.

Commercial finance and elite performers

The LTA has a big budget with its main income generated from the TV contracts and tickets sales at the Wimbledon Championships. Elite players have taken on such organisations by setting up their own player's association in order to project a 'collective voice'. For example, the PGA (Professional Golf Association), the ATP (Association of Tennis Professionals) and WTA (Womens' Tennis Association) have instigated rule changes, increases in prize money with gender equality and the extension of the competitive season to earn more money within their governing bodies. Note that the tennis IGBs are gender separate, probably because female players have had a big battle for equality with the men.

Rules and Regulations

NGBs rules and regulations have and will change considerably as technology, the impact of social media and global media evolve. NGBs (and ultimately the IGBs) are responsible for developing the rules that govern their sport based on sets of principles, policies, criteria, descriptions and or conducts governing a sport or physical activity for reasons of safety, sportsmanship, equipment or facility design and competitiveness.

- One example is the Shark suit dilemma which developed in 2009. At the 2009 World swimming championships, almost every race produced a World record swim (from 50m fly to 1500m freestyle). The suits being used were essentially wetsuits with characteristics which reduced drag when swimming. These suits were banned from the end of the 2009 season.

- Another example is the Hillsborough disaster whose report resulted in the elimination of standing terraces at all major football stadiums in England, Wales and Scotland.

- In tennis, rule changes included the introduction of the tie-breaker and Hawkeye challenges in global tournaments and the acceptance of carbon fibre rackets with a larger sweet spot and variation in stringing, to give greater spin control.

Lottery funding and team selection

NGBs are responsible for the distribution of lottery funding that supports elite athletes such as Jessica Ennis – World (2009 and 2015), Olympic (2012) heptathlon champion, and team selection for these major global events.

Each different NGB has to produce a list of supported athletes or performers, from which Sport England (or Wales, Northern Ireland or Scotland) decide on who is worthy of support depending on possible podium achievement in the next Olympic or World Championships in the sport. This support provides lifestyle funding and living expenses for the athlete.

It seems that medals to be won at major championships are the main driving force behind the NGB sense of worth. Medals produce the biggest media exposure, and therefore the best outlook for sponsorship of the sport. Hence the best guessing of the NGB administrators as to who will be most likely to win (or make the podium) will lead to the most wealthy sport.

Most of this applies to the so-called amateur sports who largely depend on lottery funding for their future. The fully professional sports (soccer, rugby, tennis, and golf for example) have built their own financial structures based on fantastic media exposure and sponsorship.

The only slight snag with this generous model, is the overlap between lottery funding and the professional sports. Examples of this are the Etihad Stadium built mostly with lottery funding for the Commonwealth Games in 2002 converted to exclusive Manchester City soccer use, and the soon to be completed (2016) conversion of the London Olympic Stadium to use by West Ham soccer club.

The rationale behind this is the future revenue possibilities (which would provide the cost of the maintenance of these expensive facilities) which the new users provide, and would therefore enable the occasional future use of the stadium for the amateur sports (for example, the 2017 World Athletics Championships at the Olympic Stadium).

Commercial pressure impact

- Over the years governing bodies have had to adapt to commercial pressures in order to maintain their status.
- Governing bodies have changed rules as a result of commercial pressures. Innovations such as the golden goal in football and the use of Hawkeye in tennis and cricket create more excitement for spectators, which increases the sport's popularity and hence the commercial revenue for both sponsors and the governing bodies.

- TV commercial breaks in play enable sponsors to advertise their products and so interruption of play is often controlled by such commercial breaks.
- Also deals made between governing bodies and the media can favour certain sports such as the alliance between Adidas and FIFA Initiatives.

- National and International Governing Bodies are continually developing initiatives. For example the English and Welsh Cricket Board's initiative 'Chance to Shine' launched in 2005.
- This initiative is aimed at reversing the decline of cricket in state schools and communities, inspiring one million more young people by 2020.
- Sports Hall Athletics provides a nationwide opportunity for all primary and secondary pupils to compete indoors in team athletics competitions that involve running, jumping and throwing.

- In addition, campaigns like '**kick racism out of football**' sponsored by major soccer clubs and governing bodies, help to defuse unacceptable racial behaviour.

- Barriers to progression in sport are discussed in detail on page 202, table 20.1. NGBs and IGBs have gone a long way to address gender, race, disability and social class issues that affect access to sporting opportunities, for example the **ParaSport Movement** and a '**Chance to Shine**' cricket scheme.
- However, some governing bodies, such as the LTA, are yet to include all members of society due to the costs and social connections needed to play tennis in the UK.

Possible corruption at the top

The IGB for athletics is the International Association of Athletics Federations - the IAAF - which has its headquarters in Monaco.

In 2015, former IAAF president Lamine Diack was arrested in France and is under investigation on suspicion of corruption and money laundering. Diack allegedly accepted '$1.2 million from the Russian Athletics Federation to cover up the positive doping tests of at least six Russian athletes in 2011'.

In late 2015, WADA (World Anti-Doping Agency) published its report, which found 'systemic failures' in the IAAF had prevented an 'effective' anti-doping programme and concluded that Russia should be banned from competing in international competitions because of its athletes' test results. This ban is still in force (July 2016), and has prevented Russia from competing in Rio.

International Governing Bodies and their function

The reason for the existence of IGBs was to coordinate the efforts of individual country's NGBs in a given sport - so that competitions should be completed on a level playing field, and people would know that competition with other countries would be fair and according to the accepted rules of the sport.

The actual function and issues faced by IGBs are summarised in figure 18.3.

The relatively recent uproar about possible corruption at the top of IGBs concerns the fact that such bodies deal with millions of dollars within the commercialisation of their sports. Some people with access to the cash feel the need to divert it into their own pockets - in spite of the good life that a sporting executive can have.

figure 18.3 – International Governing Bodies

The drug issue – anti-doping

One of the major issues in sport today is the use of legal and illegal ergogenic aids to enhance sporting performance. IGBs such as The International Olympic Committee (IOC) and International Sporting Authorities view drug taking as cheating.

- The impact of illegal drug abuse in sport has led to the development of random drug testing programmes under the supervision of **WADA** – the World Anti-Doping Agency, set up in 1998 and tasked with enforcing the international regulations on doping or drug taking.
- WADA aims to bring together governments, the IOC, International Governing Bodies and National Governing Bodies to sort out difficulties by athletes performing on the international stage.
- The impact of so many drug scandals on the society is to question whether the performances of so many great elite athletes are cheat free.

WADA has initiated a major retesting programme on global sport.

Blood and urine samples are stored in anti-doping laboratories so suspicious test results can be retested at a later date. For example, eight Russian athletes at London 2012 tested positive following retests in 2016.
Many of these athletes were medal winners and so should be stripped of their medals. These athletes can appeal against bans through Human Rights Courts, and so these disputes take a long time to resolve.

In the meantime clean athletes are waiting for medal upgrades and relevant prize money, and have lost out on opportunities of gaining commercial sponsors as well as not experiencing the glory of a medal ceremony. They may even struggle to motivate themselves to continue to training and compete within a cheating global arena.

An example of the creation and development of one of the largest and oldest national and international governing bodies is briefly cited on page 194.

Case study - football

The Football Association (The FA)

The FA is the World's oldest national governing body founded in 1863, and is responsible for all aspects of amateur and professional football in England. It is a member of FIFA and UEFA.

Before the creation of any governing bodies, the sport of football was played for centuries and originated as mob football (refer to page 173) as played by peasants and city working classes, but with no standardised rules.

Different variations on the game were played in different places, and so it was difficult for teams used to playing varying rules to play each other.

This led to the creation of 'The Football Association' (FA) - which introduced accepted formalised rules. That said, the rules for football are now controlled by the 'International Football Association Board' (IFAB), which is comprised by members of each of the associations in the UK and representatives from FIFA.

Figure 18.4 is an example of one of the first football teams (the Heathens founded in 1885) that played under the accepted rules set by the FA. Note the team kit and thousands of spectators illustrated within this figure (see page 181 for further details).

The FA was also responsible for the creation of 'The FA Cup' - which is the oldest competition in association football in the World.

Featuring prominently in the remit of the FA is control over England internationals, and team management. The FA also owns, and is based at, Wembley Stadium, in London.

figure 18.4 – the Heathens in about 1880

FIFA

With an increase in the number of international fixtures in the early 20th century it became evident that a World governing body was required. The 'Fédération Internationale de Football Association' (FIFA) is the World governing body of association football founded in 1904, and based in Zurich. It is currently comprised of 208 member national associations.

One of the main responsibilities of FIFA is the 'World Cup'. This is the World football showpiece, and is held every four years.

Women and Football

In more recent years, a World Cup for women has been formed (figure 18.5). Recent British success (bronze medal in 2015) has followed from an increase in female participation in schools.

This progression highlights the increasing standards of female players, as well as the increased interest in football by females.

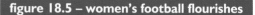

figure 18.5 – women's football flourishes

Corruption

Recently there has been alleged corruption, bribery, and vote-rigging relevant to the election of FIFA ex-president Sepp Blatter and the organization's decision to award the 2018 and 2022 World Cups to Russia and Qatar. These allegations have led to legal prosecution in the USA and the increase in popular cynicism about the fairness and honesty of the whole international sport process,

UEFA

The 'Union of European Football Associations' (UEFA) was formed in 1954 is the administrative body for association football in Europe and is by far the biggest of the confederations of FIFA, particularly in terms of money and influence.

Exam style questions

1) Discuss the part played by the British Empire in the spread of modern sports all around the World.   6 marks

2) a) What is meant by the term globalisation?   2 marks

   b) How are national cultures and cultural identities being affected by processes of globalisation?   6 marks

3) Over the years the global sports sector and global media sector have developed a self-interest relationship. Discuss.   12 marks

4) A Level. Any sport can now attract players or audiences in any part of the globe, and yet conventional wisdom suggests that as an activity takes on global stature, it becomes more controlled and competitive, disconnecting it from local origins. Discuss.   15 marks

5) The opportunity for sporting and recreational activities has varied since the 19th Century. Why were many National Governing Bodies, such as the Football Association, established in the 19th century?   3 marks

6) National Governing Bodies developed from a decentralised model. How has this model changed in the 21st century and what impact have these changes had on UK sport and society?   4 marks

7) a) Describe three functions of National Governing Bodies (NGBs)   3 marks

   b) What is the relationship between National Governing Bodies (NGBs) and International Governing Bodies (IGBs)?   4 marks

8) Describe the role Sport England plays in the development and support of National Governing Bodies.   2 marks

9) Over the years sports governing bodies have had to adapt too many external pressures in order to maintain their status with the sporting arena. How and why has this happened?   6 marks

10) Using an example from a national sport, identify a NGB sport's initiative and discuss its impact on sport and society.   5 marks

11) Identify two key functions of IGBs within today's global sports arena.   2 marks

12) All National Governing Bodies (NGBs) and International Governing Bodies (IGBs) are increasingly aware and acknowledge the need for effective sport governance. Using an example from sport, what are the effects of corruption on sport and society? How can governing bodies provide good and effective governance in sport?   10 marks

Answers link: http://www.jroscoe.co.uk/downloads/as_a1_revise_pe_edexcel/EdexcelAS_A1_ch18_answers.pdf

CHAPTER 19 - 5.2.4 The modern Olympic and other games

Characteristics and context of International Competitions

The notion of International Competitions (or World Games) is broad and can be **multi-sport** or **single sport** and usually involves the **best competitors**, the **elite**, from around the **World**. Such games may be:

- Multi-sport potentially involving all countries, for example, the Summer and Winter Olympic Games, and the Paralympic Games.
- Multi-sport involving several countries, for example, the Commonwealth Games, the African Games, and the Pan-American Games.
- Single-sport potentially involving all countries, for example, the Football FIFA World Cup, the World Athletics Championships, the World Hockey Championships, and the World Badminton Championships.

The characteristics of such global games are:
- They involve **elite performers**.
- Usually from the **whole World**, but can be regional.
- Usually require **qualification** from regional groupings or by standard.
- Most countries staging them will use them as a **shop window**.
- Often highly commercialised with **sponsorship**.
- Often with high **media** coverage (TV rights paid for as part of the finance for the event).
- Development of elite **facilities**, some or all of which will be a heritage for the future.
- Possibly involving large **spectatorship**.

Figure 19.1 outlines the factors involved in staging a global games.
- **Organisers**, the efficient handling of activities.
- **Participants**, the suitability, opportunity, comfort.
- **Spectators**, attendance provision, media provision.
- **Activities**, specified and provided.
- **Facilities**, highest standard with future potential.
- **Preparations**, ready on time.
- **Future use**, forward planning and extended value.
- **Media**, communication and commercial.
- **Travel**, convenient for training and competition.

The host country

Figure 19.2 summarises the **advantages** to a host country of staging a games:
- **Elite performers'** chance to compete against the best.
- **World audience** enlightening spectators, viewers and nations.
- **Commercial** profit through games ceremonies, merchandising and TV rights.
- The **commercial values** of successful champions.
- **Sponsorship** of performers and events.

figure 19.1 - global games

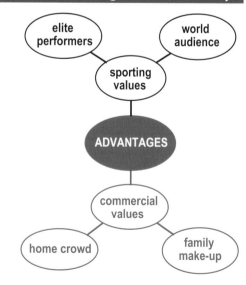

figure 19.2 - advantages to a host country

STUDENT NOTE

The influence of the USA and of the dependence of the Olympic Games on TV rights – also influenced largely by American interests – is a dominant feature of how the Olympics is allocated and organised. Commercialism, with a huge advertising audience, started in Los Angeles, 1984. This evolved into commercial TV networks owning the broadcasting rights and paying a huge price, but with World-wide advertising.

The socio-cultural factors likely to influence global games are outlined in figure 19.3:

- **Historical**, developmental background and past experience.
- **Social**, well-being of competitors, interaction during games and spectator welfare.
- **Cultural**, opportunity for nations through sport, increased awareness and wellbeing.
- **Political**, a vehicle for harmony or nationalist identity.
- **Economic**, potential national income or debt, useful future usage of facilities.
- **International**, increased national prestige, awareness and wellbeing.

figure 19.3 – socio-cultural factors

To hold a World championship may be a **shop window** for a country to display its culture and attract business and motivate a society. But recognition can be **temporary** and money spent does not necessarily help those in need in that country.

Similarly, visiting a country to compete may give a performer experience of how others do it, but it is rare if a performer will learn anything permanent from the process. It is difficult for a highly motivated and highly focused individual to learn something of a foreign culture and administration when all he or she is interested in doing is winning his or her event.

If the objective is to hold '**open**' World competition, this may be jeopardised where professionalism has led to a performing elite in some sports, which is little more than a circus. This notion of elitism and high reward has inevitably left us with an illegal drugs industry, with sports medicine and the drug testing organisations too often a step behind.

Introduction to the modern Olympic Games

Baron **De Coubertin**, founder of the Modern Olympic Games, visited English public schools including Rugby during the 1870s. He was impressed with athleticism in these schools and the linking of physical endeavour with moral integrity. He also visited the Olympian Games held at Much Wenlock, inspired by Dr Penny Brookes. De Coubertin believed that it was the character developed by exercise and games that would be the key to the re-building of France after the Franco-Prussian War. De Coubertin's Olympic dream was achieved in 1896 in Athens, when 311 athletes from 13 countries contested nine sports.

The issue of **professionalism** has always been contentious in Olympic sport. It revolved not just around whether sportsmen were paid, but whether they were gentlemen. Early Olympians would have been white, middle or upper class and wealthy. Hence moeny was not an issue - they could afford to do it!

The Olympic creed

The **Olympic Creed** was put forward in 1908: '**The most important thing in the Olympic Games is not to win but to take part, just as the most important thing in life is not the triumph but the struggle. The essential thing is not to have conquered but to have fought well'**.

The **Olympic Charter** states '**Olympism is a philosophy of life, exalting and combining in a balanced whole the qualities of body, will and mind. Blending sport with culture and education, Olympism seeks to create a way of life based on the joy found in effort, the educational value of good example and respect for universal fundamental ethical principles'**.

These statements revolve around an **ideal** notion of human behaviour including the fact that athletes should be free to participate irrespective of race, colour or creed. Mass access to sport requires that **constraints** upon cultural and sub-cultural groups should be removed. But in order for minority groups to have equality they must also have **access** and **provision**. **Access** can be denied by a numerically superior culture, self-imposed cultural constraint, and economic and topographical limitations.

The major issue, therefore, is the **exclusion** of racial minorities from existing opportunity, or the failure to **extend provision** to all. **Olympic Solidarity** programmes and the various IOC commissions are responsible for education and provision in areas of need, which are funded these days by income from television rights. The **IOC** (**International Olympic Committee**) is the organising group for the Olympic Games, and who decides policy and placement of Games.

The Summer Games are every fourth year, multiples of four: 1992, 1996, 2000, 2004, 2008 Beijing, 2012 London, 2016 Rio de Janeiro, and 2020 Tokyo. The Winter Games are also every fourth year offset by two years from the Summer Games 1994, 1998, 2002, 2006, 2010 Vancouver, 2014 Sochi, Russia, and 2018 Pyeongchang, South Korea.

Commercialisation

figure 19.4 – Montreal 1976

The commercialisation of the Olympics can be explained in terms of funding and sponsorship. The **funding** of the Olympic Games up to 1980, was largely the responsibility of the **host state** or city, which raised money out of local taxation. This nearly caused the bankruptcy of the City of Montreal (figure 19.4) following the **1976** Games. This was not quite the same with communist countries, where more general **State** funding and planning were made available.

By 1984 and the Los Angeles Summer Games, the IOC and the organising committee of this Games had realised that **sales** of anything in connection with the Games could bring in a huge income, and that global commerce would willingly pay large amounts in direct sponsorship of the Games. TV rights, clothing, logos, advertising at the venues and special edition postage stamps were all sold to bring in revenue for the games. These games' surplus was $232.5 million!

The **Atlanta Games** 1996 (figure 19.5) generated 34 sponsors and licensed 97 companies to sell products carrying the Olympic 'logo'. **The Olympic Programme** (**TOP**) was created to ensure that the main TOP sponsors are unchallenged in their category of merchandise. All TOP sponsors are multi-national companies and have the use of all Olympic symbols, **exclusive hospitality** at the Games and direct access to an advertising and public relations programme.

figure 19.5 – Atlanta 1996

Hence many global companies, Coca Cola, Kodak, McDonalds, Xerox, Swatch, and Adidas, give money to the Games organisers, so that their names will be prominently displayed.

A major problem with these arrangements is that commerce and commercials tend to dictate when events are held. **Major sponsors**, particularly the American TV networks want some say in how things are run in return for their massive investment. In some cases events are held so that TV **exposure** is maximised rather than the best time of the day for the athletes.

Opportunity

The **opportunity** for the society which holds the games – for example **London and Britain 2012** – depends on the view it takes of the **facilities** which are built. In most cases, facilities will be adapted or built to cater for the 28 sports, and 11,000+ competitors, and this has been described as the heritage to be gained by the people of Britain as reward for holding the Games. However, some facilities will be **dismantled** or **turned over** for other use after the Games. For example, athletes' accommodation was converted to domestic homes, and at present (2016) the stadium will be converted to soccer use and only made available for athletics (World Championships 2017) or other sports very occasionally.

More important to our **heritage** will be the involvement of many people in competing, watching and helping with the organisation of the Games. This will provide a big **boost** to the motivation of young people to participate in sport and possibly compete in a future Games. The desire to participate will hopefully be nurtured in the minds of many people by the sheer **proximity** of the games and identifying with **role models**.

figure 19.6 – Berlin 1936

The 'shop window' effect

The 'shop window' effect is the notion that the display of talent and excellence in both **athletic endeavour** and **organisation** of an event such as an Olympic Games, should be held up to demonstrate the high quality and **worthiness** of the National and political systems in which the games is held.

This process was first promoted by Hitler for the 1936 Games in Berlin (figure 19.6). The undesirable focus on nationalism and racism was highlighted by the dominance of some American black athletes, particularly Jesse Owens. This ideological focus was continued with the Moscow Games of 1980, but this 'shop window' effect has lessened with the fall of the USSR and its satellites.

The 'shop window'

In the Munich Olympic Games in 1972 the Black September Organisation, Palestinian terrorists used the 'shop window effect' for their own political purpose when they kidnapped and murdered eleven Israeli athletes and officials. This was the most publicised **negative event** of the Games and overshadowed the positive impact that the West German Government intended to display.

Beijing 2008

Unfortunately two million people were evicted or displaced as a result of houses being demonished to make way for transport infrastructure and facilities for the games. 40,000 protesting Chinese were imprisoned, many of these prisoners were supporters of the Tibetan freedom movement who demonstrated during the journey of the Olympic Torch around the World. These negative events tarnished the PRC's image in advance of the Games.

The IOC decided that in future the Torch would only be carried within the realms of the host country. So prior to London 2012, the torch was carried at length around the UK.

The **success** of the Beijing Olympics was dependent on several key factors:

* The Chinese State (Peoples Republic of China - PRC) spent large sums of money on the project, including superb facilities such as the Bird's Nest (the Olympic Stadium – figure 19.7).
* The **facilities** ensured that many World records were broken including 3 World records for Usain Bolt in the 100m, 200m, 4x100m relay.
* 1.4 million **volunteers**, drafted in from all over China, were crucial to the organisation of the games.
* The **security** was ever present throughout the city, and there were rigorous bag and body searches (akin to airport security procedures, but becoming more normal for entry to any venue in 2016) prior to entering the Olympic venues.
* The **population** seemed to support the games not only in person (each adult could apply for 2 tickets within a lottery system), but also on TV.
* 986 million Chinese people watched at least 1 hour of the games' coverage on TV.

figure 19.7 – the Bird's Nest - courtesy of Anwar El Bizanti

* Live games coverage was broadcast on public transport such as trains and buses.
* Up to 4 TV channels were exclusively dedicated to the games in China.
* The reward was manifested in the **overall medal table** - China 51 gold, 21 silver, 28 bronze ahead of the United States of America, Russia and Britain.
* The **1000 strong Chinese team** was thoroughly prepared to take on the World with no expense spared.
* Chinese competitors seemed to be winning not only for personal glory, but also for the honour of the PRC.

China has used the Olympic Games to **inspire its population** to participate in sports not usually engaged in in their country.
* In **cycling** 'A record breaking 7 riders were entered in the games and public interest has never been greater. People are seeing that there is much more to cycling than just transportation'. Quote in the China Post Thursday August 28th 2008.
* In **rowing**, China won its first Olympic gold medal in the women's quadruple sculls. 'We were hungry for a great leap forward in this event' quote from the Chinese rowing coach in the China Post Thursday August 28th 2008.

China ensured that their organisation, standard of participation, and number of gold medals demonstrated how wonderful the Chinese Government and people were throughout the Beijing Games of 2008. This is the 'shop window'. London 2012 enabled British sport to move forward. The success of Team GB has continued into Rio 2016!

London 2012 as a World Games

The **opportunity** for the society which holds the games – for example **London and Britain 2012** (figure 19.8 and 19.9) – depends on the view it takes of the **facilities** which have been adapted or built to cater for the 28 sports and 11,000+ competitors.

This has been described as the **heritage** to be gained by the people of Britain as reward for holding the Games. However, some facilities have been **dismantled** or **turned over** for other use after the Games. For example, athletes' accommodation have been converted to domestic homes, and the stadium is being reduced in size so that lower numbers can be accommodated for large events such as the World Athletic Championships 2017, and domestic soccer - West Ham United.

More important to our **heritage** has been the involvement of many people in **competing**, **watching** and **helping** with the organisation of the Games.

This has provided a big **boost** to the motivation of young people to **participate** in sport and possibly contribute as a **volunteer** in future Games. For example, the volunteer numbers for the Commonwealth Games in Glasgow 2014 were oversubscribed. The desire to participate will hopefully be nurtured in the minds of many people by the sheer **proximity** of the games and identifying with **role models**.

London 2012 enabled British sport to move forward and improve on the fantastic results of 2008. Unfortunately, the Government policy of **austerity** has already led to the closure of athletics facilities at the Don Valley Stadium in Sheffield - training facilities used by Jessica Ennis, Olympic Champion in the Heptathlon 2012.

figure 19.8 – London2012

figure 19.9 – facilities as a heritage

Government issues

Holding the 2012 Olympic Games was an obvious reason for Britain to join the USA, Australia, and China in a drive to achieve sporting excellence. Issues connected with this could be:
- **National pride**, highlight political superiority, prestige and advertising for the host country (shop window?).
- The British Government has a **political motive** for pouring money into sport in the UK.
- Improvement in sporting **facilities**, meeting society's demands for national sporting success.
- The **re-generation** of a whole London district.
- Improvements to trade, economy, tourism, **infrastructure** - transport, housing, hotels.
- A stimulus to a nation faced with excessive obesity.
- Encourages **mass participation** in sport.
- Enables individuals to **succeed** (due to increased provision).

Impact on the individual

Higher levels of performance have meant a need for full-time athletes. The Olympic Games of the twenty-first century now fully supports the idea of professionalism. The Games were now open but the majority of performers remain amateur or rely on state/lottery funding. Boundaries are constantly being stretched through sponsorship and funding.

But the concept of sportsmanship has been replaced by gamesmanship, and so some athletes will do anything to win, including tampering with equipment and taking performance-enhancing drugs. However, most of today's athletes will still have that love and desire to compete and demonstrate the honour that comes with competing for one's country.

We know how we felt in 2008 when Rebecca Adlington took on the World and won. Now that the Olympics are '**professional**', the limit of achievement is no longer our cricket and football. Hence we can now produce champion swimmers (figure 19.10), cyclists and athletes as well as rowers, riders and sailors who continue to provide numbers of medals.

figure 19.10 – Rebecca Adlington, swim sports star

Impact on the individual

In London 2012, **all** elite athletes, not just the socially privileged ones, had the chance to achieve their potential, because of **funding** and **organisation**. These two factors made possible the astonishing success of GB athletes who won a total of 65 medals - the greatest performance of a GB team at the Olympics to date.

Individuals are:
*   **Motivated** by high competitive drive (i.e. the will to be the best - intrinsic motivation).
*   Able to meet **personal goals** - to be number one in the World!
*   Able to develop a **career** and to gain recognition or sponsors - extrinsic motivation (rewards).
*   Inspired by **role models**.
*   **Encouraged** by peer or family.
*   Given the **opportunity**, **pride** or **satisfaction** to represent his or her own country.
*   Given the opportunity to **perform** at the **highest** level.

The disadvantages to the individual of this process are:
*   **High expectation** for individual to do well in future events.
*   **Increased pressure** on the individual to over-train and perform even whilst injured.
*   An individual may become **over-confident** or complacent with success.
*   There will be increased media attention and **intrusion** into individual's private life.

Table 19.1 – **summary of issues affecting World games**

the performer can obtain:	the spectator receives or develops:	commercial interests obtain:
celebrity status	excitement	money or revenue
sponsorship deals	entertainment	advertising
advertising deals	escapism	raised profile
personal satisfaction	fan base	boosts to business
high earning potential	encouragement into sport	association with elite performers
recognition		
respect		

Other international sporting competitions

European Championships from 2018

Each year, a number of sports have a World or European Championships and a new multi-sport European championships begins in 2018 in an attempt to coordinate the different sport into a single entity.

The European Governing Bodies for athletics, swimming, cycling, rowing, triathlon, gymnastics and golf will coordinate their individual continental championships between 1 and 12 August 2018, hosted by the cities of Berlin (already chosen as the host for the 2018 European Athletics Championships), and Glasgow - already chosen as the host for the 2018 European Aquatics Championships, and which will now also host the events of other sports.

The European Championships in cycling, rowing, triathlon, gymnastics, and mixed (both men and women) team golf will be also held in Glasgow, the golf will be held at Gleneagles, and will be the first occasion that both men and women's European golf will be coordinated via their governing bodies.

This is a **commercially driven initiative**, since the European Broadcasting Union (the umbrella body for the continent's free-to-air channels) are expected to generate more than 2700 hours of programming and reach a live television audience of more than 850 million viewers. This approach aims to bring the existing European Championships together in a sustainable format once every four years in order to continue building their prestige, profile and media exposure.

The new European Games from 2015

The European Games is an international multi-sport event in the Olympic tradition contested by athletes from European nations. The Games were envisioned and are to be controlled by the European Olympic Committees (EOC). They now have a logo (figure 19.11), an administrative structure, a president and a building!

The 2015 European Games, the first edition of the event, took place in Baku, Azerbaijan in June 2015, and further editions are planned every four years thereafter. The Baku Games catered for 20 sports with 253 events from 50 nations and including 5,898 athletes.

figure 19.11 – the European Games logo

The impact of both European Championships and Games is the broadening of **exposure** and **opportunity** for performance for elite athletes and possibly the enhancement of earning opportunities for this group. There has been significant criticism about these games because they are possibly an unnecessary addition to the global sporting calendar, hence not attractive to the sports superstars which does not therefore attract the media. This may happen because the European Olympic Committees do not control the individual sports, and therefore do not control the individual sports stars.

The first edition of the Games also received heavy criticism from organisations such as 'Sport for Rights' calling for athletes to speak out against human rights violations in Azerbaijan, since many regime opponents were jailed in the run-up to the Games.

The Commonwealth Games

This games was first held in Hamilton, Canada and was formerly known as the British Empire Games. Due to the changing relationship between the countries within the British Empire, the Commonwealth Games have had a variety of names: 1930-1950, The British Empire Games; 1954-1966, The British Empire and Commonwealth Games; 1970-1974, The British and Commonwealth Games; and from 1978 to date, The Commonwealth Games.

US athletes tended to dominate the Olympic Games (general opinion also felt that the Americans were unsporting in their behaviour), and equally, Empire countries felt a loss of international status and power. Thus, there was a desire for a smaller, more private games, with the 2006 games held in Melbourne, the 2010 games in Delhi, and the 2014 games in Glasgow. The 2018 games will be held in the Gold Coast, Australia.

The impact of such games can be evaluated in many ways. For example, official research says that the impact of the Glasgow 2014 Commonwealth Games led to £282m worth of tourism supporting 2,137 jobs, 690,000 visitors travelled to the city to attend the games and hotel occupancy in Glasgow reached 95%, thereby contributing £73m to the country's economy. However, it is too early to say whether sporting participation among the Scottish public has increased in the wake of the event.

It is notable that at the 2015 Athletics World Championships, for the first time Commonwealth athletes took a bigger share of the medals than the rest of the international community.

Exam style questions

1) A Level. In 1896 the modern Olympic Games were established around the principle of the 'amateur ideal'. Discuss whether this principle is still relevant to Olympic performers in the twenty first century.　　15 marks

2) a) Identify three goals of the Olympic movement that together define Olympism.　　3 marks

   b) Suggest two ways in which the Olympic ideal is no longer apparent today.　　2 marks

3) a) In relation to global sporting events, what is meant by the phrase 'the shop window effect'?　　2 marks

   b) Using examples from past major global games highlight some of the positive and negative impacts that the 'shop window' effect may have had on national and political groups.　　6 marks

Exam style questions

4) Describe the limitations which existed in the early Modern Olympic Games.   4 marks

5) Discuss the characteristics of World games, and explain how participation in such a games will affect the competitor.
                                                                                                                  8 marks

6) Team GB won 29 gold medals, 17 silver medals and 19 bronze medals during the London 2012 Olympic Games, finishing third in the medal table. Suggest the potential positive and negative impacts that participating in World Games can have on the elite athlete and society.   12 marks

7) The London 2012 Olympic Legacy is described as the longer-term benefits and effects of the planning, funding, building and staging of the Olympic and Paralympic Games in the summer of 2012. Evaluate the success of this legacy.   6 marks

8)

		gold	silver	bronze	total
	Montreal 1976				
1	**USSR**	49	41	35	125
2	**GDR**	40	25	25	90
3	**USA**	34	35	25	94
13	**Great Britain**	3	5	5	13
	Atlanta 1996				
1	**USA**	44	32	25	101
2	**Russia**	26	21	16	63
3	**Germany**	20	18	27	**65**
36	**Great Britain**	1	8	6	15
	London 2012				
1	**USA**	46	29	29	104
2	**China**	38	27	23	88
3	**Great Britain**	29	17	19	65
4	**Russia**	24	26	32	82

The table above lists parts of the medal league tables for 1976, 1996 and 2012 Olympic Games. Using this information answer the following questions.

a) Give reasons why the USSR and East Germany (GDR) dominated the medal league table in the 1976 Olympic Games.
                                                                                                                  3 marks

b) Account for the dramatic improvements in Team GB's medal haul from 1976 to 2012.   3 marks

c) Discuss the notion that 'a homefield' advantage plays a significant part in medal league tables.   3 marks

d) Why has the USA been consistently at or near the top of the medal league table?   3 marks

e) Following the Beijing Olympic Games in 2008, account for China's position on the 2012 London medal table league.
                                                                                                                  3 marks

f) Following the London 2012 Olympic Games, discuss the impact of the World Anti-Doping Agency (WADA) retesting programme on global sport.   3 marks

9) The global sports programme is increasing each year with new competitions, such as the multi-sports European Championships to be held in 2018. Discuss the impact of increased sporting opportunities for elite performers. 5 marks

Answers link: http://www.jroscoe.co.uk/downloads/as_a1_revise_pe_edexcel/EdexcelAS_A1_ch19_answers.pdf

CHAPTER 20 - *Barriers to participation, and mass participation*

5.3.1 Barriers to participation

Figure 20.1 outlines four factors which could be **barriers to participation.**

Table 20.1 summarises the issues which may act as barriers to participation.

figure 20.1 – barriers to participation

Table 20.1 – barriers to participation (SE = socio-economic)
         (TASS = Talented Athlete Sponsorship Scheme)

gender	race and ethnicity	disability	social class
women are discriminated against in sport - and in society	black and Asian people discriminated against in society	9% participation in sport (lower than able-bodied)	lack of financial support a big barrier
there are still stereotypical attitudes to female participation	25% soccer premiership players black, hardly any Asians	great success in Paralympics - 2nd in medal table Beijing	parental support important at young age
in Beijing, 45% of participants were female - opportunity	50% UK athletics power event competitors black	elite athletes funded from lottery same as able-bodied	elite amateur athletes funded from lottery - provision
in Athens 40% of British team were women, in IOC only 14% are women, the glass ceiling applies to female participation	in tennis no black and only one Asian competitor in UK top ten - opportunity	Sports Aid helps performers in 25 disabled sports compared with 50 able-bodied - opportunity	participation from lower SE groups about 55% lower when compared to upper SE groups
women's top soccer is still semi-professional	in UK rugby, very few black players	still lack of access to some sports facilities	some activities associated with upper SE status people
before 2007, men's prize money at Wimbledon was more than women's - esteem 2016 figures are £2 million each	no research evidence that black Afro-Caribbean people have more fast twitch muscle, or less subcutaneous fat	age limit for TASS funding raised to 35 compared with 25 for able-bodied	amateur sports have fewer low SE status elite performers
top sportswomen have 14% of income of top men, and find it harder to get sponsorship	hence stereotype of black Afro-Caribbean potential at sport incorrect	low levels of sponsorship	membership of some sport clubs only open to financially independent people
women's boxing, pole vault, triple jump, hammer & weight lifting only allowed since 1987	lack of role models in low black participation sport discourages new participants	lack of media exposure compared to able-bodied sport - lack of esteem	low SE group people have less leisure time than upper SE groups - opportunity
female sport has less social status than male sport	media reflect society's view of black people	media focus on adversity rather than ability	fewer people from low SE groups participate after 16
females get less media space or time than males in the UK	great success from male Asian boxers and cricketers		unless talent identified young, low SE people drop out
women's fitness - hence muscularity - causes media to call into question sexuality	low socio-economic status of many black Afro-Caribbean people prevents participation		
media focus on women's appearance rather than sport			

Discrimination

Deliberate **social discrimination** is largely a thing of the past in that, legally and by general public consent, discrimination should not exist in our **democratic society**.

In the past, there have been groups of **advantaged** people, primarily reflecting **social class** differences. Also the traditional place of **women** in society and attitudes to **disabled** people, have produced discrimination. In addition, newly arriving **ethnic** groups, particularly those from the old colonies, have been discriminated against on their arrival. There is little doubt that vestiges of this discrimination still exist among groups of people, but this is being fought against at individual, group and government level, especially in sport. The best example of this is probably the FA slogan '**Let's Kick Racism out of Football**'.

Stereotyping

figure 20.2 – stereotyping in sport?

In most cases of discrimination against groups of people in our society, **stereotypes** have been formed (figure 20.2), largely justifying the **presumed inferiority** of these groups. Basically, stereotyping concerns the attitudes of parts of the population about the place and capability of other parts of the population. Usually, this takes the form of assumed inferiority, which may be based on **tradition, gender, genetics or ethnicity, wealth, age** or even a resistance to change.

An example of stereotyping which presumes **superiority** in certain activities is that of the attitude of some of the white population to participation of black people in sport. The stereotype is that black people are more likely to be good at sport, but less likely to be good at academic studies. Here the stereotype has a plus and a minus **assumed** capability. Another example is that of **women** in strength, endurance and contact sports. The stereotype assumes that female sportspeople are less capable at these activities.

Inclusiveness

It has been a fundamental feature of government policy in recent years to **include all members** of society in whatever activities are available to the majority.

This contrasts with the past where there was the effective **exclusion** of certain parts of the population from some activities which most people nowadays would normally expect to do. On a very basic level, the attitude of the majority of the population to the disabled 100 years ago was to separate certain disabled people into inferior education facilities. The most disabled were locked up in asylums (mental hospitals). Such people were looked after, but not allowed participation in main-stream society.

Today there is a very strong move to engage disabled people in all aspects of society including sport (participation in the Paralympics is an example of this), and this is an example of **inclusiveness**.

The same thing used to happen to some extent for the elderly. Stereotypes of the elderly used to be that people over 60 were past it, and not capable of enjoying sporting activity. Nowadays, older people are **included** in all plans for sports facilities – and this can be productive for health as well as **self-esteem** and confidence of the people involved.

Government policy on inclusion encompasses a much wider brief than sport. Unemployment, poor skills, low incomes, poor housing, high crime, bad health and family breakdown are the very broad reasons for this policy. Sport as a vehicle for improving health and reducing crime is therefore an important element of official inclusion policy.

Prejudice

Prejudice can be defined as '**a prejudgement of a person, group, or situation usually based on inadequate information or inaccurate or biased information which reinforces stereotypes**'.

Prejudice is the outcome of negative attitudes and stereotyping by one part of the population towards another part of the population. An example of this is that women are often excluded from male dominated sports clubs or events. It is expected that females will not be interested or want to participate in the sport in question (golf, rugby, boxing). A further element of prejudice is that the minority's feelings or opinions about the situation are ignored. People prejudiced against female participation usually do not listen to or believe arguments that women should be allowed to participate.

For these reasons, **target groups** have been identified in sport so that all participants can have equal opportunity to participate. This is an on-going campaign in this country where the slogan of '**Sport for All**' is not yet achievable because of continued discrimination. This is also because of inadequate funding and lack of available facilities for the under privileged.

Disability

The term **disability** implies loss of ability in certain activities due to **impairment**. Impairment covers various categories including:

- Mental, visual, and hearing impairments.
- Cerebral Palsy.
- Les autres.
- Quadriplegic and paraplegic conditions.
- Amputees.

There has always been a conflict of attitude between ability and disability in the context of sport, since most conditions have little or no effect on the capability of a person to **participate** in and enjoy sporting activities. **Opportunity** is often limited by the **attitudes** of the able-bodied and also by the low **self-esteem** by some who suffer from impairments. The main issue being tackled is **access**, where public sport facilities are now required to have ramps and wide doorways to allow wheelchair access. The **Paralympic Games** and numerous marathons have highlighted disabled people's potential success at World level.

figure 20.3 – polo as an upper class sport

Social class

The underlying exclusiveness of certain activities lies in the traditional division of British society into **social classes**. Historically this has been based on power, where the strong dominated the weak in terms of the wealthy controlling the poor. For example, the serfs used to till the land belonging to the landed rich. This was due in the first instance to the ownership of land, and later due to the control of the workplace in industrialised Britain. Additionally, women, the disabled, the aged and immigrants have been discriminated against as part of these social constraints.

Because sport was part of these **exclusive** phases in the growth of our society, discrimination can be identified in sport as it reflected **power and influence**. For example, only the upper class was allowed to hunt in the 18th century, only the gentry went to the public schools in the early years of 19th century athleticism. Only the middle class and above could afford bicycles until the end of the 19th century and so on.

figure 20.4 – golf as a middle class sport

Today, there are traditions where certain groups try to maintain their class identity through sport. For example, sports involving horses still have an upper class association (figure 20.3), while certain games are popular among middle class (figure 20.4) and working class groups. In the case of football, this is probably the result of historic links with traditional mob football. None of these activities are exclusive, but represent vestiges of a past in which there was resistance to change because of tradition, cost and fashion. There has been no direct attempt to target the more exclusive upper class sports other than the recent ban on hunting, which was based more on its presumed cruelty than its exclusiveness.

Ethnicity

figure 20.5 – Usain Bolt superstar

Race and **ethnic** difference issues include the view that **Asian** communities who have emigrated from Kenya and Uganda into Britain have not regarded sport as a career route. Others from the Indian sub-continent have been too busy surviving and coping with the English language to participate widely in sport. In some areas, Asian soccer and cricket leagues are producing good teams with outstanding players. Many female Asian Moslems have tended to have had limited opportunities in sport.

The **Afro-Carribean** ethnic community brought cricket with them and love their cricket and have shown outstanding ability in boxing, soccer and athletics (figure 20.5).

Some of this may be a reflection of American cultural attitudes, with its high profile and role models in boxing, American football and basketball. Nowadays, black British sportspeople, male and female, have a substantial place in all our sporting activities and demonstrate a natural ability and enthusiasm. There are relatively few soccer spectators with an ethnic background, probably due to resistance from existing fans. Racism in the football ground has been largely stopped as a result of the policy of '**Let's Kick Racism out of Football**'.

Gender

STUDENT NOTE There is a full discussion of gender issues on pages 184 and 185.

Age

figure 20.6 – exercise while ageing

There is little doubt that our education system is trying to give physical education the status it should have by giving children every opportunity to participate in sport, and by allowing the talented to be recognised through the introduction of specialist schools and colleges for sport. However, in the private sector there is still a resistance to **junior** membership in clubs.

Restriction on **elderly** participation in physical recreation and sport is due to the **outmoded stereotypical views** that exercise by the old can be fatal, that to be elderly is to be inactive, and that ageing makes one incapable of enjoying competitive physical activity.

In reality, regular physical activity and sport for the elderly is most **valuable** in terms of physical health (figure 20.6), morale and self-esteem. **Opportunities** have increased in which many sports governing bodies have their veteran or masters policy which has resulted in a huge uptake for each veteran age group. **Access** to centres offering exercise and recreational facilities has been a major problem, but non-peak periods during the day are now offered free or at low cost to the elderly in many sports centres. The main problem is the lack of **esteem** of elderly females brought up as non-participants in sport, but aerobics has grown in popularity with this group of women.

This identification of **age** with **disability**, represents a minority group within each of the three main discriminated groups and is easily overlooked, but should be an additional area to recognise as a focus for **inclusiveness** in sport.

Questions

1) Outline the issues faced by top female sportspeople as they strive to obtain sponsorship from a top sporting sponsor.

2) What is meant by inclusiveness in sport?

3) With reference to figures 20.3 (page 206) and 20.5, explain how social class may affect a person's choice of sport.

Impact of wearable technology on participation

Clothing for the climate

figure 20.7 – clothing according to climate

The fashion industry for sport is a multi-million pound industry worn by the sports superstars as adverts for the product on behalf of the manufacturer - for a substantial fee!!!

The technology around this clothing is based on the production of a range of stretchable, breathable, wicking or waterproof fabrics suitable for rainproof, windproof, or cold weather, or on the other hand sun or hot temperatures (figure 20.7).

figure 20.7 – clothing according to climate

Lycra sports clothing reduces air resistance, and special shark suits (which simulate shark skin) reduces drag for the swimmers. 130 World records were set in the 2008 and 2009 seasons, which led to FINA banning the use of these shark suits in official competition from 2010.

Provided that basic decency is maintained within the rules of a sport, fashion can dictate the shape, colour, and dimensions of kit worn. The notion of showing off your purchase of the latest kit during your Park Run on Saturday mornings - this must stimulate participation.

Clothing for the sport

In the gym, the wearing of rubber belts or strapping to increase hydrostatic pressure from within the body part is becoming more widespread. Specialist one shoulder javelin suits and bench press or squatting suits in which force from the belt supports the tissue enclosed from the inside, are becoming more popular.

This is in addition to the latest trainers with foot support (including podiatratic sole inserts), all of which are expensive additions to the sporting budget and incentives for participation.

Loughborough University Sports Technology Institute

Loughborough University have a Sports Technology Institute, examples of whose tasks include reassessing how **footwear** can be made to match the **shape and mechanics** of feet on an individual basis. The foot is scanned to capture its shape, then footfall is analysed (using forceplate technology). This indicates exactly how the foot lands and moves, and leads to the construction of personalised footwear, which aims to make movement more efficient and improve performance.

> **STUDENT NOTE**
>
> The wearable technology such as GPS and heart rate monitors are discussed on page 108 above. Such technology is becoming an essential part of today's participation in events such as Park Run and mass marathons.

5.3.2 Concept of mass participation

Mass participation reflects the democratisation of sport, where everyone wishing to engage in any sport should be able to do so. This is what is meant by **mass participation**. This democratisation of sport is an ongoing process, where limits to **opportunity**, **provision** and **esteem** still exist in some sports. It suggests the availability of a sport development pyramid where ability and effort can take a performer to the top.

The opportunity, provision and esteem issues outlined above are **social problems**, caused by exclusivity, inequality and insecurity, particularly where discrimination continues to exist by **wealth**, **age**, **gender**, **race** or **disability**.

Mass participation

Mass participation is a necessary first stage at the foundation and participation levels of the sport development pyramid and the pursuit of excellence.

The sports development pyramid

This is a participation pyramid (figure 20.8) which demonstrates how the early **mass participation** either in schools or in the community provides the very broad base of the pyramid. This will lead to a broad base or **foundation** activity, where many people try things out and play many different activities, a proportion of these people would progress to **participation**, where particular sports become important at the basic competitive level.

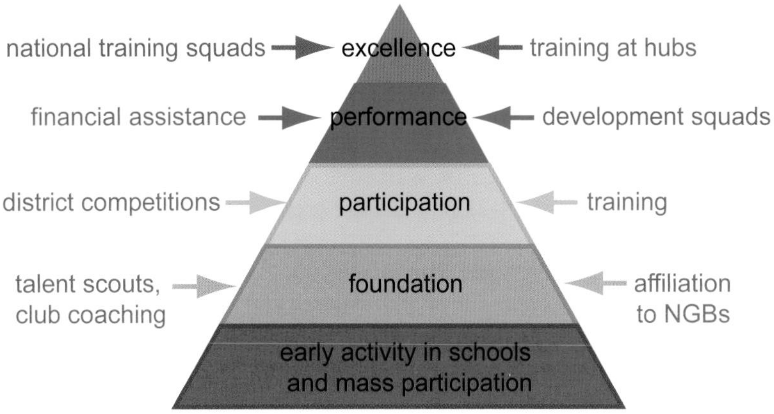

A smaller number become involved at a higher level, which involves training and directed activity where **performance** is improving, and from this group would emerge a much smaller group who would have the talent and ability to reach a stage of excellence which could be described as **elite performance**.

figure 20.8 – sports development pyramid

national training squads → excellence ← training at hubs

financial assistance → performance ← development squads

district competitions → participation ← training

talent scouts, club coaching → foundation ← affiliation to NGBs

early activity in schools and mass participation

As discussed above, this last group are the main focus of the NGBs as they strive for recognition, funding based on medal count, and media exposure which will drive sponsorship and income.

Figure 20.9 shows a breakdown of the activities and their availability for various groups in society by age, outlining the factors affecting opportunity and provision for most people in the UK.

Figure 20.10 shows the ultimate in mass participation as some 60,000 people set off on the London Marathon.

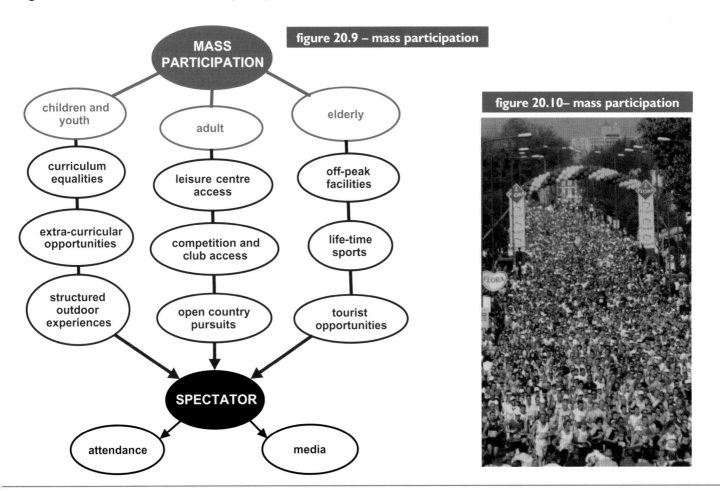

figure 20.9 – mass participation

MASS PARTICIPATION

children and youth → curriculum equalities → extra-curricular opportunities → structured outdoor experiences

adult → leisure centre access → competition and club access → open country pursuits

elderly → off-peak facilities → life-time sports → tourist opportunities

SPECTATOR → attendance, media

figure 20.10– mass participation

Initiatives to promote community participation

figure 20.11 – initiatives

Whole Sport Plans

Whole Sport Plans are the delivery contract between **Sport England** and each of the 46 funded **National Governing Bodies** for Sport (NGBs), who will be tasked with delivery of increased participation for young people under 16. The 2013-17 Whole Sport Plans will reach down to age 14, with 60% of NGB funding focused on the 14-25 year old age group.

To be eligible for Whole Sport Plan funding, NGBs must also meet high standards of **governance** and financial **control**. All public funding allocated will be published and meet Government transparency guidelines. See figure 20.11.

Sports Colleges

Sports Colleges were established by the **Youth Sports Trust** to bring into action the government (1997 to 2010) policy on school academies for sport in the age group 11 to 16. There were approximately 475 Sports Colleges in England and Wales (in November 2008), each with extra funding for facilities and staff to improve participation and develop excellence in sport among their pupils. Such facilities and expertise were also to be available to feeder junior schools.

These schools were particularly targeted for the 2 hours per week of PE or sport for every child. They aimed to improve the expertise of their staff (in terms of coaching and knowledge of sports), and made all possible use of new technologies when encouraging and developing participation in physical activity.

A new Youth Sports strategy

The present government (2016) and former coalition government (2010 to 2015) recreated the organisation and structure involved in Sport Colleges and the Youth Sport Trust to identify the role of **School Games Organiser** (**SGO**). The money for these government funded 3 days per week posts is not ring fenced to sport. The point of this policy is to enable school **autonomy** and **diversity** in respect of sport provision in schools.

Youth Sport Trust Strategic Plan

The plan outlines the core purpose, values and the impact it aims to achieve over the next 5 years - all underpinned by its mission to use the power of sport to change young people's lives.

It offers a simple overview of the Trust's vision and future ambitions for the period 2013-2018 and makes clear that:
* Every child needs the best possible sporting start in life.
* All young people deserve a sporting chance.
* All young people should be supported to achieve their sporting best in school and in life.

Sporting start

Aims to provide primary school children with a solid foundation in physical activity to prepare them for later life, helping shape them into healthy, social and active young people.

Achieved by offering primary practitioners access to a range of revolutionary teaching methods and supporting resources for Key Stage 1 PE and a national training programme to support the teaching of Key Stage 2 pupils.

Sporting chance

Aims to provide innovative and exciting ways to engage and inspire all young people, regardless of their age or ability, so they have the chance to take part in high quality physical education and meaningful school sport and enjoy being active.

Sporting best

Sporting Best is a dedicated strand of work for secondary PE and school sport. It aims to engage with teaching and school sport professionals, young leaders, coaches, volunteers and National Governing Bodies of Sport to deliver programmes, conferences and events that help young people to be the best they can be, in sport and in life.

Initiatives delivered by the Youth Sport Trust include:

- **School Games** focus on helping more young people enjoy competitive sport and impact on their learning and life skills.
- **Sky Sports Living for Sport** programme is aimed at helping disengaged young people to discover personal skills, self-confidence and achieve more through sport.
- **Matalan yoUR Activity** programme supports young people who are not motivated by more traditional sports enabling them to have the opportunity to try out alternative sports (this is part of the TOP Sport programme - see page 212).
- **Change4Life Sports Clubs** for less active youngsters helping them adopt healthly lifestyles.
- **Young Ambassadors** (page 213) and Sports leaders UK (page 212) programmes aim to empower young people to inspire their peers and to develop their leadership abilities. Plus development of the next generation of volunteers in sport.

Within the plan the Youth Sport Trust has ambitious targets over the next 5 years to have:

- Changed the lives of **one million** primary school children.
- Reached **250,000 young leaders, volunteers and teachers**, dedicating time to change young people's lives.
- Enabled **2.5 Million young people** to achieve their personal best.

The notion of **School Games** provides a framework for competitive sport at school, district, county, and national levels with funding from lottery (increased to 20% of the 'good causes' lottery budget in 2012), public and private sectors of £150million until 2015 and onwards.

The coalition government (2010–2015) introduced the **new Youth Sports strategy** in an attempt to increase participation of the Nation's youth after the age of 16 – when at present two thirds of girls and one third of boys cease to undertake any meaningful sporting activity.

The aim is to increase the number of people developing a **sporting habit for life**.

Sport England works with schools, colleges, universities, National Governing Bodies, local authorities, the voluntary sector, and County Sports Partnerships established from the Youth Sport Trust initiatives of the previous government.

The idea is to establish a **lasting network** of links between schools and sports clubs which will keep young people in sports after 25.

There is additional financial support from Sainsbury's, and the Department of Health and Sport England, whilst Adidas has pledged to provide 1600 young athletes with sport's kit.

Sportivate

Sportivate is a Sport England, London 2012 and Lottery funded initiative and was launched in June 2011 as a four-year programme aimed at 14-25 year-olds. Due to its success, additional funding of £10m per year has been invested allowing the programme to run until March 2017.
From September 2013, Sportivate extended its age group so that 11-13 year-olds can also take part.

This **London 2012 legacy project** gives young people the chance to discover a sport that they love.

Sportivate offers access to free and subsidised coaching in a variety of sports and activities in order to give young people a taste of just how fun, enjoyable and social sport can be. There is a wide range of activities on offer including judo, golf, tennis, wakeboarding, athletics, and parkour training.

During the six-to-eight weeks, those taking part can work towards an event or personal challenge, and when the free or low-cost coaching has finished they will be supported to continue playing sport.

Sportivate is **inclusive** and targets a variety of young people including those who have a disability and people from black and minority ethnic groups.

Step into Sport – Sports leaders UK

Sport relies on 1.5 million volunteer officials, coaches, administrators and managers. The government has identified a gap in the plans for expansion of participation of people in sport at all levels. This is the need for more instructors, coaches and leaders in sport. The purpose of the **Step into Sport** programme is to increase the quality, quantity and diversity of young people engaged in volunteering and leadership.

- **Sports leaders UK** is a trust (formerly The British Sports Trust) which provides opportunities for young people aged 14–19 particularly to obtain a qualification which can be recognised by those organising sports events at local or national levels.
- **Sports leaders UK** can give experience in how to organise activities and how to motivate and communicate with people.
- **Sports leaders courses** encourage volunteering in community activities and aim to reduce youth crime by including vulnerable young people in positive activities.

There are **four** levels of awards (promoted by Sportsleaders UK and the YST):

- The Junior Sports Leader Award (**JSLA**) for 14-16 year olds, graduated into **3 STEPS**:

   1. **STEP ON:** Students learn to plan, manage and run their own sports season as part of their PE programme.

   2. **STEP IN:** Focuses on how schools can utilise KS4 (Key Stage 4, 14-16 year olds). Students become active volunteers. For example, supporting inter-school competition. Volunteers are awarded the NGB Introductory Leadership Award. This then extends into how to plan, manage and deliver a festival of sport and dance.

   3. **STEP OUT:** This aspect of Step into Sport is on the movement of young people from school-based volunteering to community-based volunteering through the provision of placements in high quality community clubs. Young people are supported by their school mentor and county sport partnership (CSP) to source a volunteer placement. The final stage of the STEP OUT programme is the **Step into Sport On-line Volunteer Passport** and it allows every young volunteer to log and manage their volunteering online and supports volunteers to qualify in NGB specific coaching awards.

- The Community Sports Leader Award (**CSLA**) for the 16+ age group.
- The High Sports Leader Award (**HSLA**) develops CSLA award holders to be able to lead specific groups such as the disabled or junior children, includes first-aid and event management, and can lead to sports coaching awards.
- The Basic Expedition Leader Award (**BELA**) is aimed at people who would like to safely lead outdoor activities and organise overnight camps.

TOP programme - TOP play and TOP sport

- The TOP Programme (National Lottery funded), is a national initiative developed and coordinated by the Youth Sports Trust aimed at Primary aged children (figure 20.12).

figure 20.12 – TOP programme

TOP play 4 - 9 → TOP programme → TOP sport 7 - 11

- It is a joint curriculum (school) and community programme that is designed to encourage sports participation and develop skills associated with this.
- Developed to support teachers, leaders, coaches and other adults in introducing young people into sport, the TOP Programme appeals to all levels of ability including those with special needs.

Target groups
- TOP Play is designed to support 4 to 9 year olds as they develop core skills.
- TOP Sport provides 7 to 12 year olds with opportunities to develop skills in a range of specific sports.

Resources
TOP Play and TOP Sport are similar in that they include resource cards, equipment and training or support for teachers and leaders.
- TOP Sport equipment bags include: athletics, badminton, basketball, cricket, hockey, netball, rugby, squash, shinty, table tennis, tennis and volleyball.
- TOP Play equipment includes child friendly, multi-coloured equipment such as mini-rackets, bats, balls, beanbags and markers.
- Resource cards are available for dance, fitness, outdoor activities and gymnastics each linked to the National Curriculum.

TOP Curriculum

- PE specialists (nationally trained) deliver TOP training to class teachers.
- Secondment of a visiting PE specialist to the Sports Development team as TOP Curriculum Programme Manager.
- Top Community Leaders deliver TOP Community Programmes often on a voluntary basis.

Young Ambassador's Programme

Each year up to 2012, school sport partnerships across England recruited two young people, selected by the Head of PE or equivalent people, to take on the role of **Young Ambassador** (figure 20.13) for two years.

In their first year, they worked in their local communities championing sport and the ethos and values of the Olympic and Paralympic movements. In their second year, they took on a mentoring role with the new Young Ambassador intake. By 2012, there were 5,000 young people that had been trained through this programme. For further information about all these initiatives visit: www.youthsportstrust.org

figure 20.13 – young ambassadors in action

Links between school and clubs

In Soccer, Cricket, Rugby and Tennis, (presumably at least some predominantly female sports such as netball would be included) at least **6000 partnerships** will be established by 2017 – making it easier for young people to continue playing sport once they leave education. Football has pledged that 2,000 of their clubs will be linked to secondary schools, Cricket 1,250, Rugby Union 1,300, Rugby League another 1,000 and Tennis has pledged 1,000.

Every secondary school will have **links** with at least one local club, and every County Sport Partnership will have a specific officer responsible for creating such links, as will at least 150 Further Education Colleges. The government will ensure that three-quarters of University students will get the chance to take up a new sport or continue with an existing sport.

Facilities

£160m will be spent on new and upgraded sports facilities, on top of the £90m already invested via Sport England's Places, People, Play programme. This will include funding for the first time to allow schools to open up their sports facilities (three-quarters of all sports halls and a third of all swimming pools) to the public.

The voluntary sector

Over £50m will be made available in funds which will be open to well-run sports clubs (whether or not they are connected to an NGB), voluntary groups and others to provide an exciting and appealing sporting experience. Overall, the Government is investing over £250m from various sources (including the lottery) in community aspects of this strategy.

The role of national governing bodies

The ultimate opportunity for the British Government lay in the success of the **2012 Olympic Games** in London. People from virtually every nation were there or observed the Games by television.

figure 20.14 – London 2012 logo

The Games are now seen to have had great **commercial**, **political** and **publicity** success, particularly following from the fact that the staging of the Games was a huge outlay and gamble. Now we have to worry about the long-term value of holding them.

The advantages to **British sports men and women** are available if we can take them. It has not been possible since London 2012 to duplicate the effort made to get performers up to standard for those games. This is because of reduced funding due to austerity and the country's economic situation although positive attitudes to physical education and sport remain.

Take note of the London 2012 logo (figure 20.14) and the slogans:

- 'Winning just got easier'.
- 'We are LondONErs'.

The role of national governing bodies

National governing bodies (NGBs) must spend at least 60% of their funding on activities which promote sport as a habit for life for young people. Payment will be by results, with withdrawal of funding to governing bodies that fail to deliver agreed objectives.

NGBs, together with local partners, are tasked to create a new **satellite** club on each school setting, linked to an existing community 'hub' club, and run by coaches and volunteers from that hub club. By being located on a school site, the satellite club is within easy reach of young people, but is distinct from school PE as it is run by community volunteers.

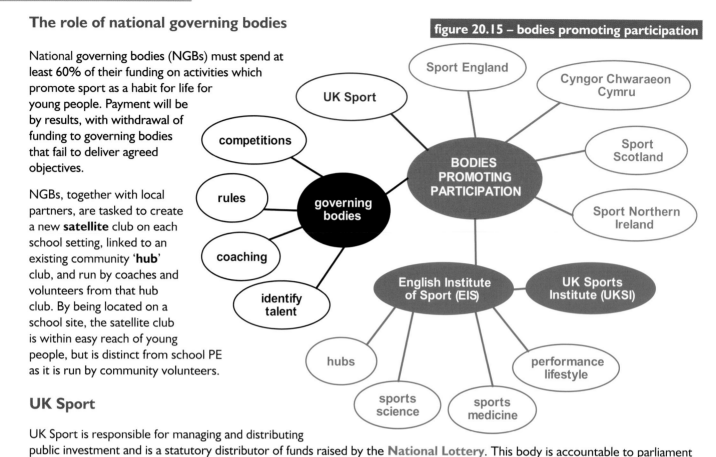

figure 20.15 – bodies promoting participation

UK Sport

UK Sport is responsible for managing and distributing public investment and is a statutory distributor of funds raised by the **National Lottery**. This body is accountable to parliament through the Department for Culture, Media and Sport (http://www.culture.gov.uk), and UK Sport's aim is to work in partnership to lead sport in the UK to World-class success. Its goals are given the title '**World Class Performance**' which is aimed to meet the challenge of the 2016 Rio Olympic Games.

The home countries of the United Kingdom are served by subdivisions of **UK Sport**, the Home Country Sports Councils:
* **Sport England**.
* **Cyngor Chwaraeon Cymru**.
* **Sport Northern Ireland**.
* **Sport Scotland**.

They distribute lottery funding to the grassroots of sport.

See figure 20.15 for a diagram showing the bodies involved in UK sport which promote participation.

Sport England

Sport England will work with **StreetGames**, amongst other partners, to extend the reach of their **Door Step Sport** programme for disadvantaged communities. This will create 1,000 sustainable Door Step Clubs, taking sport to where young people live. Sport England will also work with the **Dame Kelly Holmes Legacy Trust** (figure 20.16) to expand their '**Get on Track**' programme which will place at least 2,000 youngsters on the very margins of our society into sports projects that also teach them vital life skills.

A **five year development programme** produced by Sport England includes **nine priority sports** for development:
* Athletics.
* Basketball.
* Psychology.
* Cricket.
* Women's football.
* Netball.
* Hockey.
* Rugby Union.
* Swimming.
* Tennis.

figure 20.16 – Kelly Holmes Get-on-Track programme

The UK Sports Institute

The **UKSI** is a body, funded by UK Sport and the Lottery, which coordinates elite sport development in the UK. Its **Athlete Medical Scheme** has replaced the **British Olympic Association's Olympicare** to provide the UK's top Olympic and Paralympic athletes with free medical care. It also organises and sponsors World class **Coaching Conferences,** which present the UK's top coaches with opportunities to gain new insights and skills to develop future World, Olympic and Paralympic Champions.

The **UKSI** devolves its regional responsibilities into the **Home Country Institutes**, for example, the **English Institute of Sport** (EIS).

The EIS is a network of World class support services:
- Regional **multi-sport hub sites**.
- An evolving network of **satellite** centres.
- The **Performance Lifestyle Programme** which provides supplementary career and education advice.
- Sports science and sports medicine:
    - Applied physiology.
    - Biomechanics.
    - Psychology.
    - Medical consultation and screening.
    - Nutritional advice.
    - Conditioning and performance analysis.
    - Sports vision.

UK governing bodies

These bodies are responsible for:
- Establishing the rules.
- Organising national competitions.
- Coaching within each individual sport.
- Picking teams for international competition.

NGBs operate within the **international governing body** umbrella, for example, the IAAF for athletics, and FIFA for soccer. Those with **Olympic** participation will select teams for the Olympic Games and will abide by the Olympic rules for eligibility in respect of residence and drug status, and hence are obliged to implement a stringent anti-drug enforcement policy. **Governing body** and **government policy on participation** revolves around identifying talent and giving as many young people as possible the opportunity to learn and develop their sport.

5.3.3 Participation trends in the UK in the 21st century

Participation trends in the UK have been documented over a period of several years. The most recent trends have been surveyed in the **Active People Survey (APS) 5-7**, carried out for Sport England in conjunction with NGBs, Local Authorities, Higher and Further Education Institutions, Charities, Olympic Organisations and other funded partners to ensure that sporting opportunities are created in every community in the country. This has the fundamental aim of increasing participation and improving performance at all levels of English sport.

These surveys analyse how **participation** varies from place to place and between a range of different demographic groups in the population such as gender, ethnicity, social class, age and disability.

A number of other important measures are also captured by these surveys, such as the proportion of the adult population (aged 16 and over) who are taking at least 30 minutes of moderate intensity sport three times a week, current levels of club membership, the number of people who are currently in receipt of tuition and coaching, the levels of involvement in organised sport or competition and also overall satisfaction with levels of sporting provision in the country.

The data in table 20.2 (page 216) is from the Active People Survey 7 by Sport England showing once a week participation in funded sports.

Table 20.2 – **participation trends from 2006 to 2013 for various sports - numbers playing at least once per week**

sport	2006	2008	2012	2013
Swimming	3,273,800	3,244,300	2,824,800	2,892,200
Athletics	1,353,800	1,612,100	1,994,200	1,958,000
Football	2,021,700	2,144,700	2,198,300	1,939,700
Cycling	1,634,800	1,767,100	1,934,600	1,866,100
Golf	889,100	948,300	908,000	772,800
Badminton	516,700	535,700	538,800	499,000
Tennis	457,200	487,500	420,300	424,300
Equestrian	314,600	341,700	325,500	300,800
Squash and racketball	299,800	293,900	281,100	257,700
Bowls	251,900	277,800	231,400	223,900
Cricket	195,200	204,800	211,300	189,400
Basketball	158,300	186,000	149,400	172,300
Rugby Union	185,600	230,300	197,500	166,400
Netball	111,700	118,800	148,000	150,900
Boxing	115,500	106,800	139,200	150,100
Angling	*	*	141,000	131,500
Table Tennis	69,400	75,600	107,300	112,200
Weightlifting	107,800	118,400	86,100	106,600
Snowsport	127,400	120,600	80,800	106,400
Hockey	93,900	99,800	106,800	92,100
Mountaineering	67,000	86,100	91,600	87,800
Sailing	64,000	89,900	56,900	61,400
Gymnastics	*	*	51,100	49,100
Rugby League	73,700	82,000	58,100	48,700
Canoeing	36,500	43,500	42,400	38,500
Rowing	39,300	54,900	48,600	35,800
Volleyball	32,700	48,400	27,400	34,900
Taekwondo	19,000	23,500	26,200	23,100
Judo	17,200	18,700	23,600	19,900
Rounders	16,500	25,900	19,200	16,400

The active people survey

Samples from this survey are given in table 20.3 on page 217. From other aspects of this survey:

- 15.5 million adults in 2015 played sport at least once a week, which is 1.4 million more than in 2005/6.
- Most adults – 58% – still do not play sport.

- Gender has a big influence on sports take-up, and currently (2015) 40.6% of men play sport at least once a week, compared to 30.7% of women.
- At a younger age, men are much more likely than women to play sport, but this difference declines sharply with age.

- 54.8% of 16-to-25-year-olds take part in at least one sport session a week, compared to 31.9% of older adults (26 plus).

- More disabled people are taking part in sport – latest results (2015) show 7.4% are playing sport regularly, up from 6.1% in 2005/6.

Table 20.3 – participation trends from 2005 to 2015 for various demographic groups - % of total England groups

3 sessions per week of at least 30 min duration	2005/06 %	2007/08 %	2008/09 %	2009/10 %	2010/11 %	2011/12 %	2012/13 %	2013/14 %	2014/15 %
male	19.1	20.3	21.0	20.7	20.8	21.3	21.7	21.6	21.1
female	12.4	13.6	13.3	13.4	13.0	14.3	14.3	14.1	14.3
age 16 - 25	29.6	31.3	31.9	30.9	30.6	30.2	31.4	32.4	31.1
age 26 - 34	21.6	22.7	22.9	22.3	22.4	24.4	23.3	23.2	23.0
disabled	6.1	6.9	6.4	6.9	7.3	8.1	8.2	7.4	7.4
people in education	*	*	*	27.9	27.3	28.5	28.3	29.3	29.3
white British	15.4	16.8	16.8	16.8	16.6	17.5	17.6	17.6	17.3
black minority	17.4	17.3	18.7	18.2	17.8	19.4	19.6	18.9	19.3

* Data unavailable, question not asked or insufficient sample size.

The implications for health of the Nation from this survey

- Most preventable diseases are attributed to modified behaviours that relate directly to physical inactivity, dietary excess and obesity.
- Life-extending benefits of physical activity correlate more with preventing early mortality than improving overall life span.
- The greatest reduction in death rate from cardiovascular disease occurs when going from sedentary to a moderate fitness level.
- Hence mass participation programmes/initiatives encourage members of the public to participate actively in sports with the objectives of promoting good health, self-realisation, community development and social cohesion.

Exam style questions

1) Sport for all is not yet a reality in the UK. How can a person's opportunity to participate in sport be affected by socio-cultural factors? 5 marks

2) A Level. People from ethnic minorities, low socio-economic groups and women face more barriers in their struggle to reach elite levels in sport than those from dominant groups. Discuss. 15 marks

3) Discuss the impact of wearable technology on sports participation. 12 marks

4) Why have opportunities to participate in recreational and sporting activities improved for people with disabilities in recent decades? 4 marks

5) What are the potential barriers to participation in active recreation for individuals from ethnic minority groups? 4 marks

6) Today, some groups in society are less involved in sport and physical activity than others. Give three reasons for the lower participation rates among some ethnic minority groups. 3 marks

7) Today, social and economic conditions can restrict opportunities to participate in sport. How and why is Sport England supporting participation projects in deprived areas? 6 marks

Exam style questions

8) How have NGBs and IGBs addressed discrimination issues? Support your answer with relevant examples.   **8 marks**

9) What social and economic barriers to sport and leisure participation do women still face today?   **4 marks**

10) In the UK, a person's participation in sport and physical activity may be influenced by a variety of social factors. How might a person's ethnic background influence his or her participation in physical activity?   **4 marks**

11) Justify why governments are keen to promote a culture of mass participation in sport and physical activity.   **6 marks**

12) Identify and explain the factors that can influence an individual's participation in sporting and recreational activities **4 marks**

13) National sports organisations, such as Sport England, have devised schemes to introduce children to sport and to develop their talents. Using examples, explain how such schemes help to achieve these aims.   **5 marks**

14) a) Identify the theory behind the Sports Development Pyramid as illustrated in figure 20.17 and explain the intentions behind each section.   **6 marks**

b) Outline the roles of various agencies or bodies in the UK which have an effect on participation at the foundation level in sport.   **6 marks**

figure 20.17 – sports development pyramid

15) From table 20.2 on page 216, compute the percentage change in participation at one session of at least 30min per week between 2006 and 2013 for swimming and athletics. What are the implications for the building of facilities for sport of these results?   **6 marks**

16) From table 20.3 on page 217, compute the difference for 3 sessions per week of at least 30min duration between the improvement in males and females between 2005 and 2015. Are the policies for gender equality in the UK working?   **4 marks**

17) From table 20.3 on page 217, compute the percentage trend for participation at 3 sessions per week as between black minority and white groups in the UK. How would you amend public policy to improve participation of both groups?   **6 marks**

18) From Chapter Four of this book, identify the health risks for someone not participating in any sport whatsoever. From a sport of your choice, explain how the London Olympics 2012 may have influenced participation in sport, and hence the health of the Nation.   **12 marks**

Answers link: http://www.jroscoe.co.uk/downloads/as_a1_revise_pe_edexcel/EdexcelAS_A1_ch20_answers.pdf

Instruction/terms used in examination papers

Advantages and disadvantages

Clear statement of why one condition is better that another. Would normally need justification and/or qualification relevant to the question.

Characteristics

Common, agreed factors for a situation, structure or process.

Define/What is meant by....?

Formal and precise description frequently of a technical term/less formal by definition.

Describe

Use of quantitative or qualitative information to explain a statement or a relationship between factors. This term is maybe qualified as 'briefly describe'. Examples are frequently used.

Differences

A comparison between two states in the question. You should be precise and not be tempted to wander.

Discuss

Presentation of both sides of an argument, seeking an opinion based on knowledge and analysis with a justified conclusion.

Explain

Justification beyond simple statement or descriptions required (the why). Will frequently require examples, sometimes qualified as explain briefly. Consider number of marks allocated.

Identify and explain

Linking of cause/problem and effect/solution. Marks awarded only if links are made.

List

A number of points or features, frequently only a single word. No description required.

Name

No explanation required or credited. Will normally require use of a degree of technical language. One or two words.

Plot, Sketch and Label

Used for graphical presentation. For a sketch, graph paper is not required. Important factors are correct labelling of axes and shape of graph. Plotting requires the use of appropriate scales on axes and accurate plotting points.

Principle

Theoretical concept underpinning a practical example.

Suggest

More than one option available which require a justification linked to a question. Not to be answered from pure recall.

Assessment objectives for AS/A1 and A Level Edexcel Physical Education academic examination papers.

3 categories AO1, AO2 and AO3:

Where questions carry more than a few marks, the **indicative content** for your answer is marked up to three levels that are categorised as follows:

AO1 – is marked on recall information, and so you will be expected to demonstrate knowledge and understanding of the factors that underpin performance and involvement in physical activity and sport.

AO2 – is marked on application of theory, and so you will be expected to apply knowledge and understanding of the factors that underpin performance and involvement in physical activity and sport.

AO3 – is marked on analyses and evaluation, and so you will be expected to analyse and the factors that underpin performance and involvement in physical activity and sport.

When answering a question, consider the weighting and ensure that you have sufficient indicative content, particularly for the AO3 level. For example, an 8 mark question may consist of 4 marks for AO2 and 4 marks for AO3. An A Level 15 mark question may consist of 5 marks for AO1 and 10 marks for AO3. If the question is analyse and evaluate, then the indicative content would fall into the AO3 category. So you need read the question carefully and decide how the marks fall into these three categories.

5 banding levels

To discriminate the allocation of marks for questions that carry more than a few marks, there are up to 4 banding levels for an AS question, and up to 5 banding levels for an A Level question.

Below are a couple of examples to illustrate this mark allocation.

For example an AS 12 mark question:

Level 1 has an allocation of 1-3 marks:
- This level shows limited understanding, analysis and application of content.
- Limited links between theory and practice.
- Limited technical language supports isolated elements of knowledge and understanding.
- Limited analysis of the factors that underpin performance and involvement in physical activity and sport.
- Analysis is not used to make a judgement.

Level 2 has an allocation of 4-6 marks:
- Few links between theory and practice.
- Basic technical language supports some elements of knowledge and understanding.
- Attempts some analysis of the factors that underpin performance and involvement in physical activity and sport.
- Analysis may not is not used to make a clear judgement.

Level 3 has an allocation of 7-9 marks:
- Some links between theory and practice.
- Some appropriate technical language supports good elements of knowledge and understanding.
- Good analysis of the factors that underpin performance and involvement in physical activity and sport.
- Uses analysis to make a judgement, but without full substantiation.

Level 4 has an allocation of 10-12 marks:
- Strong links between theory and practice.
- Appropriate technical language supports a very good knowledge and understanding.
- Comprehensive analysis of the factors that underpin performance and involvement in physical activity and sport.
- Uses analysis to make a clear judgement, and supports this with examples.

For an A level question carrying 15 marks there is a fifth level:

Level 5 has an allocation of 13-15 marks:
- Excellent knowledge and understanding of factors that underpin performance and involvement in physical activity and sport. The answer is well organised, coherent throughout and communicated with clarity and precision.
- Comprehensive analyses factors that underpin performance and involvement in physical activity and sport.
- Full application of relevant skills and techniques in physical activity and sport to analyse performance.
- Sophisticated analysis used to make fully informed judgements.

For further examples of mark allocation to questions, please refer to Pearson Edexcel Level 3 Advanced Subsidiary GCE in Physical Education (8PE0), or Pearson Edexcel Level 3 Advanced Level GCE in Physical Education (9PE0) – Sample Assessment Materials.